Catalogue of Paintings and Sculpture

August Franzén, *Portrait of Dr. Dudley Peter Allen*, 1915

Catalogue of European and American Paintings and Sculpture

in the Allen Memorial Art Museum

Oberlin College

Oberlin College, Oberlin, Ohio   1 9 6 7

This catalogue was made possible by a matching grant from
The Ford Foundation

Designed and printed by Clarke & Way, Inc., New York

Contents

F. E. László, *Portrait of Mrs. F. F. Prentiss*, 1932

Introduction

From its inception the Allen Memorial Art Museum of Oberlin College was conceived of as a teaching museum. It has become, however, a particular kind of teaching museum, with a recognizable character all its own. This character derives in great part from the talents and interests of the art department, the museum staff, the acquisitions committee and from a common determination to acquire only works of the highest quality possible. The areas of strength or of weakness in the collections that emerge from this catalogue are a part of the museum's character and of its history. It is not a teaching museum as the term is currently used, for there has never been an attempt to include all periods of art regardless of quality. Nor can it be considered a miniature version of a large metropolitan museum with only works of the highest caliber on display. Rather, the unique character of the collections derives from the firm desire on the part of all who have ever been associated with it to maintain both teaching and quality in balance and harmony.

In the decades immediately preceding and following 1900 interest in a teaching museum for Oberlin College was first fostered and then maintained by Professors Adelia A. Field Johnston and Charles Beebe Martin. Through their efforts and the efforts of their students a number of temporary exhibitions were arranged in various public rooms of the College, thus emphasizing the need for a permanent collection and for permanent housing of that collection. An Art Association was founded in 1912 to encourage this nascent interest in art among the undergraduate body and to acquire works of art for the college as funds became available. Upon her retirement in 1900 Madame Johnston had announced her intention to devote her considerable energies to raising funds for the construction of an art building to house a museum and classes in art.

The need for a museum building became acute with the bequest of Charles F. Olney in 1904. Although uneven in scope and quality, the Olney bequest was the first major gift of works of art to the College. The first recorded donation was a Ming vase given in 1894 by D. A. Bunker of the class of 1893. The Olney collection remained in Cleveland until 1908 when it was installed on a temporary basis in the newly completed Carnegie

Catalogue

The organization of the present catalogue owes much to many models, most of all, perhaps, to a German type which was established by Weizsäcker's pace-setting catalogue of the Städelsche Kunstinstitut in Frankfurt as far back as 1900.

Each entry is preceded by a short *vita* of the respective artist which is restricted to the chief biographical facts and dates. This basic information, which may be particularly helpful in regard to less well-known artists, cannot hope to escape flaws and errors, in spite of the utilization of many dictionaries and a few documents.

No new catalogue numbers have been created; each work is sufficiently identified by its inventory number which is given to the right of the title; added to this is the date of the work in those cases in which an exact date or at least a helpful *terminus ante quem* has been fully established. Titles have sometimes been changed from earlier publications for the sake of clarity; foreign titles have been translated into English.

The type of wood on which panel pictures were painted and from which pieces of sculpture were carved has been identified wherever possible but many question marks remain, since precise identification is much harder to obtain than is often realized. In the painting section of the catalogue the medium is oil (or tempera) unless otherwise specified. Watercolors, unless of an opaque medium such as tempera or gouache, have been omitted. Measurements are given in inches and in centimeters, with height preceding width; in the case of relief sculpture depth has usually been added. This is followed by information concerning signatures and other essential inscriptions on front or back. Next comes the provenance of the work in question, from the oldest mention known to us to the last owner and the method of acquisition by the Museum, followed by the figure number when the piece is reproduced in the present catalogue.

The next paragraph first informs about the state of preservation, generally in brief form except in cases of special interest. This is followed by what we hope is a succinct statement concerning the work's subject and art historical position, with brief reference (author's name and date of

3

publication) to the literature provided at the end of the entry; this statement is brief when the work is well known through publication.

The list of exhibitions in which the work was included contains the exhibition title, the year, and the number under which the work was catalogued. The following paragraph lists the additional literature on the work in so far as it is known to us, with the exclusion of popular items and mere listings (except where these fill special gaps or convey opinions of prominent writers). In the case of articles in which these works are mentioned without being the main item of discussion, the full title is given, and the pagination refers to the beginning of the article, with the page of interest in the present context added in parenthesis. References to illustrations have been omitted in the list of exhibition catalogues and of the other literature, with the exception of reasonably good color plates; photographs of each item can be secured from the Museum. The abbreviation AMAM has been used throughout in reference to the Allen Memorial Art Museum, including its Bulletin. The selection of the plates has been made with the intention of illustrating the most significant works and, in addition, other pieces which may claim attention because of rarity or other considerations besides quality. They are arranged in roughly chronological order, paintings followed by sculpture, the American paintings grouped separately from the European.

The cataloguer owes a very great debt of gratitude to a large number of collaborators, most of all to the Curator of the Museum, Mrs. Chloe Hamilton Young, and to Mrs. Laurine Mack Bongiorno whose support has been indispensable with regard to the works of the Italian Renaissance; in the text on several of these many a colleague will recognize her hand. Mr. Richard D. Buck and Mr. Delbert Spurlock of the Intermuseum Laboratory at Oberlin have been untiring in their efforts to penetrate the secrets of preservation and technical construction of the works of art. Mrs. Athena Tacha Spear has provided much valuable information, particularly on bronzes, and Mrs. Jan Keene Muhlert has helped in many ways. Others who have given generous advice on one or more problems are: Dr. Justus Bier, Raleigh, N.C.; Miss Ellen Callmann, New York; Mr. Ralph Coe, Kansas City; Dr. A. Contini-Bonacossi, New York; Dr. John D. Cooney, Cleveland; Prof. Helmut von Erffa, Albuquerque; Mr. William H. Forsyth, New York; Miss Geraldine Fowle, Bayside, N.Y.; The Frick Art Reference Library, New York; Dr. Klara Garas, Budapest; Prof. Jan G. van Gelder, Utrecht; Prof. Horst Gerson, Groningen; Prof. Creighton Gilbert, Waltham, Mass.; Prof. Donald E. Gordon, Carlisle, Pa.; Prof. Lawrence Gowing, London; Dr. David Lawall, Charlottesville, Va.; the late Dr. Karl Lilienfeld, New York; Mr. Loring McMillen, Richmondtown, Staten Island; Mr. Denis Mahon, London; Prof. Lise Lotte Möller, Hamburg; Prof. Theodor Müller, Munich; Mr. Benedict Nicolson, London; Prof. Gert von der Osten, Cologne; Prof. Erwin Panofsky, Princeton; Mr. John W. Pope-Hennessy, London; Dr. Kurt Schwarzweller, Frankfurt; Mrs. Fern Rusk Shapley, Washington; Miss Dorothy Shepherd, Cleveland; Dr. Hanns Swarzenski, Boston; Dr. Cornelius Vermeule, Boston; Mr. Tom Virzi, New York; Mr. Burton B. Fredericksen, Malibu, Calif.; Mr. Terence Mullaly, London. To those here overlooked go my apologies; to all, my thanks.

WOLFGANG STECHOW

Paintings

ADAMS, WAYMAN. Born in Muncie, Indiana, in 1883. Pupil of W. Chase, W. Forsyth and R. Henri in New York. Traveled in Italy and Spain. Active in Indianapolis and (after 1918) in New York. Died in 1959.

Portrait of George C. Calvert   *52.17*

Canvas, 37½ × 31 in. (95.3 × 78.7 cm). Signed, lower right: Wayman Adams. Coll. G. C. Calvert, Indianapolis. Gift of G. C. Calvert, 1952.

ALLSTON, WASHINGTON. Born near Georgetown, S.C., in 1779. After graduation from Harvard (1800) went to Europe (England, France, Italy) to study, 1801–08. Active in Boston (1808–11 and 1818–30), London and Bristol (1811–18) and Cambridgeport, Mass. (from 1830), where he died in 1843.

Tavern Scene   *56.17*

Pencil and oil sketch on canvas, 27⅝ × 37⅞ in. (70.2 × 96.2 cm). Colorman's stamp on canvas: T. Brown/High Holborn/LINEN, crown with monogram, and LINENS 99. Estate of the artist, 1843; Coll. Richard Henry Dana, Cambridge, Mass. Gift of Henry L. deRham as trustee of the Dana Collection of Allston Pictures, 1956.

Partly disfigured by water stains.

To judge from the marks on the canvas and from the style, a work of the English years, 1811–18. The subject has not been identified beyond doubt, but it is probably the scene of Rip van Winkle being harassed by his wife outside the inn, after the story by Washington Irving, who was a close friend of the painter. His *Sketch-Book*, which made Rip van Winkle famous, was not published until 1820 but Allston may well have known it a few years earlier.

Exh.: Boston, Museum of Fine Arts, Allston Memorial Exhibition, 1881, no. 260.

Lit.: E. P. Richardson, *Washington Allston*, Chicago, 1948, p. 217, no. 186.

AMERICAN (Ohio), ca. 1840.

Portrait of William Bushnell   *51.25*

Canvas, 31½ × 27½ in. (80 × 69.9 cm). Gift of Mrs. Katharine Bushnell Spencer and Martin Bushnell, 1951.   *Fig.* 159

The sitter (1800–1893) was the great-grandfather of the donors. He was a physician and resident of Mansfield, Ohio. Judging from his appearance, the portrait was painted during his middle years (according to a family tradition, by a patient unable to pay his bill).

ANGUISSOLA (ANGUISCIOLA), SOFONISBA. Born in Cremona in 1528. Pupil of Bernardino Campi and Bernardino Gatti (Sojaro). Later active in Madrid (1559 ff.), Genoa (1584 ff.) and Palermo. Died in Palermo in 1625.

Double Portrait of a Boy and a Girl of the Attavanti Family
61.84

Panel (softwood mounted on a mahogany veneer), diam. 15¾ in. (40 cm). Of the inscription below can be read, left: . . . attavanti filius . . . attav. . . . .; right: Ottavia(?) attavanti . . . mancina . . . nobile . . . Private collection in England; Coll. Samuel H. Kress, 1939. Kress Study Coll., 1961.   *Fig.* 26

Surface somewhat abraded.
The Attavanti are a Florentine family.

Lit.: W. Stechow, "The Samuel H. Kress Study Collection, Catalogue," *AMAM Bulletin*, XIX, 1961–62, pp. 35 ff., no. 7.

APOLLONIO DI GIOVANNI. Florentine painter of cassoni and book illuminations, also called "Dido Master" and "Master of the Jarves Cassoni." Born in 1415. Jointly with Marco del Buono, head of a busy workshop for wedding cassoni and birth salvers in Florence. Died in 1465.

Panel (hardwood like poplar), 16¼×60¾ in. (41.3×154.3 cm).
Coll. Pier Francesco Vettori, Florence (1463); Giuseppe Toscanelli,
Pisa, sold in Florence, April 9–23, 1883, no. 57 (as Dello); A.
Werner, Vienna; E. Weinberger, Vienna (1923), sold Oct. 22–24,
1929, no. 456 (as Anghiari Master); P. Drey, New York. Purchased
from R. T. Miller, Jr. Fund, 1943.   *Fig.* 10

Reasonably well preserved. Cleaned in 1966.

Painted for the wedding of Pier Francesco Vettori and Catarina
Rucellai in Florence and paid 50 florins (bottega book of the firm
of Marco del Buono and Apollonio di Giovanni, 1446–1463, Florence, Bibl. Naz. Ms. cl. XXXVII, cod. 305, found by Aby Warburg;
Schubring 1915); the arms of both families are liberally distributed
over the panel, establishing the occasion and workshop identification beyond doubt (Stechow 1944), the more so as they are joined
by the Strozzi arms on a horse to the left (the mother of the bride
was a Strozzi). Gombrich (1955) has proved that of the two workshop owners it was Apollonio di Giovanni who was responsible
for the design of this cassone since two of the stylistically related
Jarves cassoni (Yale University, New Haven, Conn.) were described as his work and singled out for special praise in Ugolino
Verino's *Flametta*, written between 1458 and 1464. The inter-
mingling of the names "Serses," "Cimon," "Temistocles" and
"Pericles," and the costumes point to a fanciful rather than historical interpretation of the event, combined with a moralizing
tendency based on Boccaccio's account in "De casibus virorum
illustrium" (Gombrich 1955). A companion panel representing the
Triumph of the Greeks over the Persians was owned by Dr. Ernö
Wittmann in Budapest and taken to England, where it was destroyed during the second world war. The report that the Oberlin
panel was once in the Stroganoff Coll. in Rome (Weinberger sale,
1929) has not been verified.

Lit.: P. Schubring, *Cassoni*, Leipzig, 1915, pp. 111, 282 (nos.
277–279), pp. 430 ff. (437); W. Stechow, "Marco del Buono and
Apollonio di Giovanni, Cassone Painters," *AMAM Bulletin*, I,
1944, pp. 4 ff.; E. H. Gombrich, "Apollonio di Giovanni," *Journal
of the Warburg and Courtauld Institutes*, XVIII, 1955, pp. 16 ff.
(reprinted in E. H. Gombrich, *Norm and Form, Studies in the Art*

of the Renaissance, London, 1966, pp. 11 ff.); F. B. Robinson, "A Mid-Fifteenth Century Cassone Panel," *Museum of Fine Arts Bulletin, Springfield, Mass.*, XXIX, 1963, no. 3 (Feb.–March).

ARNEST, BERNARD PATRICK. Born in Denver, Colorado, in 1917. Studied at the Colorado Springs Art Center. Professor and Head of the School of Art, Colorado College and Colorado Springs Art Center.

View of La Roche 1945 *46.51*

Gesso board, 15½×22 in. (39.4×55.9 cm). Signed lower left: Arnest—.45. Inscribed on back: "View of La Roche, Belgium, Bernard Arnest, 45 (this town was destroyed during the German Ardennes counter offensive)." Coll. Kraushaar Gallery, New York; Mrs. Malcolm L. McBride, Cleveland. Gift of Mrs. McBride, 1946.

AUSTRIAN (Salzburg), ca. 1470–80.

St. Michael Weighing Souls On the reverse: *Presentation in the Temple.* *43.113*

Panel (softwood?), 36¾×30½ in. (93.4×77.5 cm). Coll. Mrs. Emma Dernburg, Berlin; H. J. Dernburg, New York. Purchased from R. T. Miller, Jr. Fund, 1943. *Fig.* 16

The front is reasonably well preserved; more extensive restorations on the reverse (gold ground, larger areas in the front figures but none of the faces except chin and mouth of the pigeon-holding servant).

Formerly called School of Ulm or Augsburg (the panel was acquired in that region by the first recorded owner) but certainly originating in Salzburg, as was first pointed out by Friedrich Winkler (orally). Related to other Salzburg works of the time (see L. von Baldass, *Conrad Laib und die beiden Frueaufs*, Vienna, 1946, pl. 54 ff.; for the city view of the *Presentation* see pl. 56, and for the pigeon-holding servant, the woman looking up under the Cross on pl. 57). There is also some connection with the (greatly superior) "Throne of Grace," formerly at St. Peter's in Salzburg, now in the Berlin Museum no. 2149 with attribution to Jos Ammann (see

F. Winkler in *Jahrbuch der Berliner Museen*, I, 1959, pp. 97 ff.).
Lit.: R. Arnheim, *Art and Visual Perception*, Berkeley and Los Angeles, 1954, pp. 9 f.

BACCANTE, ENZO. Born in Soloma, Italy in 1887. After the first world war active in New York, where he died in 1938. Sculptor, singer.

The Prayer Before 1932 *43.303*

Canvas, 42 × 35 in. (106.7 × 88.9 cm). Signed, lower left: BAC-CANTE. Coll. Margaret Brisbine (Baccante) Preble, Arlington, Va. Gift of Mrs. Preble in memory of Elizabeth Green Preble, 1943.

Exh.: "Enzo Baccante and Margaret Brisbine," New York, Barbizon-Plaza Art Galleries, 1932; "Paintings," New York, Balzac Galleries, 1933, no. 4; Memorial Exhibition Enzo Baccante, New York, Barbizon-Plaza Art Galleries, 1942, no. 13.

BARKER, THOMAS, CALLED BARKER OF BATH. Born in Pontypool (Monmouthshire) in 1767. Mostly self-taught; 1791–94 in Italy. Active in Bath. Exhibited in the Royal Academy between 1791 and 1829. Died in Bath in 1847.

Interior of a Mill 1807 *40.41*

Canvas, 40½ × 26 in. (102.9 × 66 cm). Signed, lower right: Tho. Barker Pinx. 1807. Private Coll., Westchester, N.Y.; Norman Hirschl Gallery, New York. Purchased, 1940. *Fig.* 89

A drawing which was lithographed in "Forty Lithographic Impressions from Drawings by Thomas Barker, Selected of Rustic Figures after Nature," Bath, 1813, was used for the girl in the background, with the sheaf of gleanings and bag, in the present picture. Another drawing reproduced in the same collection shows the model here used for the miller, similarly dressed but somewhat younger looking and standing outside the mill.

Lit.: L. Gowing, s. v. *Barker*, in *Kindlers Malerei-Lexikon*, I, Zürich, 1964, pp. 202 f.

BASSANO, JACOPO (GIACOMO) DA PONTE, CALLED; FOLLOWER OF. Born in Bassano about 1517/18. In Venice by 1535 as pupil of Bonifazio Veronese. Active chiefly in Bassano (from 1540), where he died in 1592.

Nativity   *55.8*

Panel (poplar), 22⁵⁄₁₆ × 15¹⁵⁄₁₆ in. (56.7 × 40.5 cm). Coll. Earl of Egremont; William Wyndham, Orchard Wyndham, Williton, Devon; David M. Koetser, New York. Purchased from R. T. Miller, Jr. Fund, 1955.   *Fig. 27*

This is a variant of the *Adoration of the Magi* in Vienna (Arslan 1962, fig. 127), of which many other versions exist, rather than of the Vicenza Lunette, to which Arslan (p. 173) referred. It is certainly not a work by Bassano's workshop or by one of his brothers and looks rather like an exercise in the style of Bassano by a somewhat later Italian (not necessarily Venetian) artist of considerable rank.

Lit.: Edoardo Arslan, *I Bassano*, Milan, 1962, pp. 119 and 173 ("judging from photograph good work, very close to the Vicenza Lunette").

BAZZANI, GIUSEPPE. Born in Mantua in 1690. Pupil of Giovanni Canti but mainly formed by his study of older masters such as Veronese, Feti, Rubens and van Dyck, as well as some contemporary Italian and French painters (Cignaroli, Dorigny). Director of the Accademia di Belle Arti in Mantua from 1767 until his death in 1769.

The Death of Sapphira   *43.278*

Canvas, 36¼ × 55⅛ in. (92 × 140 cm). Coll. Eduard Hirschler, Vienna, sold April 26, 1900, no. 49 (as G. B. Tiepolo); Prince Henry of Bourbon, Vienna, sold April 2, 1906, no. 87 (as Piazzetta); Ernst Lang, Berlin (1927); Fritz Haussmann, Berlin (1930–35); Schaeffer Galleries, New York. Purchased from R. T. Miller, Jr. Fund, 1943.
                                                                            Fig. 78

The rare subject is taken from *Acts V*, 7–10. The relative restraint in brush stroke and color suggests a date of ca. 1735–40, rather than ca. 1750 as proposed by Goering (1938) and Perina (1964, without knowledge of the original).

Exh.: "Italienische Malerei des 17. und 18. Jahrhunderts," Berlin (Wertheim), 1927, no. 15 (as "The Apostles Attending the Fainting Mary"); "Italienische Malerei des 17. und 18. Jahrhunderts," Wiesbaden Museum, 1935, no. 15; "Gems of Baroque Painting," Schaeffer Galleries, New York, 1942, no. 2; Pittsfield, Mass., Berkshire Museum, 1942; "Italian Baroque Painting," Smith College Museum of Art, Northampton, Mass., 1947, no. 26; "Paintings and Drawings from Five Centuries" (AMAM), New York (Knoedler's), 1954, no. 50; "Great Traditions in Painting from Midwestern Collections," Department of Art, University of Illinois, Urbana, 1955, no. 2; "Masterworks from University and College Art Collections," University of Kansas Museum of Art, Lawrence, 1958, no. 73; "An American University Collection" (AMAM), Kenwood (London County Council), 1962, no. 14; "Treasures from the Allen Memorial Art Museum," Minneapolis Institute of Arts, 1966.

Lit.: Vitale Bloch, "La pittura italiana a Berlino," *Vita artistica*, 1927, pp. 174 ff. (178); H. Voss, "Spätitalienische Gemälde in der Sammlung Dr. Fritz Haussmann in Berlin," *Zeitschrift für bildende Kunst*, LXV, 1931–32, pp. 161 ff. (165); G. Delogu, "Pittura italiana del 600 e del 700 nella collezione Haussmann," *Emporium*, LXXXII, 1935, pp. 327 ff. (331); M. Goering, "Eine Bilderfolge von Bazzani," *Pantheon*, XXI, 1938, pp. 93 ff. (95); Nicola Ivanoff, Cat. Exh. Bazzani, Mantua, 1950, p. 67; A. Pigler, *Barockthemen*, Budapest-Berlin, 1956, I, p. 381; C. Perina, "Some Unpublished Paintings by Giuseppe Bazzani," *Art Bulletin*, XLVI, 1964, pp. 227 ff. (229 f.).

Allegory of Peace (?)   *61.86*

Canvas, 46 × 44⅜ in. (116.8 × 112.7 cm). Coll. Samuel H. Kress, 1941. Kress Study Collection, 1961.   *Fig. 79*

Part of a series of overdoors, probably painted ca. 1750, the iconography of which remains to be identified. Four of these (all illustrated by Stechow, 1961) were exhibited from the Kress Collection at the *Mostra del Bazzani*, Mantua, 1950, Cat. (by Nicola Ivanoff) nos. 60 (*La Maestà*, fig. 64; the present canvas), 62 (*La Luce*, now Amherst College), 66 (*Il Buon Governo*, now Bowdoin College) and 68 (*La Forza*, now Howard University). Three others are in a private collection in Rome. The present picture shows a young woman with a scepter, to whom a boy is offering crown and pearls, an old woman with a caduceus, and a soldier on the left. The caduceus is often related to Peace (see Guy de Ter-varent, *Attributs et symboles dans l'art profane, 1450–1600*, Geneva, 1958, I, col. 57 f.) as well as to Justice, the Arts and Eloquence. The contained pose of the soldier may point to an allegory of Peace rather than Victory (which the crown could signify but which the caduceus does not fit).

Lit.: Nicola Ivanoff, Cat. Exh. "Bazzani," Mantua, 1950, no. 60; W. Stechow, "The Samuel H. Kress Study Collection, Catalogue," *AMAM Bulletin*, XIX, 1961–62, no. 9, pp. 43 ff.

BEAULIEU, EMILE F.   Worked in Philadelphia, 1852–57, and in New York after 1858. Exhibited landscapes at the National Academy of Design, 1859–62. According to the present picture, active in Paris in 1873.

By the Riverside   1873   *04.1286*

Canvas, 17¾ × 24⁷⁄₁₆ in. (45.1 × 62.1 cm). Signed, lower left: EF. Beaulieu. / PARIS 73. (EF in ligature). Coll. Charles F. Olney, Cleveland, acquired in 1889. Olney Gift, 1904.

BEERS, JULIE HART.   Born in Pittsfield, Mass., in 1835. Went to New York with her brothers James and William Hart in the mid-1850's. Exhibited at the National Academy in 1867, and in the Boston Athenaeum in 1867–68. Later married a Mr. Kempson and lived in Metuchen, N.J. Died in Trenton, N.J., in 1913.

Cattle near a Creek   Before 1887   *04.1098*

Canvas, 6½ × 12¼ in. (16.5 × 31.1 cm). Coll. Charles F. Olney, Cleveland, acquired before 1887. Olney Gift, 1904.   *Fig. 180*

Exh.: "American Artists Discover America," AMAM, 1946,

no. 2; "Women Artists of America, 1704–1964," Newark, N.J., Museum, 1965, p. 24 of cat.

BEGEYN, ABRAHAM JANSZ. Born in Leyden in 1637 or 1638. Traveled in Italy and France; in the Leyden guild from 1655 to 1667. Later active in Amsterdam (1672 ff.), The Hague (1681–85) and as court painter to the Grand Elector of Brandenburg in Berlin from 1688 until his death in 1697.

Ruins of a Castle 1665 *19.6*

Canvas, 18¾ × 16¾ in. (47.6 × 42.5 cm). Signed, lower left: A Begijn f. 1665. Gift of A. Augustus Healy, 1919. *Fig.* 61

Before cleaning in 1944, the signature had become illegible, and the picture was attributed to Jan Fransz. Soolmaker.

Lit.: W. Stechow, "Italianate Dutch Artists in the Allen Art Museum," *AMAM Bulletin*, XXII, 1964–65, pp. 3 ff. (18 f.); Cat. Exh. *Nederlandse 17e Eeuwse Italianiserende Landschapschilders*, Utrecht, 1965, p. 28.

BERCHEM, NICOLAES. Born in Haarlem in 1620, son of the still-life painter Pieter Claesz. Pupil of Claes Moeyaert in Amsterdam. Must have been in Italy before 1642, when he entered the painters' guild in Haarlem. Active in Haarlem until 1677, later in Amsterdam, where he died in 1683.

Resting Shepherds *59.125*

Panel (oak), 16⁷⁄₁₆ × 18⁹⁄₁₆ in. (41.8 × 47.2 cm). Coll. J. van der Linden van Slingeland in Dordrecht (1752), sale in Dordrecht on August 22, 1785, no. 19, bought by Beekmans (original size, see below); Mr. and Mrs. Arthur Erlanger, New York. Gift of Mr. and Mrs. Erlanger, 1959. *Fig.* 60

Until 1960 the picture was attributed to Hendrick Mommers (1623–93), a gifted follower of Berchem. However, as H. Gerson was first to point out (orally, 1961), it is a characteristic early work by Berchem, closely related to pictures dated between 1643 and 1646 (see the examples adduced by Gerson 1964 and Stechow 1964). The suggestion (Gerson 1964) that the picture can be identified with that mentioned by Hofstede de Groot (1926) no. 637 is borne out by the fact that it shows distinct traces of having been cut at the top and the bottom (probably with the concomitant loss of its signature). It is therefore as good as certain that it originally measured ca. 61 × 47 cm and had a companion piece described by Hofstede de Groot under no. 296.

Exh.: "Italy through Dutch Eyes," University of Michigan Museum of Art, Ann Arbor, Michigan, 1964, no. 5; "Seventeenth Century Painters of Haarlem," Allentown (Pa.) Art Museum, 1965, no. 3.

Lit.: G. Hoet, *Catalogus of Naamlyst van Schilderyen . . .*, The Hague, 1752, II, p. 491; C. Hofstede de Groot, *Beschreibendes und kritisches Verzeichnis . . .*, IX, 1926, p. 226, no. 637; H. Gerson, "Italy through Dutch Eyes," *Art Quarterly*, XXVII, 1964, pp. 342 ff. (346); W. Stechow, "Italianate Dutch Artists in the Allen Art Museum," *AMAM Bulletin*, XXII, 1964–65, pp. 3 ff. (11 ff.); Cat. Exh. *Nederlandse 17e Eeuwse Italianiserende Landschapschilders*, Utrecht, 1965, p. 150.

The Country Farrier 62.15

Panel (oak), 20 × 16¼ in. (50.8 × 41.3 cm). French Collection, probably de Flavigny, Les Andelys, late 18th century; Hart Davies, sale in London, June 1, 1814, no. 7; C. Sestieri, Rome. Purchased from Mrs. F. F. Prentiss Fund, 1962. *Fig. 62*

The picture was engraved with the title "Le Maréchal de Campagne" by J. J. Le Veau (1729–86), with a dedication to Mr. de Flavigny, who is not otherwise known as a collector. The engraving shows the wine glass, later overpainted, which is held upside down by the girl on the mule. A characteristic work by Berchem of the early 1660's.

Exh.: "An American University Collection" (AMAM), Kenwood (London County Council), 1962, no. 15; "Italy through Dutch Eyes," University of Michigan Museum of Art, Ann Arbor, Michigan, 1964, no. 6.

Lit.: H. de Winter, *Beredeneerde catalogus van alle de prenten van Nicolaes Berchem*, Amsterdam, 1767, no. 204 (Le Veau's print); John Smith, *A Catalogue Raisonné* . . ., V, London, 1834, p. 57, no. 169 (erroneously identified with a picture of different composition, painted on canvas and measuring ca. 71 × 61 cm, in the Crozat sale, Paris, June 1751); C. Hofstede de Groot, *Beschreibendes und kritisches Verzeichnis* . . ., IX, 1926, p. 102, no. 178 (same erroneous identification); E. Schaar, *Studien zu Nicolaes Berchem*, Diss. Cologne, 1958, p. 70; W. Stechow, "Italianate Dutch Artists in the Allen Art Museum," *AMAM Bulletin*, XXII, 1964–65, pp. 3 ff. (15 ff.).

BERCKHEYDE, JOB. Born in Haarlem in 1630. Pupil of Jacob de Wet. After extended journeys with his brother Gerrit in West Germany, master in the Haarlem guild in 1654. Died there in 1693.

The Bakery Shop   *56.62*

Canvas, 18⅞ × 15½ in. (47.9 × 39.4 cm). Coll. Arthur Hunter, Liverpool; sale P. Dalton a. o., London (Christie's), June 15, 1956, no. 106; Schaeffer Galleries, New York. Purchased from R. T. Miller, Jr. Fund, 1956.   *Fig.* 65

The large loaf is a "duivekater" (rather than a "tai-tai"), baked in North Holland on St. Nicholas Day. The pretzel rack appears in very similar form in two other Bakery Shop paintings by Berckheyde (see Stechow 1957 and Gammelbo 1960).

Unusually close in quality and style, particularly in color, to Metsu and Ochtervelt in their more Vermeer-like works. Painted about 1680; very similar in style to another *Bakery Shop* dated 1681 (Stechow 1957).

Exh.: Menstrie Museum, Bath (before 1956); "The Art that Broke the Looking Glass," Museum for Contemporary Arts, Dallas, Texas, 1961, no. 125; "An American University Collection" (AMAM), Kenwood (London County Council), 1962, no. 16; "Fêtes de la Palette," Isaac Delgado Museum of Art, New Orleans, 1962–63, no. 16; "Ten Baroque Paintings," Ohio State University School of Art Gallery, Columbus, Ohio, 1964; "Seventeenth

Century Painters of Haarlem," Allentown (Pa.) Art Museum, 1965, no. 7.

Lit.: W. Stechow, "Job Berckheyde's 'Bakery Shop,' " *AMAM Bulletin*, XV, 1957–58, pp. 4 ff. (reprinted in *Art Quarterly*, XX, 1957, pp. 485 ff.); E. Meyer-Hessig, "Festliches Brot," *Der Weisse Turm*, III, 1960, pp. 19 ff.; P. Gammelbo, *Dutch Still Life Painting in Danish Collections*, Copenhagen, 1960, p. 138, under no. 207; B. N(icolson) in *Burlington Magazine*, CIV, 1962, p. 310.

BERGEN, DIRCK VAN. Born in Haarlem ca. 1640–45. Pupil of Adriaen van de Velde in Amsterdam, later active in England (?) and Haarlem where he died. Dated pictures from 1661 (?) to 1690.

The Bull   59.3

Canvas, 10⅝ × 13⁵⁄₁₆ in. (27 × 33.8 cm). In the Berlin trade in 1931; Coll. Dr. George Katz, Great Neck, L.I., N.Y. Gift of Dr. Katz, 1959.   *Fig.* 63

Between 1931 and cleaning in 1956 the bull was overpainted.

In the style of Adriaen van de Velde, to whom the picture was formerly attributed. Most clearly related to an undated picture in the Louvre (no. 2326), probably of the 1680's, and (less closely) to one in the J. and M. Ringling Museum in Sarasota (no. 283, indistinctly dated 1682).

Lit.: W. Stechow, "Italianate Dutch Artists in the Allen Art Museum," *AMAM Bulletin*, XXII, 1964–65, pp. 3 ff. (19).

BIERSTADT, ALBERT. Born in Solingen (Rhineland) in 1830. Came to New Bedford, Mass., in 1832. Studied at Düsseldorf and Rome, 1853–57. After his return he traveled extensively in the American West, settled in New York in 1860 and became a member of the National Academy in the same year. Visited Europe again in 1867, 1878, 1883 and 1887. Died in New York in 1902.

Sphinx Rock   Before 1888   *04.1181*

Canvas, 5⅛ × 5¾ in. (13 × 14.6 cm). Inscribed, lower left: Sphinx
Roch (sic). Coll. Charles F. Olney, Cleveland, acquired in 1888.
Olney Gift, 1904.   *Fig.* 178

Probably a motif at Sphinx, Montana, near Yellowstone Park
which Bierstadt visited in 1863 and in 1872/73.

Exh.: "American Artists Discover America," AMAM, 1946,
no. 3.

BLACKMAN, WALTER.   Born in Chicago (?) in 1847. Studied in
Paris with J. L. Gérôme in 1877–78, when he exhibited pictures in the
Paris Salon. Probably resident of New York in 1878, when he exhibited
with the Society of American Painters. Lived in London and Paris, ca.
1913–28. Died in Chicago in 1928.

Autumn on the Beaverkill   Before 1889   *04.1211*

Panel, 7¼ × 10½ in. (18.4 × 26.7 cm). Coll. Charles F. Olney, Cleveland, purchased in 1889. Olney Gift, 1904.

Exh.: "Art Loan Exhibition," Cleveland, 1894, letter G (p. 110).

BLAKELOCK, RALPH A.   Born in New York in 1847; self-
taught. Traveled in the Far West; later active in New York. Became insane
and was interned in an asylum in 1899. Member, National Academy, in
1916. Died in the Adirondacks in 1919.

California Ranch   Before 1887   *04.412*

Canvas, 12 × 10 in. (30.5 × 25.4 cm). Signed, lower left: R. A.
Blakelock. Coll. Charles F. Olney, Cleveland, acquired before 1887.
Olney Gift, 1904.   *Fig.* 189

BLOEMAERT, ADRIAEN.   Born in Utrecht after 1609. Son and
pupil of Abraham Bloemaert, also influenced by Roelandt Savery and

18

Gijsbert d'Hondecoeter. Visited Italy and worked for a while in Salzburg. Active in Utrecht where he died in 1666.

Hilly Landscape 1657   *63.3*

Panel (oak), 11⅛ × 9⅞ in. (28.3 × 25.1 cm). Signed, lower right: A Blommaert 1657. Coll. Loss, Paris; Schaeffer Galleries, New York. Gift of Dr. and Mrs. H. S. Schaeffer in honor of Wolfgang Stechow, 1963.   *Fig.* 57

This is the earliest known dated work by Bloemaert; perhaps of the same year is a picture in Leningrad, no. 3609 (dated 16.7, third digit illegible).

Lit.: W. Stechow, "Italianate Dutch Artists in the Allen Memorial Art Museum," *AMAM Bulletin*, XXII, 1964–65, pp. 3 ff. (5).

BOCCATI, GIOVANNI. Born in Camerino (Umbria) ca. 1420. Active in Camerino and Perugia, where he became a citizen in 1445. Dated altarpieces between 1446 and 1480. Died after 1480.

St. John the Baptist and St. Sebastian   *61.79*

Panel (hardwood like poplar), 59½ × 40¼ in. (151.1 × 102.2 cm). Coll. Sterbini, Rome (1906); Samuel H. Kress (1939). Kress Study Collection, 1961.   *Fig.* 9

Reasonably well preserved; severe paint losses only in right upper arm of St. John.

Part (dexter wing?) of an altarpiece to which the following panels may also have belonged: *Crucifixion* (central pediment), Turin Museum (ill. in R. van Marle, *The Development of the Italian Schools of Painting*, XV, The Hague, 1934, p. 9); two groups of two saints each, Rome, Vatican Gallery, no. 121–122 (lateral pediments; ill. *AMAM Bulletin* 1961–62, fig. III–IV); *Madonna with Angels* (central panel?), Ajaccio, Musée Fesch (ill. *ibid.*, fig. II).

Dated ca. 1450–60 by R. Longhi (*in litteris*) because of strong reminiscences of Andrea del Castagno and Domenico Veneziano.

On the other hand, the figure of St. John is most closely related to that of St. Roch in the altarpiece of 1468 in the Church of St. Eustace, Belforte sul Chienti (ill. in Cat. Exh. "Carlo Crivelli e i Crivelleschi," Venice, 1961, no. 58).

Exh.: Washington, National Gallery (1941). *Lit.*: A. Venturi, *La Galleria Sterbini in Roma*, Rome, 1906, no. 37 (as "Maniera di Francesco Benaglio"); *Preliminary Catalogue, National Gallery, Washington*, 1941, no. 518 (*Book of Illustrations*, p. 72); F. Zeri, *Due dipinti, la filologia e un nome: il maestro delle tavole Barberini*, Turin, 1961, p. 53, note 1; W. Stechow, "The Samuel H. Kress Study Collection, Catalogue," *AMAM Bulletin*, XIX, 1961–62, pp. 14 ff., no. 2.

BOHROD, AARON. Born in Chicago in 1907. Studied at the Art Institute of Chicago and the Art Students League of New York. Active in Chicago. War correspondent in France, 1944–45. Since 1948, artist-in-residence at the University of Wisconsin at Madison.

Advertising Pillar, Paris   1945   *50.5*

Gouache on board, 11½ × 7¼ in. (29.2 × 18.4 cm). Signed, center bottom: Aaron Bohrod. Coll. Mrs. Malcolm L. McBride, Cleveland (acquired through Associated American Artists Galleries). Gift of Mrs. McBride, 1950.

Since one of the posters attached to the *Colonne Morris* announces a concert and dance in celebration of the 27th anniversary of the Red Army, the picture was apparently painted in 1945.

BONE, STEPHEN. Born in London in 1904, son of Muirhead Bone. Died in London in 1958. Author and critic.

Caldey from Lydstep   *44.107*

Canvas, 12 × 16 in. (30.5 × 40.6 cm). Signed, lower right: Stephen Bone. Coll. Mrs. Malcolm L. McBride, Cleveland. Gift of Mrs. McBride, 1944.

The Isle of Caldey lies 3 miles off the seaside resort of Tenby (Pembroke, Wales); the view is from Lydstep, south of Tenby. *Lit.*: Nancy Coe, *The History of the Collecting of European Paintings and Drawings in the City of Cleveland* (Oberlin Master's Thesis, typewritten), 1955, II, p. 134, no. 6.

BOUGUEREAU, see EVANS, DE SCOTT.

BOURDON, SÉBASTIEN. Born in Montpellier in 1616; 1623 in Paris, 1630 in Bordeaux, 1634 in Rome; from 1637 to 1652 in Paris. Court painter to Queen Christina of Sweden, 1652–54; after that, active in Paris until his death in 1671, except for the years from ca. 1659 to 1663 when he worked in Montpellier.

Encampment *57.9*

Canvas, round, diam. 22½ in. (56.2 cm). Coll. Lebrun . . . , Paris, sale March 12ff., 1782, no. 112 (to Dufour); Edouard Napoléon Edmond Nortier, Duc de Trévise; Julius Weitzner, New York. Gift of John J. Burling in memory of his wife, Marguerite Bensinger Burling, Oberlin Class of 1913.   *Fig.* 72

As pointed out by Miss Geraldine Fowle (*in litteris*, 1966), a picture listed as by Bourdon in sale Prince de Conti, March 15 ff., 1779, no. 52 (bought by Dulac) had an identical or near-identical composition as is proved by Gabriel de Saint-Aubin's sketch in his copy of the sale catalogue (see E. Dacier, *Gabriel de St. Aubin*, Paris and Brussels, 1931, II, no. 1062). The size of the picture is given as 12 pouces, which may be a misprint for 21 pouces, the size given in the Lebrun catalogue and the approximate size of the Oberlin painting. The picture is closer in style to the Netherlandish "Bamboccianti" than are Bourdon's other genre scenes of this type (e.g., Louvre, Algiers, Kassel, Hartford, Montpellier, Dulwich) and presumably somewhat earlier than the latter, but the same hand is recognizable in all of them. The possibility of an attribution to

Pieter van Laer suggested by P. Rosenberg (1964) must be ruled out.

Lit.: P. Rosenberg, "Quelques tableaux inédits du dix-septième siècle français . . .," *Art de France*, IV, 1964, pp. 297 ff. (299, no. 15), as by either Bourdon or Pieter van Laer.

BRADLEY, I. J. H. American painter, active in New York and Connecticut in the 1830's, about whose life nothing is known. Some of his best signed portraits bear the dates 1832 and 1833. Whether a miniature painter John Bradley, who resided in New York between 1837 and 1845, can be identified with him is not clear.

Portrait of a Lady 44.176

Canvas, 33½ × 26½ in. (85.1 × 67.3 cm). Signed, lower right: "by J. Bradley 128 Spring St." Coll. A. Seligmann, Rey & Co., New York. Purchased from the Charles F. Olney Fund, 1944.

Fig. 158

According to tradition, the portrait represents a Mrs. Stevens. Undoubtedly from the early 1830's; in style and quality closely related to the signed paintings of 1832 and 1833 (nos. 1–4 in the œuvre catalogue appended to Jean Lipman, "I. J. H. Bradley, Portrait Painter," *Art in America*, XXXIII, 1945, pp. 154 ff.). Painted in the artist's New York studio and clearly not of the "stock" type employed by him as an itinerant limner.

Exh.: "American Portraiture before the Civil War," Akron, Ohio, Art Institute, 1956.

Lit.: W. Stechow, "Another Signed Bradley Portrait," *Art in America*, XXXIV, 1946, pp. 30 ff.

BRAQUE, GEORGES. Born in Argenteuil-sur-Seine, near Paris, in 1882. 1890 moved to Le Havre. 1902–04, art student in Paris: Académie Humbert and École des Beaux-Arts. Exhibited at the Salon des Indépendants (1906) and the Salon d'Automne. Active in L'Estaque 1906–10; later mostly in Paris, where he died in 1963.

Blue Guitar 1943   *48.297*

Canvas, 28⅜ × 21 in. (70.9 × 52.5 cm). Signed, lower right: "G. Braque." Inscribed on back of stretcher, by artist: "La Guitare bleue." Coll. Stragiotti, Paris; Theodore Schempp, New York. Purchased from R. T. Miller, Jr. Fund, 1948.   *Fig.* 141

Exh.: Salon d'Automne, Paris, 1943, no. 1793; "Braque," Stedelijk Museum, Amsterdam, 1945, no. 8; "Braque-Rouault," Tate Gallery, London, April, 1946, no. 13; "Braque," Galerie Maeght, Paris, June, 1947, no. 2; Junior Art Gallery, Louisville, Kentucky, 1954; "Art in the 20th Century," San Francisco Museum of Art, 1955, p. 11; "10th Anniversary Exhibition: Current Painting Styles and their Sources," Des Moines Art Center, Iowa, 1958; "Paintings, Drawings, Prints and Sculptures from American College and University Collections," Ackland Memorial Art Center, University of North Carolina, Chapel Hill, 1958, no. 94; "Art from Ingres to Pollock," University of California, Berkeley, 1960, p. 43; "An American University Collection," (AMAM), Kenwood (London County Council), 1962, no. 17; "Treasures from the Allen Memorial Art Museum," Minneapolis Institute of Arts, 1966.

Lit.: *Cahiers d'art, 1940–1944,* p. 104 ("La guitare et le pot blanc"); Stanislas Fumet, *Braque* (Collection Couleurs des Maîtres), Mulhouse-London-New York, 1946, pl. 9 (as "La Guitare Bleue," 1943); S. Fumet, *Braque* (Collection des Maîtres), Paris, n.d., p. 54 (as "Pichet et Guitare," 1943); S. Fumet, *Braque* (Ed. Braun), Paris, 1948, no. 49; Maurice Gieure, *G. Braque,* Paris and New York, 1956, p. 102, no. 108; *Catalogue de l'œuvre de Georges Braque: Peintures 1942–1947,* Paris, 1960, p. 45.

BRIGGS, EASY.   Lived in Watertown, Wisconsin (?) and in Michigan (Eaton Rapids?), 2nd half 19th century.

Cows in a Pond   Painted ca. 1880   *45.141*

Canvas, 11 × 7 in. (27.9 × 17.8 cm). Coll. Karl W. Gehrkens, Oberlin; Chester Shaver, Oberlin. Gift of C. Shaver, 1945.   *Fig.* 170

BRIL, PAULUS. Born in Antwerp in 1554. Pupil of Damiaen Wortelmans in Antwerp. Active in Rome from 1574, partly in collaboration with his brother Matthijs Bril, as painter of landscapes in fresco and easel paintings. Died in Rome in 1626.

Landscape with Nymphs and Satyrs   1623   *53.257*

Canvas, 27¾ × 40⅝ in. (70.5 × 103.2 cm). Signed, lower right: Paolo Brill 1623. Coll. Earl of Lonsdale, Lowther Castle (1854); Alan P. Good, Glympton Park, Woodstock, Oxon.; P. de Boer, Amsterdam. Purchased from Friends of Art, A. A. Healy, C. F. Olney and R. T. Miller, Jr. Funds, 1953.   *Fig.* 51

Characteristic work of the artist's late period, under strong influence of Adam Elsheimer. The picture is very similar to the *Landscape with Tobias and the Angel* of 1624 in Dresden, which shows the same landscape motif, as does a picture in the Museum of Algiers (Jean Alazard, *Cent chefs-d'œuvre du musée national des beaux-arts d'Algier*, Paris, 1951, no. 13). The same Italian artist, probably Agostino Tassi, painted the figures in the Oberlin and Dresden pictures as well as in a landscape of 1621 in the Denis Mahon Collection in London (subject of the staffage the same as here but with more numerous figures), on which see Exh. "Art Historians and Critics as Collectors," London (Agnew's), 1965, no. 6.

Exh.: Art Dealers' Fair, Delft, 1953; "Paintings and Drawings from Five Centuries" (AMAM), New York, Knoedler Galleries, 1954, no. 38; "Landscape, Massys to Corot," Fogg Art Museum, Harvard University, Cambridge, Mass., 1955, no. 1.

Lit.: G. F. Waagen, *Treasures of Art in Britain*, III, London, 1854, p. 260; W. Stechow, "A Landscape by Paul Bril," *AMAM Bulletin*, XII, 1954–55, pp. 22 ff.; G. T. Faggin, "Per Paolo Bril," *Paragone*, XVI, no. 158, 1965, pp. 21 ff. (p. 24, and p. 33, no. 67).

BROOKS, NICHOLAS A. Active in New York City between 1880 and 1904. Nothing else is known about him.

Handbill of the Play at the Night of Lincoln's Assassination
04.593

Panel (oak), 22⅜ × 15⅝ in. (56.8 × 39.7 cm). Signed, lower right:

N. A. Brooks—N.Y. Coll. Charles F. Olney, Cleveland, acquired in 1890 or 1893. Olney Gift, 1904. *Fig.* 184

Probably painted in 1888; a check for $700, drawn on the Fifth National Bank of New York on Feb. 21 of that year to the order of James A. Bostwick and signed by Robert Fullerton, is the top object on the table. The bill is the "Brown Reprint" of the playbill at Ford's Theatre on the night of Lincoln's assassination (see Frankenstein, 1953). The newspaper clipping refers to Charles Muller's "General Robert Fullerton's Old Curiosity Shop," which is probably identical with a picture by Muller once likewise in the Olney Collection.

Exh.: 'Still Life Paintings, 17th to 19th Centuries," AMAM, 1945; "Illusionism and Trompe l'Oeil," San Francisco, California Palace of the Legion of Honor, 1949, no. 61.
Lit.: A. Frankenstein, *After the Hunt*, Berkeley—Los Angeles, 1953, p. 149.

BROWN, WILLIAM MASON. Born in Troy, New York, in 1828. Had settled in New York City by 1859; exhibited at the National Academy between 1859 and 1890. Died in Brooklyn in 1898.

River Valley Before 1887   *04.1097*
Panel (academy board), 9¾ × 8 in. (24.8 × 20.3 cm). Signed, lower left, with monogram WMB. Coll. Charles F. Olney, Cleveland, acquired before 1887. Olney Gift, 1904.

BRUYN, BARTHEL, THE ELDER. Born in Haarlem (?), probably in 1493. After 1515 active in Cologne as painter of altarpieces and portraits; 1549 and 1552 member of the City Council. Died at Cologne between 1553 and 1557.

Portrait of a Lady   *40.42*
Panel (oak), 12¼ × 10½ in. (31.1 × 26.7 cm). Coll. Garthe, Cologne, sale Sept. 17, 1877, no. 53; Constantin Raderschatt, Cologne (not

in sale July 9, 1885); Franz Hax, Cologne (1904); Manoli, Berlin; P. Cassirer, Berlin; Wildenstein & Co., New York; Ernst Rosenfeld, New York (1928); M. Knoedler & Co., New York. Purchased from R. T. Miller, Jr. Fund, 1940.

Fig. 39

Somewhat cut below; otherwise in excellent condition. On the brocaded belt the (not uncommon) inscription: ALS I FREN (for: ALS IN EREN; Everything in Honor; see Olsson, 1953) and the initials (?) N and W. Possibly the same woman who appears in a portrait (with companion piece) now in the Landesmuseum in Hannover (Cat. 1954, no. 45). For the setting compare the pair of portraits, dated 1534, in the Berlin Museum (nos. S 20 and S 21), but the Oberlin panel is probably somewhat later; Westhoff-Krummacher (1965) dates it ca. 1539.

Exh.: "Kunsthistorische Ausstellung," Düsseldorf, 1904, no. 78; "German Primitives," New York, F. Kleinberger & Co., 1928, no. 50; "Forty Masterpieces," City Art Museum of St. Louis, 1947, no. 3; "Holbein and His Contemporaries," J. Herron Art Museum, Indianapolis, 1950, no. 11; "Paintings and Drawings from Five Centuries" (AMAM), New York, Knoedler Galleries, 1954, no. 28; "Barthel Bruyn, 1493–1555," Cologne, Wallraf-Richartz Museum, 1955, no. 115; "Paintings, Drawings, Prints and Sculptures from American College and University Collections," Ackland Memorial Art Center, University of North Carolina, Chapel Hill, N.C., 1958, no. 93.

Lit.: E. Firmenich-Richartz, *Bartholomaeus Bruyn und seine Schule*, Leipzig, 1891, p. 101; L. Scheibler, "Die kunsthistorische Ausstellung zu Düsseldorf 1904 . . . ," *Repertorium für Kunstwissenschaft*, XXVII, 1904, pp. 524 ff. (561); *International Studio*, XCII, February 1929, cover (color pl.); C. L. Kuhn, *A Catalogue of German Paintings of the Middle Ages and Renaissance in American Collections*, Cambridge, Mass., 1936, p. 27, no. 30; W. Stechow, "The Bruyn Portrait," *Art Quarterly*, IV, 1941, pp. 248 f.; M. Olsson, "Korset på Gustav Vasas Kista," *Arkaeologiska Forskningar och Fynd*, 1953, pp. 229 ff. (231); *Katalog der Gemälde alter Meister in der niedersächsischen Landesgalerie Hannover*, 1954, p. 44, no. 45; H. Westhoff-Krummacher, *Barthel Bruyn der Ältere als Bildnismaler*, Munich, 1965, p. 68 and p. 180, cat. no. 111.

BUISSERET, LOUIS. Born in Binche (Hainaut, Belgium) in 1888. Studied at the Academies at Brussels and Mons. Director of Mons Academy, 1931.

Meditation 1929 *48.47*

Canvas, 28½ × 21½ in. (72.4 × 54.6 cm). Signed, lower right: L. Buisseret 1929. Coll. Mrs. Malcolm L. McBride, Cleveland. Gift of Mrs. McBride, 1948.

Lit.: Nancy Coe, *The History of the Collecting of European Paintings and Drawings in the City of Cleveland* (Oberlin Master's Thesis, typewritten), 1955, II, p. 135, no. 7.

BURI, MAX. Born in Burgdorf, Switzerland, in 1868. Studied in Munich and Paris; closely allied with Ferdinand Hodler. Active mostly in Brienz (Berner Oberland). Died in Interlaken in 1915.

Head of a Woman *50.15*

Paper, 4⁹⁄₁₆ × 6¹⁄₁₆ in. (11.6 × 15.4 cm). Coll. F. A. Goerner, Oberlin. Gift of the owner, 1950. *Fig.* 111

BYZANTINE, 17th century.

Virgin and Child *44.34*

Panel (softwood), 20 × 14⅝ in. (50.8 × 37.1 cm). Coll. Robert Lehman, New York. Gift of Robert Lehman, 1944.

Icon of the Hodegetria type, closely related to paintings by Cretan artists active in Crete and Venice.

BYZANTINE, 17th century(?)

Head of a Saint *40.40*

Fresco fragment, newly mounted, 14⅞ × 9½ in. (37.8 × 24.1 cm). Coll. Joseph Brummer, New York. Purchased from R. T. Miller, Jr. Fund, 1940. *Fig.* 19

The style of this fragment points to a late phase of the group of icons listed as "Italo-Cretan, 15th–16th century," by N. P. Kondakov, *L'Icone russe*, Prague, 1929, II, pls. 134–135. The modelling of the face with short white strokes is there prefigured; it was also imitated in Russian icons (such as Kondakov, pls. 33, 52, 63), and Miss Der Nersessian (orally, 1957) is inclined to consider the Oberlin fragment a Russian work.

CALDER, ALEXANDER. Born in Philadelphia in 1898. Son of the sculptor, Alexander Stirling Calder. Studied engineering in New York, 1915–19. Active as sculptor and painter in Paris (1927 ff.) and Roxbury, Conn. (since 1933).

View of Brooklyn Bridge   Painted ca. 1923–26   *57.28a*

Canvas, 20 × 24 in. (50.8 × 61 cm). Signed, lower right: Calder. Coll. Mr. and Mrs. A. Stirling Calder, New York; Miss Marion Sims, Oberlin (from ca. 1930). Gift of Miss M. Sims, 1957.

Landscape with Country House   Painted ca. 1923–26   *57.28b*

Canvas, 16⅛ × 20 in. (41 × 50.8 cm). Signed on upper member of stretcher: CALDER. Coll. Mr. and Mrs. A. Stirling Calder, New York; Miss Marion Sims, Oberlin (from ca. 1930). Gift of Miss M. Sims, 1957.   *Fig. 199*

CARLONE, CARLO. Born in Scaria (Val d'Intelvi, Lombardy) in 1686. Son and pupil of the sculptor Giovanni Battista Carlone. In 1698 pupil of Giulio Quaglio in Venice, afterwards of F. Trevisani and C. F. Poerson in Rome. Active in Ljubljana (1707), in Switzerland, and (most extensively) in Germany and Austria (mainly 1710–25); later again in Northern Italy. Died in Como in 1775.

Lamentation over Christ   *60.44*

Canvas, 25½ × 17¼ in. (64.8 × 43.8 cm). Gift of Dr. George Katz, Great Neck, N.Y., 1960.   *Fig. 75*

Modello for an altarpiece, probably painted in the 1730's or 1740's.

The body of Christ in Carlone's *Deposition from the Cross* in St. Martin, Weingarten (Matteo Marangoni, *I Carloni*, Florence, 1925, fig. 71) is painted in a very similar attitude. A similar profile of a woman appears in both. The list of bozzetti from Carlone's studio published by Fausto Lechi ("Un elenco di abbozzi delle opere di Carlo Carloni," *Arte Lombarda*, X, 1965, pp. 121 ff.) contains (p. 126) "La Vergine Addolorata col Cristo morto"; as this measured only 6 × 4 inches, it could not have been identical with the present work but might have been an oil sketch proper for the same composition.

Lit.: K. Garas and S. Barigrozzi Brini, *Carlo Carlone* (in print at Milan).

CARLSON, JOHN FABIAN. Born in Ukna (Kalmar, Sweden) in 1874. Family moved to Buffalo, N.Y., in 1886. Studied at the National Academy in New York; associate member 1911, full member 1925. Active in New York and Woodstock, N.Y., where he died in 1945.

The Passing of Spring Before ca. 1918 *00.19*

Canvas, 25 × 32 in. (63.5 × 81.3 cm). Signed, lower left: John F. Carlson. Purchased by the Oberlin Art Association, ca. 1918.

CARRIERA, ROSALBA. Born in Venice in 1675. Pupil of G. Diamantini and A. Balestra. Member of the Accademia di San Luca in Rome, 1705. Visited Paris in 1720–21, and Vienna in 1730–31. Active mostly in Venice, where she died in 1757.

Portrait of a Lady *64.15*

Tempera on ivory, oval, 2¹¹⁄₁₆ × 2 in. (6.8 × 5.1 cm) without frame; 3¼ × 2⅝ in. (8.3 × 6.7 cm) with frame. Private collection, England, sale London (Christie's), May 2, 1961, no. 63; F. Kleinberger & Co., New York. Purchased from Mrs. F. F. Prentiss Fund, 1964.

Fig. 77

29

Probably early 18th century; comparable in style to a lady's portrait on ivory in the Correr Museum in Venice (*Il museo Correr di Venezia, Dipinti del XVII e XVIII secolo*, Venice, 1960, p. 49, no. 706).

CÉZANNE, PAUL. Born in Aix-en-Provence in 1839. Began painting about 1860. Went to Paris in 1861; also worked in Aix and L'Estaque. 1873/74 with Pissarro at Auvers-sur-Oise. Later active in Paris, other places in the Île-de-France, and in Provence; settled permanently in Aix-en-Provence about 1898 and died there in 1906.

The Viaduct at L'Estaque *50.3*

Canvas, 17¾ × 21⅛ in. (45.1 × 53.6 cm). Coll. Ambroise Vollard, Paris; Paul Cassirer, Berlin (1913?); Oskar Schmitz, Dresden (1932–36); Wildenstein & Co., New York (1947). Purchased from the R. T. Miller, Jr. and Mrs. F. F. Prentiss Funds, 1950. *Fig.* 107

The Viaduct of L'Estaque, located not far from Cézanne's home at Aix-en-Provence, was painted repeatedly by him but only once from this particular angle. Since he and Renoir painted this motif together in the spring of 1882 and Renoir's canvas in the Boston Museum approaches it from the same viewpoint, the present picture is very likely to have been painted at that time, probably in February, 1882 (Johnson 1963).

Exh.: "Berliner Secession," Berlin, 1913; "Sammlung Oskar Schmitz," Zürich, Kunsthaus, 1932, no. 29; "Französische Malerei des 19. Jahrhunderts," Zürich, Kunsthaus, 1933, no. 78; "La Collection Oskar Schmitz," Paris, Wildenstein & Co., 1936, no. 12; "Loan Exhibition of Cézanne," New York, Wildenstein & Co., 1947, no. 21; "Six Masters of Post Impressionism," New York, Wildenstein & Co., 1948, no. 4; "Cézanne: Paintings, Watercolors and Drawings," Chicago, Art Institute, and New York, Metropolitan Museum, 1952, no. 56; "Inaugural Exhibition," Forth Worth, Texas, Art Center, 1954, no. 8; "Paintings and Drawings from Five Centuries" (AMAM), New York, Knoedler Galleries, 1954, no. 61; "Paul Cézanne, 1839–1906," The Hague, Gemeente Museum, 1956, no. 25; "Cinquantenaire de la mort de

Cézanne," Aix-en-Provence, Pavillon de Vendôme, 1956, no. 25;
"Paul Cézanne, 1839–1906, Zürich, Kunsthaus, 1956, no. 25;
"Paul Cézanne, 1839–1906," Munich, Haus der Kunst, 1956,
no. 31; "Cézanne," Cologne, Wallraf-Richartz-Museum, 1956/57,
no. 16; "Six Great Painters," Milwaukee, Art Institute, 1957;
"Cézanne," New York, Wildenstein & Co., 1959, no. 22; "Art
from Ingres to Pollock," Berkeley, University of California, 1960,
p. 22; "Paul Cézanne," Vienna, Oesterreichische Galerie, 1961, no.
20; "Cézanne," Aix-en-Provence, Pavillon Vendôme, 1961, no. 9;
"Treasures from the Allen Memorial Art Museum," Minneapolis
Institute of Arts, 1966.

Lit.: C. Glaser, "Die XXVI. Ausstellung der Berliner Secession,"
Die Kunst, XXVII, 1913, pp. 457 ff. (469); M. Dormoy, "La collection Schmitz à Dresde," *L'Amour de l'art*, VII, 1926, pp. 338 ff.
(341); K. Pfister, *Cézanne, Gestalt, Werk, Mythos*, Potsdam, 1927,
p. 6; E. Waldmann, "La Collection Oscar Schmitz," *Documents*, II,
1930, p. 320; Maurice Denis, "Cézanne," *Kunst und Künstler*, XII,
1914, pp. 208 ff. (215); Lionello Venturi, *Cézanne*, Paris, 1936, I,
p. 152, no. 401; Ellen Johnson, " 'The Viaduct at l'Estaque' of
Paul Cézanne," *AMAM Bulletin*, VII, 1949/50, pp. 4 ff. (reprinted
in *Art Quarterly*, XIII, 1950, pp. 353 f.); Ellen Johnson, "The
Viaduct at l'Estaque: a Footnote," *AMAM Bulletin*, XXI, 1963/64,
pp. 24 ff.

CHAGALL, MARC. Born in Vitebsk, Russia, in 1887. Studied in
St. Petersburg, 1907–09. In Paris, 1910–14, then returned to Vitebsk and
Moscow. Moved to Paris in 1923; traveled widely in France. In the United
States, 1941–46; returned to France in 1946. Settled at Vence in 1950.

In the Mountain   1930   *56.23*

Canvas, 28¾ × 23¾ in. (71.9 × 59.4 cm). Signed, lower left: Marc
Chagall 930. Coll. Mr. and Mrs. Joseph Bissett, New York. Bissett
Gift (life interest retained), 1956.   *Fig. 134*

The landscape is a view of Peyra Cava near Nice, a vacation home
of the artist in 1930. For similar motifs painted in the same year
see Franz Mayer, *Marc Chagall*, London, 1964, nos. 575–578.

Exh.: "Marc Chagall," New York, Museum of Modern Art—
Chicago Art Institute, 1946, no. 37.

Lit.: J. J. Sweeney, *Marc Chagall*, New York, 1946, p. 58, and
p. 88, no. 37.

Green Dream 1945 *56.24*

Canvas, 30×24 in. (76.2×61 cm). Signed, lower right: Marc
Chagall 1945. Coll. Pierre Matisse Gallery, New York; Mr. and
Mrs. Joseph Bissett, New York. Bissett Gift (life interest retained),
1956. *Fig.* 135

When Mr. and Mrs. Bissett acquired the painting in February,
1946, it was neither signed nor dated, as older photographs prove;
it is probable that signature and date were added by the artist at a
later date. The dating to 1947 (Meyer 1964) is refuted by the
history of the painting.

Exh.: Pierre Matisse Gallery, New York, 1946; "What is
Modern Art?," Toledo, Ohio, Museum of Art, 1960.

Lit.: Franz Meyer, *Marc Chagall*, London, 1964, repr. no. 771
(as of 1947) and p. 758, no. 771 (no date given).

CHARDIN, JEAN-BAPTISTE SIMÉON. Born in Paris in
1699, son of a wood carver. Pupil of Pierre Jacques Cazes, Noël Nicolas
Coypel and Jean-Baptiste van Loo. In 1728, member of the Academy,
which he served as treasurer (1755 ff.) and organizer of exhibitions
(1759 ff.). Active in Paris, where he died in 1779.

Still Life with Rib of Beef 1739 *45.32*

Canvas, 16×13⅛₆ in. (40.6×33.2 cm). Signed, right center: char-
din 1739. Private Coll. in England; John W. Simpson, New York;
Knoedler Galleries, New York. Purchased from the R. T. Miller,
Jr. Fund, 1945. *Fig.* 82

The genuineness of the signature and date has been doubted by
Martin (1951) but this view is not supported by technical evidence;
the inscription appears to be sound. Martin's re-dating to 1728 or
slightly later must therefore be abandoned, the more so as it is not

convincing from the point of view of style. A replica of the painting (Canvas, 40 × 31.5 cm, signed but not dated; probably later than the present picture) is in the Norton Simon Coll. in Los Angeles (G. Wildenstein, *Chardin*, Zürich, 1963, p. 146, no. 62); it has a companion piece showing a similar kitchen still life with a ray (*ibid.*, no. 63). Other such pairs with various dates are mentioned elsewhere (Martin 1951 and 1957); the Oberlin picture, too, is reported to have had such a companion piece but it has not been rediscovered. The pair (of the Simon Coll.?) was copied by a certain Jamin in 1743 (Dumbarton Oaks Coll.; Martin 1957).

Exh.: "Still Life Paintings, 17th to 19th Century," AMAM 1945; "French Still Life from Chardin to Cézanne," New York, A. Seligmann-Helft Galleries, 1947, no. 15; "Paintings and Drawings from Five Centuries" (AMAM), New York, Knoedler Galleries, 1954, no. 51; "Painters' Painters," Buffalo, N.Y., Albright Art Gallery, 1954, no. 14; "French 18th Century Painters," Minneapolis Institute of Arts, and New York, Wildenstein Galleries, 1954, no. 4; "The Century of Mozart," Kansas City, Nelson Gallery and Atkins Museum of Fine Arts, 1956, no. 11; "An American University Collection" (AMAM), Kenwood (London County Council), 1962, no. 18; "In Focus—A Look at Realism in Art," Rochester, N.Y., Memorial Art Gallery, 1964/65, no. 16; "Treasures from the Allen Memorial Art Museum," Minneapolis Institute of Arts, 1966.

Lit.: K. Martin, "Notes on a Still Life by Chardin," *AMAM Bulletin*, IX, 1951, pp. 17 ff.; K. Martin, "Bemerkungen zu zwei Kopien nach Stilleben von J. B. S. Chardin," *Festschrift Kurt Bauch*, Munich, 1957, pp. 238 ff. (243 n. 9).

CHARLOT, JEAN. Born in Paris in 1898. Went to Mexico in 1921. In the United States since; taught and painted in Georgia (1941–44), at Smith College and Colorado Springs (1948–49). Since 1950 active at the University of Hawaii. Writer on Mexican art.

Rest on the Flight into Egypt 1943   *47.43*

Canvas, 16 × 12 in. (40.1 × 30.5 cm). Signed, lower left: Jean Charlot 1943. Purchased through Associated American Artists from Friends of Art Fund, 1947.   *Fig.* 212

"If there are any Mayan elements in the picture, they are part of my general style. . . . I remember that when I painted the picture I was more preoccupied with the seventeenth century and Nicolas Poussin" (letter from the artist, July, 1948).

Exh.: "Contemporary American Painting," AMAM, 1947, no. 6.

CHARNAY, ARMAND. Born in Charlieu (Loire) in 1844. For a short while pupil of I. Pils and F. N. A. Feyen-Perrin in Paris but mainly self-taught. Exhibited at the Salon, 1865–97. Later active in Normandy and Marlotte (Seine-et-Marne), where he died in 1916.

The Park of Sansac, Autumn   *19.13*

Canvas, 13¾ × 19 in. (34.9 × 48.3 cm). Signed, lower left: A. Charnay. Coll. Oliver Ames (Governor of Massachusetts), sale New York, Jan. 16, 1919, no. 12; A. Augustus Healy, Brooklyn. Gift of A. A. Healy, 1919.   *Fig.* 106

Close variant of the somewhat smaller (11⅝ × 15½ in.) picture of 1885 in the Tate Gallery, London (Cat. by R. Alley, 1959, p. 42, no. 2290), and possibly identical with the "Autumnal Evening— Park of Sansac," exhibited at the Paris International Exhibition of 1889.

Exh.: Brooklyn Museum, 1919.

CHASE, WILLIAM MERRITT. Born in Franklin, Indiana, in 1849. Pupil of B. J. Hayes in Indianapolis and of J. O. Eaton in New York (1869). After a stay in St. Louis (1871) he spent six years in Munich, studying with A. Wagner and K. Piloty. Settled in New York in 1878 and taught at the Art Students League; member of the National Academy, 1890. Frequent travels to Europe. Died in New York in 1916.

Still Life in Copper   Before 1893   *18.12*

Canvas, 14 × 16⅞ in. (35.6 × 42.7 cm). Signed, lower right: WM. M. C. Gift of Grace A. Fairchild, Cleveland, 1893.   *Fig.* 192

The painting probably dates from the early 1890's. Compare the *Still Life with Fish* of 1892, reproduced exh. cat. "William Merritt Chase," Parrish Art Museum, Southampton, Long Island, N.Y., 1957, no. 98.

Exh.: "Still Life Paintings, 17th to 19th Centuries," AMAM, 1945; "Chase and Hawthorne, Two American Teachers," Toledo, Ohio, Museum of Art, 1957.

CHIRICO, GIORGIO DE. Born in Volo (Greece) in 1888. Studied at the Academies of Athens, Florence (1905–07) and Munich. Active in Paris (1911–15 and 1935–38), Milan, Florence and Rome; from 1919 member of the "Valori plastici" group.

Self Portrait   Painted ca. 1935   *38.1*

Canvas, 10 × 7½ in. (25.4 × 19.1 cm). Signed, lower right: G. de Chirico. Purchased from anonymous donations, 1938.   *Fig.* 139

Exh.: "Modern French Paintings," AMAM, 1940, no. 4.

CHURCH, FREDERICK EDWIN (?). Born in Hartford, Conn., in 1826. Pupil of Thomas Cole at Catskill. Went to live in New York in 1848; became a member of the National Academy of Design in New York in 1849. Except for many travels in the Western Hemisphere and in Europe, active in New York until his death in 1900.

"The Letter Revenge"   Before 1892   *04.579*

Canvas, 8¼ × 10¼ in. (21 × 26 cm). Coll. Charles F. Olney, Cleveland, bought in New York in 1892. Olney Gift, 1904.   *Fig.* 186

The letter is addressed to "Mr. F. E. Church, Art Union Building, New York." A tradition preserved through a note in Olney's possession maintains that the picture was "painted to deceive a friend who had made the statement that 'a work of art is meritorious only as it may be mistaken for the original.' " The absence of a stamp on the letter suggests a date before 1847. No similar work by Church is known today, and the attribution of the

present picture to him has been doubted (Exh. Cat. 1966). However, the fact that it was sold as his work in New York during his
lifetime cannot be easily ignored, and it may also be worth while
mentioning that a painting by him called *Retaliation* was exhibited
by F. G. Hecker of Detroit in Cleveland (Art Association) in 1895,
no. 490.

Exh.: "Still Life Paintings, 17th to 19th Century," AMAM,
1945; "American Artists Discover America," AMAM, 1946, no. 9;
"Frederick Edwin Church," Washington, National Collection of
Fine Arts—Albany, New York, Institute of History and Art—
New York, M. Knoedler & Co., 1966, no. 156.

Lit.: A. Frankenstein, *After the Hunt*, Berkeley-Los Angeles,
1953, pp. 53 f. (the statement that the picture was acquired by Mr.
Olney from the artist himself cannot be substantiated).

CIARDI, EMMA. Born in Venice in 1879. Pupil of her father,
Guglielmo, and her brother, Beppe Ciardi. Active mostly in Venice, where
she died in 1933.

Garden of a Villa 1912   *19.24*

Canvas, 27 × 22 in. (68.6 × 55.9 cm). Signed, lower right: Emma
Ciardi/Venezia (?) 1912. Gift of A. Augustus Healy, 1919.

Fig. 116

COLE, THOMAS. Born in Bolton-le-Moor (Lancashire) in 1801.
Moved to Philadelphia in 1818 and to Steubenville, Ohio, in 1820, where
he was active until 1823. Moved to Philadelphia in 1823 and to New York
in 1825; traveled in Europe, 1829–32 and 1841; settled at Catskill, N.Y. in
1836, died there in 1848.

Lake with Dead Trees (Catskill) 1825   *04.1183*

Canvas, 27 × 34 in. (68.6 × 86.4 cm). Signed, center below: T. Cole.
Coll. William Dunlap, New York (1825); Philip Hone, New York
(1825), sold at Ludlow's, April 28, 1852, no. 259 (as "painted for
the late owner"); Charles F. Olney, Cleveland (acquired before
1887). Olney Gift, 1904.   *Fig.* 153

Painted after Cole's first visit to the Catskill Mountains in 1825; belongs to the paintings exhibited at Coleman's frame maker's shop in New York that attracted the attention of John Trumbull, Asher Durand, and William Dunlap. Exhibited (by Dunlap?) later in the same year at the Academy, where it was described in detail by a reviewer, as pointed out by D. Lawall (*in litteris*, Jan. 1966). Listed by the artist in "Some notes of pictures painted New York 1825–26" as no. 7 and sold to Dunlap for $25 (Writing Book no. 1, Detroit Institute of Arts).

Exh.: At Coleman's, New York, 1825; "Paintings of the late Thomas Cole," New York, American Art-Union, 1848, no. 72; "American Artists Discover America," AMAM, 1946, no. 11; "Thomas Cole: Paintings by an American Romanticist," Baltimore Museum of Art, 1965, no. 1.

Lit.: "A Review of the Gallery of the American Academy of Fine Arts . . .," *The Atheneum Magazine*, II, 1825, Dec., p. 77; William Dunlap, *A History of the Rise and Progress of the Arts of Design in the United States* (1834), ed. F. W. Bayley and C. E. Goodspeed, Boston, 1918, III, pp. 149 f. and 277; Allan Nevins, ed., *The Diary of Philip Hone, 1828–1851*, New York, 1927, II, p. 838; George Washington Greene, *Biographical Studies*, New York, 1860, p. 92; Louis L. Noble, *The Course of Empire, Voyage of Life, and Other Pictures of Thomas Cole, N. A.*, New York, 1853, p. 57 (reprinted under the title: *The Life and Works of Thomas Cole*, ed. Elliot S. Vesell, Cambridge, Mass., 1964, p. 35); David B. Lawall, "Note on the Date of Catskill Lake by Thomas Cole, N. A.," *AMAM Bulletin*, XIII, 1955/56, pp. 165 ff.

The Ruins   *04.1184*

Canvas, 5¼ × 6¾ in. (13.3 × 17.1 cm). Coll. Charles F. Olney, acquired before 1887. Olney Gift, 1904.   *Fig.* 154

Used for a painting entitled "An Italian Autumn," signed and dated 1844, 32 × 48½ in., in the Walker Art Center, Minneapolis (Seaver, 1948–49), but possibly painted during the artist's first visit to Italy (1831–32).

Exh.: "American Artists Discover America," *AMAM*, 1946, no. 12.

Lit.: Esther I. Seaver, *Thomas Cole, One Hundred Years Later*, Exhibition Catalogue, Hartford, Wadsworth Atheneum, 1948–49, p. 33 under no. 43.

Sunset across the Water   *04.1185*

Canvas (glued to fir wood), 6½ × 9⅞₁₆ in. (16.5 × 24 cm). Signed, lower left: Cole. Coll. Charles F. Olney, Cleveland, acquired before 1887. Olney Gift, 1904.   *Fig.* 155

Probably painted in the early 1840's.

CORNWALL, N. E. Minister of the Episcopal Church on Scranton and Mentor Avenues in Cleveland in the 1880's, took over the pastorate of the Episcopal Church in Stratford, Connecticut, shortly before 1890.

A Glimpse of Mount Everett   1890   *04.448*

Academy board, 6⅞₁₆ × 4⅞₁₆ in. (16.4 × 11.3 cm). Signed: N.E.Cornwall '90. Coll. Charles F. Olney, Cleveland, acquired as a gift of the painter in 1892. Olney Gift, 1904.   *Fig.* 187

COURBET, GUSTAVE. Born in Ornans (Franche-Comté) in 1819. Studied at the École des Beaux-Arts in Besançon and after 1840 in Paris, where he sent pictures to the Salon from 1844. Active also in Ornans (after 1854), Honfleur and in Normandy. Fled to Switzerland in 1873, died in La Tour de Peilz near Vevey in 1877.

Castle of Chillon, Evening   1872?   *58.47*

Canvas, 25½ × 31¹³₁₆ in. (64.8 × 80.8 cm). Signed, lower left: G Courbet 72. Sale in Paris (Hôtel Drouot), May 12, 1923, no. 70; Coll. Bähler, Château Meggen, Lucerne; F. Nathan, Zürich. Purchased from R. T. Miller, Jr. Fund, 1958.   *Fig.* 98

The same site was often painted by Courbet and his assistants, with dates ranging from 1873 (painting in the Springfield, Mass., Museum) to 1876 (Cat. Exh. 19th and 20th Century French Masters, Finch College Museum of Art, 1962, no. 9). If the date

1872 on the present picture is correct it would be the earliest representation of the motif and would have to have been painted during a visit of Courbet to Switzerland in that year rather than after he took up residence there in 1873. The possibility of a trip to Switzerland is indicated in Courbet's letter to Cornuel, from Ornans, Oct. 6, 1872 (*Courbet raconté par lui-même et par ses amis*, Geneva, 1950, II, p. 149). However, the present picture is closely related in style to the painting of 1873 in Springfield, which shows the castle from a different viewpoint. The possibility that the date 1872 is unreliable is further underlined by the occurrence of the inexplicable date (18)71 on another *View of Castle Chillon* (from the other side), reproduced in Hans Naef, *Courbet*, Berne, 1947, no. 48.

Lit.: A. T. Lurie, "Grand Panorama of the Alps with the Dents du Midi," *Bulletin of the Cleveland Museum of Art*, LIII, 1966, pp. 74 ff. (80).

COXIE, MICHIEL. Born in Malines in 1499. After a sojourn in Rome (1532–39) he entered the painters' guild in Malines. Active as painter of altarpieces and a few portraits, designer for tapestries, stained glass and prints. Court painter to Mary of Hungary at Brussels, patronized by Charles V and Philip II. Died in 1592.

Portrait of Christina of Denmark 1545   *53.270*

Panel (oak), 28 × 21¹⁵⁄₁₆ in. (71.1 × 55.7 cm). Signed, lower right: MICHEL COCXYIE PINGEBAT ANNORUM 1545 (see below). Coll. Count Arco, Munich; A. S. Drey, Munich; Knoedler Galleries, New York, 1925; Drey & Co., New York, 1928; Viscount Rothermere, 1938, sale at London (Christie's), Dec. 12, 1947, no. 18; Sabin Galleries, London; Kleinberger & Co., New York. Purchased from the Prentiss Fund, 1953.   *Fig. 32*

Christina of Denmark, born in 1521, married in 1534 to Francesco II Sforza, Duke of Milan, widowed in 1535; married to Francis I, Duke of Lorraine, in 1540, widowed in 1545.

The brown background of the painting is recent and seems to have replaced a green one, from which the somewhat garbled present inscription (ANNORUM for ANNO DOM or DNI?), which lies over a varnish coating, can be assumed to have been copied. The identification of the sitter (formerly wrongly called Mary of Hungary), of the painter and of the date can be considered assured. Coxie seems to have used an anonymous portrait of Christina (head only) as his model (Budapest Museum, Cat. 1954, no. 6709, listed in Coll. Archduke Leopold Wilhelm in 1659); both may reflect a lost portrait of Christina by Titian which was in the collection of Mary of Hungary in 1556 (Rose 1963).

Exh.: "Selected Pictures from Lord Rothermere's Collection," Budapest Museum, 1938, no. 4; "Le portrait dans les anciens Pays-Bas," Musée Communal, Bruges, 1953, no. 85; "Paintings and Drawings from Five Centuries" (AMAM), Knoedler Galleries, New York, 1954, no. 31; "An American University Collection" (AMAM), Kenwood (London County Council), 1962, no. 19; "Le siècle de Bruegel," Brussels Museum, 1963, no. 84; "Sixteenth Century Paintings from American Collections," Vassar College, Poughkeepsie, N.Y., 1964, no. 5.

Lit.: G. Glück, "Bildnisse aus dem Haus Habsburg, II," *Jahrbuch der kunsthistorischen Sammlungen in Wien*, n. s. VIII, 1934, pp. 173 ff.; G. Marlier, "Altniederländische Bildnisse in Brüssel," *Weltkunst*, XXIII, Aug. 15, 1953, p. 9; L. van Puyvelde, *La peinture flamande au siècle de Bosch et Breughel*, Paris, 1962, p. 412 (with faulty reading of the inscription and obsolete ownership); P. Rose, "Christina of Denmark by Michael Coxie," *AMAM Bulletin*, XXI, 1963, pp. 29 ff.

COZZARELLI, GUIDOCCIO. Active in Siena between 1450 and 1499. Closely related in style to Matteo di Giovanni.

Madonna with Child and Two Angels   *43.237*

Panel (hardwood like poplar), 27¾ × 17¾ in. (70.5 × 45.1 cm). Coll. Dowdeswell, London; George A. Hearn, New York (1908); sale George A. Hearn in New York, Feb. 28, 1918, no. 306; John E. Aldred, New York; Acquavella Galleries, New York. Purchased from the R. T. Miller, Jr. Fund, 1943.   *Fig. 11*

Berenson's remark (1918) that the picture is "sugared down by restoration" is probably too harsh but there are many restored spots and a heavy layer of varnish.

Called Matteo di Giovanni in the Hearn Coll.; correct attribution to Cozzarelli by Berenson (1918), who on the basis of comparison with the Madonna of the Walters Art Gallery in Baltimore (no. 586; van Marle 1937, fig. 220) suggests a date shortly after the latter, ca. 1485. Also very similar to a Madonna in the former Joseph Spiridon Coll. (sale Berlin, May 31st, 1929, no. 49, as Matteo di Giovanni but with the remark by Oskar Fischel that it is more probably by Cozzarelli; as such in van Marle 1937, p. 382).

Exh.: Museo de Bellas Artes, Caracas, Venezuela; "Old Masters," Wichita, Kansas, Art Association, 1945; "Old Masters from Midwestern Museums," Grand Rapids, Michigan, Art Gallery, 1948–49.

Lit.: B. Berenson, *Essays in the Study of Sienese Painting*, New York, 1918, p. 89; *Catalogue of the Collection of Foreign and American Paintings owned by Mr. George A. Hearn*, New York, 1908, p. 149, no. 188 (as Matteo di Siena); R. van Marle, *The Development of the Italian Schools of Painting*, XVI, The Hague, 1937, p. 382.

CROPSEY, JASPER FRANCIS. Born in Rossville, L.I., N.Y., in 1823. Studied architecture for five years; traveled in Europe, mostly Italy, from 1847 to 1850. Active in New York; member of the National Academy, 1851. From 1857 to 1863 active in London, where he exhibited at the Royal Academy. Returned to New York in 1864; died in Hastings-on-Hudson, 1900.

Temple of the Sibyl, Tivoli 1876   *04.1186*

Canvas, 9⅛ × 12⅛ in. (23.2 × 30.8 cm). Signed, lower left: J. F. Cropsey 1876. Coll. Charles F. Olney, Cleveland, acquired before 1887 (as "Early Morning at Paestum"). Olney Gift, 1904. *Fig. 173*

Exh.: "American Artists Discover America," AMAM, 1946, no. 14.

Lake Wawayanda 1876   *04.1187*

Canvas, 12×20¼ in. (30.5×51.4 cm). Signed, lower left: J. F.
Cropsey 1876. Coll. Charles F. Olney, Cleveland, acquired before
1887. Olney Gift, 1904.   *Fig.* 174

Lake Wawayanda (Winding Water) is part of Greenwood Lake,
N.Y. and N.J., where Cropsey worked during several summers
beween 1850 and 1856.

Exh.: "Art Loan Exhibition," Cleveland, 1894, no. 29 (p. 27);
"American Artists Discover America," AMAM, 1946, no. 15.

CROSS, HENRI EDMOND. Real name H. E. Delacroix. Born in
Douai in 1856. In 1876, pupil of François Bouvin in Paris. In the later
1880's member of the Salon des Artistes Indépendants, under the guidance
of Seurat and Signac. Died in Saint-Clair (Var) in 1910.

The Return of the Fisherman (Pêcheur Provençal) 1896
                                                    53.271

Canvas, 26×37 in. (66×94 cm). Signed, lower right: Henri Edmond Cross 96. Deposited by the artist at the Galérie Druet; sale
Atelier H. E. Cross, Paris (Drouot), Oct. 28, 1921, no. 30; Coll.
Maximilien Luce (1858–1941), Paris; M. F. Luce, Paris; Wildenstein Galleries, New York. Gift of Nate B. Spingold, 1953.
                                                    Fig. 112

The site represented is the way along the beach at St. Clair, at
the level of the rocks, "Les Baleines."

A preparatory drawing was in the Cross Exhibition at Bernheim
Jeune, 1913, no. 131; a water color with the landscape but without
the figure is in a private collection in Paris; a letter by Cross,
addressed to Signac in the fall of 1896, shows a colored crayon
drawing after this picture (Compin 1964).

Exh.: Société des Artistes Indépendants, Paris, 1897, no. 273;
La Libre Esthétique, Brussels, 1901, no. 140; "H. E. Cross,"
Galérie Druet, Paris, 1905, no. 12; "H. E. Cross," Galérie Bern-
heim Jeune, Paris, 1937, no. 29; "Seurat and his Friends," New
York, Wildenstein Galleries, 1953, no. 58; "The Two Sides of the

Medal," Detroit Institute of Arts, 1954, no. 130; "Muse or Ego—Salon and Independent Artists of the 1880's," Pomona College, Claremont, Cal., 1963, no. 22; "The Seashore in Paintings of the 19th and 20th Centuries," Pittsburgh, Carnegie Institute, 1965, no. 21; "Seven Decades, 1895–1965, Crosscurrents in Modern Art," New York, Public Education Association, 1966, no. 23 (P. Rosenberg).

Lit.: Madeleine Octave-Maus, *Trente années de lutte pour l'art*, Brussels, 1926, p. 260; Isabelle Compin, *H. E. Cross*, Paris, 1964, cat. no. 58.

DAUBIGNY, CHARLES-FRANÇOIS. Born in Paris in 1817, son and pupil of Edmonde-François Daubigny. In Italy, 1835–36; then active in Paris, where he exhibited at the Salon from 1838, and in Auvers (1861 ff.). Traveled in England (1866), Spain (1868) and Holland (1869). Died in Paris in 1878.

River Banks 1874   *44.57*

Panel (mahogany), 9⅞ × 17¼ in. (25.1 × 43.8 cm). Signed, lower right: Daubigny 1874. Coll. J. J. Carnaud; M. Tauber; J. P. Labey and Glenn Hall, New York; Mrs. F. F. Prentiss, Cleveland (acquired in 1919). Prentiss Bequest, 1944.   *Fig.* 99

Exh.: "Paintings, Drawings and Prints by Charles François Daubigny," New York, Gallery of Modern Art, and Oshkosh, Wisconsin, Paine Art Center, 1964, no. 76.

A Showery Day in Spring 1876   *19.12*

Panel (mahogany), 15 × 26 in. (38.1 × 66 cm). Signed, lower left: Daubigny 76. Seal in back: C. D. (estate of Daubigny?). Coll. A. Augustus Healy, Brooklyn, N.Y., sale in New York, Feb. 15, 1907, no. 57 (bought by Carll de Silver, but apparently re-sold to Healy). Gift of A. A. Healy, 1919.   *Fig.* 100

DAVIES, ARTHUR BOWEN. Born in Utica, N.Y., in 1862. Pupil of Dwight Williams in Utica, 1877; studied in Chicago (1878, 1882) and New York (1886). In Europe in 1893. Active in New York; member of

"The Eight," 1908; main organizer of the Armory Show in 1913. Died in Florence, 1928.

Child with a Toy   *19.18*

Canvas, 10 × 6⅝ in. (25.4 × 16.8 cm). Signed, lower right: A. B. Davies. Coll. A. Augustus Healy, Brooklyn. Gift of A. A. Healy, 1919.   *Fig.* 195

The child is a niece of the artist, Miss Rostan Betts, who was born in 1887; this suggests a date of ca. 1895 for the picture, which is corroborated by stylistic analogies with other works of the 1890's such as *The Throne*, painted in 1895 (R. Cortissoz, *Arthur B. Davies*, New York, 1931, p. 71).

DELACROIX, EUGÈNE. Born in Charenton-Saint-Maurice in 1798. Moved to Paris in 1807. Pupil of Guérin in 1815, friend of Géricault and Bonington. Visited England in 1825. Active in Paris, where he first exhibited in the Salon of 1822; died in 1863. His diary runs from 1822 to 1824 and from 1847 to 1863.

The Beheading of St. John the Baptist   *43.224*

Canvas, 13 × 16⅝ in. (33 × 42.2 cm). Coll. Durand-Ruel, Paris; Adolph Lewisohn, New York; R. Stora, New York. Purchased from the R. T. Miller, Jr. Fund, 1943.   *Fig.* 93

Sketch for one of the four spandrels of the fourth cupola of the ceiling of the Library of the Palais Bourbon in Paris, which the artist executed between 1838 and 1847 (see the illustration of this spandrel in Maurice Sérullaz, *Les peintures murales de Delacroix*, Paris, 1963, figs. 49 and 51). Lassalle-Bordes retouched the final version after Nov. 5, 1842 (Sérrulaz, p. 57). Of the sketches for the same set of spandrels, that for the *Captivity in Babylon* was likewise in the Lewisohn Collection. Alfred Robaut, *L'œuvre complet de Eugène Delacroix*, Paris, 1885, nos. 859–861, lists three pencil drawings connected with this composition, one of which (no. 860) looks like the present sketch, judging from the illustration. A later version of the same composition (rectangular; canvas,

56 × 46 cm), signed and dated 1858, is now in the Museum at Berne, Switzerland (Huggler 1958).

Exh.: "Paintings and Drawings and Prints by Eugène Delacroix," Art Institute of Chicago, 1930, no. 16; "Paintings and Drawings from Five Centuries" (AMAM), Knoedler Galleries, New York, 1954, no. 57; "French Masters, Rococo to Romanticism," UCLA Art Galleries, Los Angeles, 1961, p. 42.
Lit.: J. Meier-Graefe, *Eugène Delacroix*, second ed., Munich, 1922, p. 61, repr. p. 160; St. Bourgeois, *The Adolph Lewisohn Collection of Modern French Paintings and Sculptures*, New York, 1928, p. 20; R. Escholier, *Delacroix*, Paris, 1929, III, p. 68; M. Huggler, "Eugène Delacroix: Die Enthauptung Johannes des Täufers, 1857–58," *Mitteilungen, Berner Kunstmuseum*, no. 20, Feb. 1958, pp. 1 ff.

DERAIN, ANDRÉ. Born in Chatou in 1880. Studied at the Académie Carrière in Paris, 1898–99. Exhibited at the Salon des Indépendants and the Salon d'Automne, 1905. Active mostly in Paris and in Chambourcy (from 1934) until his death in 1954. Sculptor.

Bust of a Woman *33.80*

Canvas, 21¼ × 17¾ in. (54 × 45.1 cm). Signed, lower right: a derain. Coll. Mme. Lederlin, Paris, sale March 23, 1933, no. 117; Theodore Schempp, New York. Purchased from C. F. Olney and Friends of the Museum Funds, 1933. *Fig.* 133

Painted ca. 1927; closely related in design to the *Tête* of that year in the P. Guillaume Coll. (André Salmon, *André Derain*, Paris, 1929, pl. 25) and also to the *Portrait of Mme. Derain* of 1927 (G. Hilaire, *Derain*, Geneva, 1959, pl. 150) but emotionally and coloristically more subdued. Strictly frontal busts of this kind are frequent in the 1920's.

Exh.: "Modern French Paintings," AMAM, 1940, no. 6.

DETTI, CESARE A. Born in Spoleto in 1847. Pupil of M. Fortuny, F. Podesti, and the Accademia di San Luca in Rome. Active in Rome, Naples, and (after 1880) in Paris, where he died in 1914.

The Lost Game 1889 *04.1227*

Canvas, 23¾ × 28¾ in. (60.3 × 73 cm). Signed: C. Detti/Paris. 89. Coll. Charles F. Olney, Cleveland, acquired in 1889. Olney Gift, 1904.

In a damaged condition.

Exh.: "Art Loan Exhibition," Cleveland, 1894, no. 28 (as "The Game's Off").

DICKINSON, SIDNEY E. Born in Wallingford, Conn., in 1890. Studied in New York with F. A. Bridgman, D. Volk and W. Chase. Active in New York.

Portrait of Edward Dickinson 1917 or 1919 *31.87*

Canvas, 39½ × 33½ in. (100.3 × 85.1 cm). Signed, upper left: SIDNEY E. DICKINSON 1917 (or 1919). Gift of the sitter, 1931.

The sitter (died in 1946) was a Professor at the Oberlin Conservatory, 1895–1922, and an uncle of the artist.

DIEBENKORN, RICHARD. Born in Portland, Oregon, in 1922. Studied at University of California (1940–43), Stanford University and California School of Fine Arts (1946) where he also taught. Taught at University of Illinois and California College of Arts and Crafts. Now lives in Berkeley, California.

Woman by a Large Window 1957 *58.118*

Canvas, 70⅞ × 65 in. (177.2 × 162.5 cm). Signed, lower left: RD 57. Coll. Poindexter Gallery, New York. Purchased from R. T. Miller, Jr. Fund. *Fig. 207*

Exh.: Los Angeles County Museum, 1957, loan no. 57–586; "Recent Paintings: Richard Diebenkorn," Poindexter Gallery, N.Y., 1958; "Aspects of Representation in Contemporary Art," William Rockhill Nelson Gallery of Art, Kansas City, Mo., 1959; "New Imagery in American Painting," Art Center Gallery, Indiana University, Bloomington, Indiana, 1959, no. 6; "The

46

Figure in Contemporary American Painting," circulated by the American Federation of Arts, New York, Nov. 1960–Nov. 1961; "Six Americans," The Arkansas Arts Center, Little Rock, 1964, no. 1.

Lit.: Ellen Johnson, "Diebenkorn's 'Woman by a Large Window,' " *AMAM Bulletin*, XVI, 1958/59, pp. 18 ff.

DINE, JIM. Born in Cincinnati, Ohio, 1935. Graduated (B.F.A.) from the Ohio University, Athens, 1958. Active in New York since 1959.

Charcoal Self-Portrait in a Cement Garden 1964   *65.47*

Charcoal and oil on canvas with five cement objects, 108³⁄₁₆ × 47¹⁵⁄₁₆ × 27 in. (274.8 × 116.7 × 68.5 cm). Signed on back: Jim Dine 1964. Coll. Sidney Janis Gallery, New York. Purchased from the Ruth C. Roush Fund for Contemporary Art, 1965.   *Fig.* 209

Exh.: "Jim Dine," New York, Sidney Janis Gallery, 1964, no. 22; "Works by the Oberlin Artist-in-Residence: Jim Dine," AMAM, 1965.

DOUGHTY, THOMAS. Born in Philadelphia in 1793. Worked as a leather currier until 1820. Self-taught as a painter. Member of the Pennsylvania Academy in 1824; of the National Academy in 1827. Active in Philadelphia, Boston (1826–30 and 1832–37), England (1836–38 and 1845–47), Newburgh, N.Y. (1839–40) and from 1841, in New York City, where he died in 1856.

Tuckerman's Ravine   *04.1208*

Canvas, 19 × 27 in. (48.3 × 68.6 cm). On a label attached to the stretcher inscribed: "Thomas Doughty, Tuckerman's Ravine, White Mountains, N.H." Coll. Charles F. Olney, Cleveland. Olney Gift, 1904.   *Fig.* 157

The date of the picture is difficult to determine. Scenes from New Hampshire were repeatedly painted by Doughty at a later date "from recollection." The total lack of human figures is comparatively rare with Doughty.

47

DUBOIS, FRÉDÉRIC. Dates of birth and death unknown. Painter of miniature portraits, active in Paris (1780–1804), St. Petersburg (1804–18) and London (1818–19).

Miniature Portrait of a Lady Writing a Letter   *61.72*

Tempera on ivory, round, diam. 3⅛ in. (7.9 cm). Signed on the table: Dubois. Coll. G. Cramer, The Hague. Purchased from R. T. Miller, Jr. Fund, 1961.   *Fig. 84*

The letter the sitter is holding in her hand begins with: "Mon cher ami." To judge from the costume, painted about 1795. A "Portrait de jeune femme" by the artist (signed, canvas 53 × 44 cm) was in the sale X . . ., Paris, May 8, 1925 (Bénézit, 1950, III, 353); another is in the Louvre. For reproductions of other signed portraits by this excellent but little known artist see H. Bouchot, *La miniature française, 1750–1825*, Paris, 1907, IV, pl. opp. p. 178; sale cat. Hermann Emden, IV, Hamburg, May 2, 1911, no. 130; L. R. Schidlof, *The Miniature in Europe in the 16th, 17th, 18th and 19th Centuries*, Graz, 1964, I, pp. 214 f. and III, pl. 181. He is often confused with François Dubois (*Unknown Man*, signed f. Dubois and dated 1810, National Museum, Warsaw, no. 31813, Exh. "Dessins, Estampes, Miniatures Françaises du XIX. siècle jusqu'au début du XX.," Warsaw, 1956, Min. no. 9). Similar letter-writing motifs were favored by the miniaturist Jean-Laurent Mosnier (1743/44–1808), who moved to St. Petersburg two years prior to Dubois; see P. Lespinasse, *La miniature en France au XVIII. siècle*, Paris-Brussels, 1929, p. 147 and fig. 68.

DU BOIS, GUY PÈNE. Born in Brooklyn, N.Y., in 1884. Pupil of C. Beckwith, W. M. Chase, F. V. Dumond, R. Henri, and K. H. Miller. 1905–06 in Europe. Active in New York, where he died in 1958. Writer on art.

In the Wings 1921   *48.44*

Panel (hardwood veneer), 19½ × 14¾ in. (49.5 × 37.5 cm). Signed,
upper right: Guy Pene du Bois 21. Coll. Mrs. Malcolm L. McBride,
Cleveland. Gift of Mrs. McBride, 1948.   *Fig.* 200

DUBREUIL, VICTOR. American painter of the 1880's and 1890's
about whose life nothing is known.

Take One Before 1890   *04.442*

Canvas, 10 × 12 in. (25.4 × 30.5 cm). Signed, lower left: V. Dubreuil. Coll. Charles F. Olney, Cleveland, acquired in 1890. Olney
Gift, 1904.   *Fig.* 183

Painted after 1880 (bill of that year's series in lower right
corner; the series was used for 20 years).

Exh.: "Harnett and His School," American Federation of Arts,
1953–54 (circulated to San Francisco, Dallas, Portland, Phoenix,
Tulsa, Sarasota, Coral Gables, Akron, Minneapolis, Louisville,
Ithaca).

Lit.: Alfred Frankenstein, *After the Hunt*, Berkeley-Los Angeles, 1953, p. 151.

Is It Real? Before 1890   *04.1213*

Canvas, 12⅛ × 14⅛ in. (30.8 × 35.9 cm). Signed, left of center below:
V. Dubreuil. Coll. Charles F. Olney, Cleveland, acquired in 1890.
Olney Gift, 1904.   *Fig.* 182

Exh.: "Art Loan Exhibition," Cleveland, 1894, letter A (p. 110);
"Illusionism and Trompe l'Oeil," San Francisco, California Palace
of the Legion of Honor, 1949, no. 62; "Harnett and His School,"
American Federation of Arts, 1953–54; "Still Life Paintings from
the XVI. Century to the Present," Atlanta, Georgia, Atlanta Art
Association, 1958, no. 56; "Collage International from Picasso to
the Present," Houston, Texas, Contemporary Arts Museum, 1958,
no. 4.

DUBUFFET, JEAN.   Born at Le Havre in 1901. Studied at the École des Beaux-Arts, Le Havre 1916 and at the Académie Julian, Paris 1918. Traveled in Italy, Switzerland and South America, 1923–24. In 1925 gave up painting and resumed it in 1942. Visited New York, 1951–52. Active chiefly in Paris.

Lili (Lili, noir de fumée)   1947   *61.93*

Board, 45 × 33 in. (112.5 × 82.5 cm). Coll. Mr. and Mrs. Joseph Bissett, New York (acquired in 1948). Bissett Gift, 1961 (life interest retained).   *Fig.* 146

Exh.: "Jean Dubuffet, Retrospective Exhibition," Pierre Matisse Gallery, New York, 1959, no. 18.

Head (Tête sableuse)   1950   *60.98*

Masonite, 28¾ × 23⅝ in. (71.9 × 59.1 cm). Signed, upper right: en l'honneur de Enid Bissett. J. D.; lower left: J. Dubuffet, Avril 50. Coll. Mr. and Mrs. Joseph Bissett, New York. Bissett Gift, 1960 (life interest retained).

Body of a Woman (Corps de dame—Château d'Étoupe)   1950   *63.33*

Canvas, 45¾ × 35 in. (114.4 × 87.5 cm). Signed, lower left: J. Dubuffet juin 50. Coll. Pierre Matisse Gallery, New York (acquired from the artist, 1951); Mr. and Mrs. Joseph Bissett, New York. Bissett Gift, 1963 (life interest retained).   *Fig.* 147

Exh.: Pierre Matisse Gallery, New York, 1951, no. 12; "Jean Dubuffet, Retrospective Exhibition," Pierre Matisse Gallery, New York, 1959, no. 34.

Table with Watch and Ink Bottle   1951   *63.32*

Canvas, 28 × 36½ in. (70 × 91.3 cm). Signed, upper left: J. Dubuffet 51. Coll. Pierre Matisse Gallery, New York (acquired from the artist in 1952); Mr. and Mrs. Joseph Bissett, New York. Bissett Gift, 1963 (life interest retained).   *Fig.* 148

Exh.: "Landscaped tables, landscapes of the mind, stones of philosophy," Pierre Matisse Gallery, New York, 1952, no. 13;

"Jean Dubuffet, Retrospective Exhibition," Pierre Matisse Gallery, New York, 1959, no. 40.

Wooded Landscape (Pays boisé) 1953 *65.45*

Canvas, 34¹⁵⁄₁₆ × 45⁹⁄₁₆ in. (88.7 × 115.7 cm). Signed, upper right: J. Dubuffet 53. Titled and dated on back: Pays boisé mars 1953. Coll. Mr. and Mrs. Joseph Bissett, New York (acquired from the artist in 1953). Bissett Gift, 1965.

DUFY, RAOUL. Born in Le Havre in 1877. Pupil of Léon Bonnat in Paris, 1900. Exhibited at the Salon des Artistes Français 1901 and the Salon des Indépendants 1902. Active in Paris, on the Riviera and in Sicily; in the United States, 1951. Died at Forcalquier (Vaucluse) in 1953.

Vence *53.248*

Canvas, 18⅛ × 21¹¹⁄₁₆ in. (46 × 55.1 cm). Signed, lower right: Raoul Dufy. Coll. Goldschmidt, Paris; Schoneman Galleries, New York, 1953. Gift of Norbert Schimmel, New York, 1953. *Fig.* 128

Painted ca. 1920, together with many other views of Vence.

Boats at Le Havre 1938 *58.177*

Canvas, 13 × 32⅜ in. (32.5 × 80.9 cm). Signed, lower left: Raoul Dufy 1938. Coll. Bignou Gallery, New York (1939): Mr. and Mrs. Joseph Bissett, New York. Bissett Gift, 1958 (life interest retained).

Fig. 129

Exh.: San Francisco Museum of Art, 1939, loan no. 964.39.

DUGHET, GASPARD, OR CLOSE FOLLOWER OF. Born in Rome in 1615. 1631–35, pupil of Nicolas Poussin, who was his brother-in-law and for whom he occasionally called himself Poussin. Active in Naples, Perugia, Florence, and (chiefly) Rome, where he died in 1675.

Classical Landscape with Waterfalls *45.34*

Canvas, 38½ × 48½ in. (97.8 × 123.2 cm). Probably Coll. Sir Richard Worsley (died in 1805); Coll. Earls of Yarborough in London

(1854), sold in London (Christie's), July 12, 1929, no. 67; Schaeffer
Galleries, New York. Purchased from R. T. Miller, Jr. Fund, 1945.

Fig. 71

The picture, highly praised by Waagen and accepted by W.
Friedlaender (Exh. Cat. 1946), is based on the master's style of the
1650's (see in particular the *Falls of Tivoli* in the Wallace Collection in London, reproduced by Denys Sutton in *Gazette des Beaux-
Arts*, ser. 6, vol. LX, p. 303) but, on account of a certain flatness of
texture and tone, does not quite seem to measure up to the same
standards. Given the almost total lack of authenticated canvases
by Dughet no firm decision on the traditional attribution can be
ventured here. The figures are closely related to those on several
more or less generally accepted works by Dughet such as the one
in the Wallace Coll. mentioned above and on landscapes at Holkham
(Courtauld Negatives B 60 / 617 and 618) and Stourhead (B 60 / 78
and 79); however, a similar hand was responsible for the figures in
landscapes given to Jan Frans van Bloemen which are related to the
present work but not by the same hand (Holkham, Courtauld Neg.
B 60 / 62 and 628).

Exh.: London, British Institution, 1849, one of nos. 14, 20 or 49
(see Waagen, 1854); "French Painting of the Time of Louis XIIIth
and Louis XIVth," New York, Wildenstein & Co., 1946, no. 15;
"Nicolas Poussin, Peter Paul Rubens," Cincinnati, Ohio, Art
Museum, 1948, no. 22; "Héritage de France," Montreal Museum
of Fine Arts—Musée de la Province de Quebec—National Gallery
of Canada, Ottawa—Art Gallery of Toronto, 1961–62, no. 24.

Lit.: G. F. Waagen, *Treasures of Art in Great Britain*, II, London, 1854, p. 86, and Supplement (*Galleries and Cabinets of Art
in Great Britain*), London, 1857, p. 67.

DUTCH, second half 17th century.

Still Life with Lobster *54.93*

Canvas, 36 × 46½ in. (91.4 × 118.1 cm). Coll. Robert E. Eisner, New
York (1908). Gift of R. E. Eisner, 1954.

Painted by an as yet unidentified Dutch (Utrecht?) follower of Jan Davidsz de Heem, to whom the picture had been attributed in 1908 and by M. J. Friedländer (expertise, 1954). The painter is comparable, but hardly identical, with Michiel Simons.

DYCK, ANTHONY VAN. Born in Antwerp in 1599. Pupil of Hendrik van Balen in 1609, independently active from 1615 on; member of the painters' guild in 1618, in close collaboration with Rubens on many projects until 1620. 1620–21 in England, 1621–27 in Italy, 1627–32 in Antwerp; 1632 as court painter of Charles I. in London, active there until his death in 1641, except for a third stay in Antwerp and Brussels, 1634–35.

Portrait of a Bearded Man *44.28*

Panel (oak), 29 × 24¼ in. (73.7 × 61.6 cm). Coll. Leopold Koppel, Berlin (1914); M. Knoedler & Co., New York. Purchased from R. T. Miller, Jr. Fund, 1944. *Fig.* 49

In excellent condition.
A very early work of the master, painted ca. 1616, not far removed from the portrait of Jan Vermeulen, dated 1616, in the Liechtenstein Coll. in Vaduz, and certainly before all portraits dated 1618. Under strong influence of Rubens' style of ca. 1614–15. The striking resemblance of some van Dyck portraits of this phase with (early) works by Frans Hals has already been remarked upon by Rosenbaum (1928).

Exh.: "Werke alter Kunst aus dem Privatbesitz von Mitgliedern des Kaiser Friedrich Museum Vereins," Berlin, 1914, no. 38; "Rubens and van Dyck," Los Angeles County Museum, 1946, no. 44; "Old Masters from Midwestern Museums," Dayton, Ohio, Art Institute, 1948, no. 9; "Paintings and Drawings from Five Centuries" (AMAM), New York, Knoedler Galleries, 1954, no. 37; "Notable Paintings from Midwestern Collections," Joslyn Art Museum, Omaha, Nebraska, 1956–57; "An American University Collection" (AMAM), Kenwood (London County Council), 1962, no. 21.

Lit.: W. van Bode, *Die Meister der holländischen und vlämischen*

Malerschulen, 3rd ed., Leipzig, 1921, p. 348 (4th ed. by E. Plietzsch, Leipzig, 1951, p. 446); H. Rosenbaum, "Über Früh-Porträts von van Dyck," *Cicerone*, XX, 1928, pp. 323 ff. (332 as "formerly with Colnaghi in London"); G. Glück, *Van Dyck, Des Meisters Gemälde* (*Klassiker der Kunst*, XIII, 2nd ed.), London, 1931, pp. 76, 528 (ca. 1615–16); W. Stechow, "Two Seventeenth Century Flemish Masterpieces," *Art Quarterly*, VII, 1944, p. 298; B. N[icolson] in *Burlington Magazine*, CIV, 1962, p. 310.

ESSELENS, JACOB. Born in Amsterdam in 1626 or 1628. Nothing is known about his training. A well-to-do merchant, widely traveled, with a small *œuvre* of great diversity. Died at Amsterdam in 1687.

Portrait of a Lady *62.40*

Panel (oak). 11¾ × 8¹⁵⁄₁₆ in. (28.9 × 22.7 cm). Signed, lower left: J. Esselens. Private Coll. in Switzerland; F. Mont, New York. Purchased from Mrs. F. F. Prentiss Fund, 1962. *Fig. 67*

Painted ca. 1665–70; most clearly related to the woman of a pair of portraits first published by A. Bredius (*Künstler-Inventare*, II, 1916, 549, present whereabouts unknown). This group is more reminiscent of Nicolaes Maes than of Terborch and Barent Graat as are some other portraits by Esselens.

Lit.: W. Stechow, "A Portrait by Jacob Esselens," *AMAM Bulletin*, XXI, 1963–64, pp. 2 ff.

EVANS, DE SCOTT. Born in Boston, Indiana, in 1847. Self-taught. Taught at Smithson and Mt. Union Colleges. Settled as portrait painter in Cleveland in 1874; in 1877 went to Paris for two years and studied with A. W. Bouguereau. Taught at the School of Art in Cleveland, 1879–87, then moved to New York. Was drowned in 1898 on the ocean liner *La Bourgogne*.

War (First Discord) *04.404*

Canvas, 33¾ × 41¾ in. (85.7 × 106 cm). Falsely signed, upper right:

W. Bouguereau 1864. Coll. Charles F. Olney, Cleveland, acquired of the painter in 1892 as by Bouguereau. Olney Gift, 1904.

Fig. 194

Copy of the original (same date, same size) painted by Bouguereau and last recorded (with reproduction) in sale Comte Daupias, Paris, May 16–17, 1892, no. 81 (85×106 cm). The composition is a variant of Leonardo's *Christ Child and St. John* group known from many copies.

The authorship of Evans and dating to the time when Evans studied in Bouguereau's atelier (1877–79) is mentioned in a ms. note by F. Grover in his copy of the original Olney list drawn up about 1900. Bouguereau's signature and date on this copy would seem to point to a *mala fide* handling of what originally may have been an honest copy.

FAISTAUER, ANTON. Born in St. Martin bei Lofer (Salzburg) in 1887. Studied briefly at the Vienna Academy. Active mostly in and near Salzburg. Died in Vienna in 1930.

Flower Still Life   *58.54*

Canvas on board, 24⅞×17⅞ in. (63.2×45.4 cm). Remains of a signature or date, upper right. Inscribed on back (not a signature): "Anton Faistauer, Wien." Coll. Elisabeth Lotte Franzos, Vienna (probably acquired from the artist) and Washington. Franzos Bequest, 1958.

Probably a rather early work, closely related to a *Flower Still Life* of 1917 (?), reproduced as color plate in Arthur Roessler, *Der Maler Anton Faistauer*, Vienna, 1947, after p. 24.

FANTIN-LATOUR, (IGNACE) HENRI (JEAN THÉO-DORE). Born in Grenoble in 1836. Studied with his father, Théodore, at Lecoq de Boisbaudran's drawing school and, for a short time, at the École des Beaux-Arts and in Courbet's studio. Exhibited at the Salon from 1861, and in the Salon des Refusés, 1863. Visited England (1859, 1861, 1864). Died at Buré (Orne) in 1904.

The Traveler (Le Voyageur) *19.25*

Canvas, 8¾ × 13⅝ in. (22.2 × 34.1 cm). Coll. A. Augustus Healy, Brooklyn. Gift of A. A. Healy, 1919.

Heavy paint losses and overpainting.

The subject cannot be identified, partly because of the poor condition of the painting. This is possibly identical with one listed (as having been done in 1904) in Mme. Fantin-Latour's *Catalogue*, Paris, 1911, no. 2043: "Allégorie. Toile, H. 0 m 23. L. 0 m 35. Composition de 8 figures et d'un cheval."

FLEMISH, ca. 1500–15.

Holy Face *59.113*

Panel (oak), panel size 10¹⁵⁄₁₆ × 8¼ in. (27.8 × 21 cm), painted surface 9⅝ × 7 in. (24.4 × 17.8 cm). Letters O. D. B. scratched onto the back. Coll. G. M. Gardella, Milan; J. J. Klejman, New York. Purchased from Charles F. Olney Fund, 1959. *Fig.* 29

Not the "Veronica" (Sudarium) but the "Mandilian" type of the Face of Christ. Small panels of this sort were frequently exported to Italy and Spain. Somewhat reminiscent of Mostaert in his more Flemish phase (E. Panofsky *in litteris*, 1959, points to the *Man of Sorrows* illustrated by M. J. Friedländer, *Altniederländische Malerei*, X, pl. X); in any case closer to Antwerp than to Bruges.

Exh.: "An American University Collection" (AMAM), Kenwood (London County Council), 1962, no. 33.

FLEMISH, early 16th century.

Lamentation over Christ *44.44*

Panel (oak), 7⅝ × 5½ in. (19.4 × 14 cm). Coll. Robert Lehman, New York. Gift of Robert Lehman, 1944. *Fig.* 30

School of Bruges, from the wider circle of Gerard David and Adriaen Isenbrandt.

FLEMISH, 1525.

Holy Family with St. Anne and St. Joachim 1525   *45.10*

Panel (oak), 37 × 29¼ in. (94 × 74.3 cm). Dated, bottom center: 1525. Coll. Count Andrássy, Budapest (not in the sales of Dec. 1, 1930 and April 24, 1931); Hans Wendland, Berlin; E. and A. Silberman Galleries, New York; John Bass, New York, sale Jan. 25, 1945, no. 18. Gift of Robert Lehman, New York, 1945. *Fig.* 31

The figure on the right is certainly meant to be Joachim, not a donor, as formerly suggested. The iconography of the panel, with Mary so subservient to Anne and with the lively turning of Joseph to Anne, is exceptional.

Gustav Glück (certificate, Dec. 28, 1934) considered this a work of Dirck Vellert; however, this attribution seems to be erroneous and was also opposed by M. J. Friedländer (orally, from photograph, 1947). The master is more closely related to the Bruges than to the Antwerp School, and particularly to Lancelot Blondeel.

Exh.: "Paintings and Drawings from Five Centuries" (AMAM), New York, Knoedler Galleries, 1954, no. 27; "Portrait of the Madonna," Akron, Ohio, Art Institute, 1960–61; "Le siècle de Bruegel," Brussels, Musée des Beaux-Arts, 1963, no. 261.

FRANZÉN, AUGUST REINHOLD. Born in Drothem, Östergötland (Sweden) in 1863. In the U.S., 1881–85; then studied under C. Larsson in Göteborg and the Académie Julian in Paris. Settled in New York in 1891. Member of the National Academy, 1920. Died in New York in 1938.

Portrait of Dr. Dudley Peter Allen 1915   *44.59*

Canvas, 38⅛ × 31 in. (96.8 × 78.7 cm). Signed, left center: Aug. Franzén. Coll. Mrs. F. F. Prentiss, Cleveland. Prentiss Bequest, 1944.   *Frontispiece*

The sitter (1852–1915) was a well-known Cleveland surgeon and the first husband of Mrs. Prentiss; see the introduction to this catalogue.

FROESCHL, DANIEL. Born in Augsburg before 1572. In 1601 he is called miniature painter in the service of Emperor Rudolf II at Prague but returned there in 1604 from Italy, where he had been active for the Grandduke of Tuscany. Antiquarian to Rudolf II, 1607–1612. Died in Prague in 1613. Very few of his works are known.

Allegorical Figure representing Faith and Hope 1609   *59.2*

Tempera on vellum, 7⁷⁄₁₆ × 6¼ in. (18.9 × 15.8 cm). Signed lower right: D. F. 1609. Coll. Philipp Hainhofer, Augsburg, 1610; Dr. George Katz, Great Neck, New York. Gift of Dr. Katz, 1959.

Fig. 35

Mentioned in Ph. Hainhofer's letter of July 28, 1610, addressed to Duke Philip II of Pomerania-Stettin: "I have in my album only two little pieces from his hand, a half-length figure which represents Fides . . ."; also mentioned in the list of the works contained in his album in the same year ("Fides and Spes (sic), likewise by Froeschel"). Both Brulliot (1833) and Nagler (1860) fail to indicate where they saw the miniature; and only Nagler describes it unequivocally.

Painted in close imitation of the style of Hendrick Goltzius; compare the engraving B. 79 = Hirschmann 87, also the one by J. Saenredam after Goltzius, B. 82.

Lit.: F. Brulliot, *Dictionnaire des Monogrammes* . . ., Munich, II, 1833, no. 586; G. K. Nagler, *Die Monogrammisten*, Munich, 1860, II, p. 422, no. 1090; Oscar Doering, *Des Augsburger Patriciers Philipp Hainhofer Beziehungen zum Herzog Philipp II. von Pommern-Stettin (Quellenschriften für Kunstgeschichte und Maltechnik* . . ., new series, ed. A. Ilg, VI), Vienna, 1894, pp. 12, 38.

GAERTNER, CARL FREDERICK. Born in Cleveland in 1898. Pupil of F. N. Wilcox and H. G. Keller in Cleveland. Taught at the Cleveland Institute of Art and the Toledo Museum of Art. Died in Willoughby, Ohio, in 1952.

Easter Evening 1949   *49.238*

Gouache on board, 18 × 30 in. (45.7 × 76.2 cm). Signed, lower right: CARL GAERTNER / 1949. Inscribed on the back: Easter Evening /

Demonstration at Oberlin / Carl Gaertner / May 23, 1949. Gift of the artist, 1949.

GALL, FRANÇOIS (FERENC). Born in Kolozsvár (Klausen-burg, Cluj) in 1912. Studied in Rome and Paris. Active in Kolozsvár, 1940–45, and since 1946 in Paris.

Woman by a River   Painted after 1946   *59.124*

Canvas, 24 × 19⅞ in. (61 × 40.5 cm). Signed, lower right: F. Gall Argenteuil. Anonymous Gift, 1959.

GAULLI, GIOVANNI BATTISTA, CALLED IL BACICCIO. Born in Genoa in 1639. Came to Rome in the mid-1650's. Sponsored by Giovanni Lorenzo Bernini. Active in Rome until his death in 1709.

Death of Adonis   *66.2*

Canvas, 60¼ × 48¼ in. (153 × 122.5 cm). Coll. Leger Galleries, London; Giovanni Salocchi, Florence; Gualtiero Volterra, Florence. Purchased from Mrs. F. F. Prentiss Fund, 1966.   *Fig.* 46

Dated on stylistic grounds ca. 1683–85. A preparatory drawing for this painting is in the British Museum, London (published by M. V. Brugnoli in *Paragone*, VII, no. 81, 1956, pp. 28 ff.). A painting of *Venus and Adonis*, perhaps a companion piece to ours, belongs to the Marquis of Exeter, Burghley House, Stamford, Lincs., England. Another, probably earlier painting of the *Death of Adonis* was in the Paul Ganz collection, New York (Enggass 1966), now in the Ponce Art Museum, Puerto Rico.

Exh.: "Genoese Masters, Cambiaso to Magnasco, 1550–1750," Dayton, Ohio, Art Institute—Ringling Museum of Art, Sarasota, Fla.—Wadsworth Atheneum, Hartford, Conn., 1962–63, no. 36; "G. B. Gaulli," Oberlin, 1967, no. 13.

Lit.: F. Zeri, "Quattro tele del Baciccia," *Paragone*, VI, no. 67, 1955, pp. 56–57; R. Enggass, *The Painting of Baciccio*, University Park, Penna., 1964, p. 133; R. Spear, "Baciccio's Pendant Paintings of *Venus and Adonis*," *AMAM Bulletin*, XXIII, 1965–66, pp. 98 ff.; R. Enggass, "Addenda to Baciccio: III," *Burlington Magazine*, CVIII, 1966, p. 365.

GAY, EDWARD. Born in 1837 in Dublin, Ireland. In 1848 he came to Albany, N.Y., where he became a pupil of James M. Hart. After further study with K. F. Lessing and J. W. Schirmer in Karlsruhe, 1862–67, he settled in New York. Associate member of the National Academy in 1869, full member in 1907. Died in Mt. Vernon, N.Y., in 1928.

By the Brookside 1875 *04.1189*

Panel (pine), 12⅝ × 9⁷⁄₁₆ in. (32.1 × 24 cm). Signed, lower right: Edward Gay 75. Coll. Charles F. Olney, Cleveland, acquired before 1887. Olney Gift, 1904. *Fig. 172*

Exh.: "American Artists Discover America," AMAM, 1946, no. 18.

GELLI, EDOARDO (ODOARDO). Born in Savona in 1852. Studied at the Academy in Lucca (until 1870) and under A. Ciceri in Florence (1870–73). Active in Florence and Vienna (1886 ff.). Died in Florence in 1933.

Portrait of Frederick Norton Finney *16.7*

Canvas, 43½ × 33½ in. (110.5 × 85.1 cm). Signed, upper right: EGelli (E and G in ligature) 1894 Firenze. Coll. Frederick Norton Finney, Milwaukee. Bequest of the owner, 1916.

The sitter (1832–1916) was the son of Charles Grandison Finney (see under WALDO and Jewett) and a trustee of Oberlin College, 1883–1916.

GERGELY, TIBOR. Born in Budapest in 1900. Studied art in Vienna; active there as a set designer, designer of puppets, newspaper caricaturist, and book illustrator. Came to America in 1939. Active in New York City as children's book illustrator.

In the Tent 1940 *43.122*

Tempera on paper board, 11½ × 20³⁄₁₆ in. (29.2 × 51.3 cm). Signed, lower right: Gergely. Purchased from R. T. Miller, Jr. Fund, 1943.

Final version for illustration, pp. 36–7, to *Topsy Turvy Circus*, New York (Harper & Bros.), 1940, text by Georges Duplaix.

Circus Parade 1940 *43.123*

Tempera on paper board, 5¹¹⁄₁₆ × 8⅛ in. (14.5 × 20.6 cm). Signed, lower left: Gergely. Purchased from R. T. Miller, Jr. Fund, 1943.

Final version for tailpiece illustration to *Topsy Turvy Circus*, New York (Harper & Bros.), 1940, text by Georges Duplaix.

GERMAN (South), ca. 1515–20.

Portrait of a Young Man *49.89*

Panel (softwood like pine), 13¼ × 9½ in. (33.7 × 24.1 cm). Coll. Richard von Kaufmann, Berlin, sale Dec. 4–5, 1917, no. 146 (as Swabian Master, ca. 1520); Camillo Castiglioni, Vienna, sale Berlin, Nov. 28, 1930, no. 38 (do.); A. S. Drey, Munich and New York, 1931; J. Goudstikker, Amsterdam; Schaeffer Galleries, New York. Purchased from Mrs. F. F. Prentiss Fund, 1949. *Fig. 38*

The portrait has been attributed to Martin Schaffner (mentioned in the Castiglioni sale; Toronto Exh. Cat., 1931) and to Hans Burgkmair (M. J. Friedländer in certificate of August 2, 1949) but neither suggestion is convincing. Its origin in Augsburg is probable, and there is some evidence of kinship with both Burgkmair and Leonhard Beck. The brocaded background, which goes back to Dürer's *Elsbeth Tucher* of 1499 in Kassel, is a comparatively rare feature which also occurs in Schaffner's *Eitel Besserer* (1510) in the Ulm Minster, in a portrait of 1533, in the Munich trade, 1917 (according to M. J. Friedländer, in the Kaufmann Cat., by the same hand as the Oberlin picture), and in the portraits of a couple, dated 1521, in the Innsbruck Ferdinandeum, there given to Leonhard Beck but attributed to Jörg Breu by K. Löcher in *Alte und Moderne Kunst*, XI, 1966, pp. 15 ff. The parallel pen hatchings on the front side of the face are a distinguishing feature.

Exh.: "Italian Old Masters and German Primitives," Art Gallery of Toronto, 1931, no. 58 (as Martin Schaffner); "The Renaissance

Image of Man and the World," Columbus, Ohio, Gallery of Fine Arts, 1961, no. 19.

Lit.: *Pantheon*, VII, 1931, p. 49.

GERMAN (South) or SWISS, ca. 1520.

St. Mary Magdalen Raising the Wife of the Prince of Marseilles

41.73

Panel (oak) 37⅞ × 19½ in. (95.5 × 48.6 cm). Coll. Count Wilczek, Castle Kreuzenstein near Vienna; E. and A. Silberman Galleries, New York. Purchased from R. T. Miller, Jr. Fund, 1941. *Fig.* 36

The subject after Jacobus de Voragine, *Golden Legend*, Caxton IV, 81. Nos. 41.73 and 41.74 formed part of an apparently large altarpiece dedicated to the Life of St. Mary Magdalen of which two other panels have survived (formerly Coll. de Lancey Kountze in New York: ca. 1943 with Victor Spark, New York); these represent the *Conversion of the Prince of Marseilles and his Wife* and the *Arrival of Mary Magdalen in the Harbor of Marseilles*. Another panel from the same altarpiece, in bad condition, was left behind in the Wilczek Coll. when the two now at Oberlin were acquired by Messrs. Silberman.

The style of the panels points to the Swabian-Swiss border region around Lake Constance. Related, though not by the same hand, are: a panel of 1523 in the chapel of the Castle at Vaduz (*Die Kunstdenkmäler von Liechtenstein*, Basel, 1950, p. 203) and two in the Kunsthaus at Zürich, inv. no. 1908–09 (*Bilder nach Skulpturen und Gemälden der Sammlung*, 1936, pl. 51); to be compared also to the *Visitation*, sale Eduard von Grützner, Munich, June 24, 1930, no. 223 (as School of Lake Constance, ca. 1510).

Exh.: "Swiss Painting from the 15th to the 18th Centuries," Berne Art Museum, 1936, no. 59.

St. Mary Magdalen Raising a Dead Knight for Confession

41.74

Panel (oak), 38 × 19½ in. (96.5 × 48.6 cm). Same provenance as the companion piece, 41.73. *Fig.* 37

The subject after Jacobus de Voragine, Golden Legend, Caxton IV, 87. See further under 41.73.

GIACOMETTI, ALBERTO. Born in Stampa im Bergell (Graubünden, Switzerland) in 1901. Studied at the École des Arts et Métiers in Geneva. In Rome, 1920–21. After 1922 active mostly in Paris. Died at Chur in 1966. Sculptor.

Figure 1951 *64.25*

Canvas, 43¼ × 20½ in. (109.8 × 52.1 cm). Signed, lower right: Alberto Giacometti 1951. Coll. Galerie Maeght, Paris (1951); Mr. and Mrs. Joseph Bissett, New York. Bissett Gift (life interest retained), 1964. *Fig. 150*

Exh.: "Alberto Giacometti," New York, Museum of Modern Art, 1965, p. 117, no. 85.

GIAMPIETRINO? Lombard painter about whose life and real name (Giovanni Pedrini?) no authentic information exists. Probably pupil, in Milan, of Leonardo da Vinci whom he imitated; active ca. 1520–40.

Cleopatra *61.81*

Panel (mounted on mahogany), 29⅞ × 21⅛ in. (75.9 × 53.7 cm). Coll. Ferroni, Florence (not in sales of Coll. Gioacchino Ferroni, Rome 1909 and 1910); Samuel H. Kress, New York (1939). Kress Study Collection, 1961. *Fig. 23*

Considerable rubbing.

A near-identical composition of the same size is in the Louvre (Cat. 1926, no. 1686 as Giampietrino; published as by Sodoma by Ch. Marcel-Reymond in *Gazette des Beaux-Arts*, 5. per., IV, 1921, II, pp. 211 ff.); the architecture in the right background is different (see reproductions in Stechow 1961–62).

The composition is an adaptation of Leonardo's lost *Standing Leda* which is known from many copies (cf. also the "Neuwied" copy of Leonardo's (?) *Kneeling Leda*, usually attributed to Giampietrino). The pose was repeated almost exactly for the *Lucretia* of

63

the Kress Coll., now in the Museum of the University of Wisconsin (Cat. *The Samuel H. Kress Study Collection of Italian Renaissance Art*, n.d., no. 3), which is attributed to the same artist. However, the softer modelling and facial features of the Oberlin *Cleopatra* differ from those of the Louvre version, of the Madison *Lucretia*, and of its companion piece, a second *Cleopatra* of the Kress Coll. (no. 347; now Bucknell University, Lewisburg, Pa.) and seem to point to a different hand.

Lit.: W. Stechow, "The Samuel H. Kress Study Collection, Catalogue," *AMAM Bulletin*, XIX, 1961–62, pp. 24 ff., no. 4.

GIFFORD, ROBERT SWAIN. Born in Naushon, Mass., in 1840; pupil of A. van Beest and B. Russell in New Bedford. Active in Boston (1864–66) and New York (from 1866); traveled widely in the U.S., Europe and North Africa. Associate member of the National Academy, 1867; full member, 1878. Died in New York in 1905.

Autumn Woods, Nonquitt   *19.16*

Canvas, 13½ × 23½ in. (34.3 × 59.7 cm). Sale in New York, Feb. 2, 1906, no. 64; A. Augustus Healy, Brooklyn, N.Y. Gift of A. A. Healy, 1919.

Nonquitt is situated south of New Bedford, Mass.

GIOLFINO, NICCOLÒ. Born in Verona in 1476. Pupil of Liberale da Verona. Active as painter of altarpieces, frescoes and cassone panels in Verona, where he died in 1555.

Lucretia   *61.82*

Panel (mounted on mahogany), 16¼ × 12⅞ in. (41.3 × 32.7 cm). Coll. Samuel H. Kress, 1941. Kress Study Collection, 1961.

Fig. 24

The tree, formerly overpainted, has been revealed by recent cleaning. Probably a fragment of a full-length figure; the painting has been cut on all sides. The convincing attribution to Giolfino was first made by F. Mason Perkins.

Lit.: W. Stechow, "The Samuel H. Kress Study Collection, Catalogue," *AMAM Bulletin*, XIX, 1961–62, p. 29, no. 5.

GIORDANO, LUCA. Born in Naples in 1632. Pupil of his father Antonio but predominantly influenced by Lanfranco and Ribera in Naples, Pietro da Cortona in Rome, Veronese and Rubens. Active in Naples (member of the guild, 1655), Venice, Florence (1682 ff.) and Madrid (1692–1702). Died in Naples in 1705.

Christ Expelling the Money-Changers from the Temple 1684
52.28

Canvas, 38⅛ × 47⅝ in. (97 × 121 cm). Coll. Butler, Woollen Hall, Berwick; Frederick Mont, New York (ca. 1945); J. Weitzner, New York (1948). Purchased from R. T. Miller, Jr. Fund, 1952. *Fig.* 47

Modello for the large fresco of 1684 on the entrance wall of the Gerolomini Church (San Filippo Neri) in Naples, which deviates from it in a few details, primarily in the extension on all four sides, and in the distance where the fresco has introduced a landscape behind Christ instead of the oculus of the modello. The area occupied by the actual door in the final setting is painted in the shape of a door in the modello. Perhaps identical with the picture of this subject by Giordano in sale Duke of Orléans, London, Feb. 14, 1800, no. 36. W. Rolfs (*Geschichte der Malerei Neapels*, Leipzig, 1910, p. 346 n. 2) and Pigler (1956) mention a sketch for the fresco as being preserved in the sacristy of the Naples church (no information available). The fresco was immensely popular in the eighteenth century and was copied, among others, by Hubert Robert and Fragonard; the colored drawing in the Brera in Milan (no. 2092), there considered a preparatory study, is apparently also by an eighteenth-century hand.

Exh.: "Italian Paintings of the Seventeenth Century," AMAM, 1952, no. 6; Akron Art Institute, 1954; "Masterpieces from Ohio Museums," Zanesville Art Institute, 1954; "Dedication Exhibition," Athens, Georgia, Museum of Art, University of Georgia,

1958, no. 80; "Luca Giordano in America," Memphis, Tennessee, Brooks Memorial Art Gallery, 1964, no. 14.
Lit.: A. Pigler, *Barockthemen*, Budapest-Berlin, 1956, I, p. 328; O. Ferrari & G. Scavizzi, *Luca Giordano*, Naples, 1966, Vol. II, p. 133 ("un preteso bozzetto"); Vol. III, p. 369, fig. 247.

GORKY, ARSHILE. Born in Tiflis (Tblissi) in 1904 (baptized Vosdanig Adoian). Came to the United States in 1920 and studied painting in Boston and New York. Taught at Grand Central School of Art and the New York School of Design, 1925–32. Active in New York until his death in 1948.

The Plough and the Song 1947 *52.16*

Canvas, 50¾ × 62¾ in. (126.9 × 156.9 cm). Signed, lower right: "A Gorky 47." Coll. Julian Levy, New York. Purchased from R. T. Miller, Jr. Fund, 1952. *Fig.* 206

One of three versions of the subject; the other two are in the Art Institute of Chicago (Mr. and Mrs. Lewis Larned Coburn Coll.) and in the S. J. Wolf Coll., New York.

A preparatory drawing is in the AMAM (see Seitz 1954–55).

Exh.: "Twenty-five Years of American Painting," USIA Traveling European Exhibition, 1959–1960, Darmstadt and Göteborg, no. 22; "Paintings and Drawings from Five Centuries" (AMAM), Knoedler Galleries, N.Y., 1954, no. 77; "Some Points of View in Modern Painting," William Rockhill Nelson Gallery of Art, Kansas City, Missouri, 1957, no. 22; "Some Contemporary Works of Art," Cleveland Museum of Art, 1958, no. 21; "XXXI. Esposizione Biennale Internazionale d'Arte," Venice, 1962, no. 25; "Arshile Gorky," Museum of Modern Art, New York, 1962–1963; "Arshile Gorky," Gallery of Modern Art, Washington, D.C., 1963, no. 112; "Art Since 1889," University of New Mexico Art Gallery, Albuquerque, 1964, no. 39; "Arshile Gorky," Tate Gallery, London; Palais des Beaux-Arts, Brussels; Museum Boymans-Van Beuningen, Rotterdam, 1965, no. 92; "Treasures from the Allen Memorial Art Museum," Minneapolis Institute of Arts, 1966.

Lit.: W. C. Seitz, "Arshile Gorky's 'The Plough and the Song,' " *AMAM Bulletin*, XII, 1954–55, pp. 4 ff.; E. K. Schwabacher, *Arshile Gorky*, New York, 1957, p. 143.

GOYEN, JAN VAN. Born in Leyden in 1596. Pupil of some smaller masters including Willem Gerritsz. in Hoorn. Traveled in France; after his return pupil of Esajas van de Velde in Haarlem (1617). Active in Leyden (1619 ff.); after 1634 (at the latest) in The Hague, where he died in 1656.

Landscape with Dunes 1647   *41.76*

Panel (oak), 18½ × 28 in. (47 × 71.1 cm). Signed, lower right: VG 1647. Coll. M. Focke, Bremen (1904); E. J. van Wisselingh, Amsterdam (1932); M. Knoedler & Co., New York. Purchased from R. T. Miller. Jr. Fund, 1941.   *Fig.* 55

Exh.: "Gemälde aus bremischem Privatbesitz," Bremen, 1904, no. 180; "Dutch and Flemish Pictures of the Seventeenth Century," Amsterdam, E. J. van Wisselingh, 1932, no. 3; "Old Masters of the 17th and 18th Centuries," Vassar College, Poughkeepsie, N.Y., 1938, no. 7; Houston, Texas, Museum of Fine Arts, 1940, no. 7; "Masterworks from University and College Art Collections," University of Kansas Museum of Art, Lawrence, Kansas, 1958, no. 74.

Lit.: C. Hofstede de Groot, *A Catalogue Raisonné* . . ., VIII, London, 1927, p. 81, no. 295 (erroneously as signed "Van Goyen," no date); W. Stechow, *Dutch Landscape Painting of the Seventeenth Century* (*National Gallery of Art, Kress Foundation Studies in the History of European Art*, I), London, 1966, p. 28.

HAMMER, JOHN J. Born in Westhofen (Germany; not clear which town of the name) in 1838 or 1842; came to the United States as a youth. Active in Baltimore and, after a visit to Paris, in New York (after 1869). In 1876 student of L. von Löfftz and Alexander Wagner at the Munich Academy; visited Italy. Lived in Pittsburgh, 1888–89; later (1898) again active in Munich. Died in New York in 1906.

Mount Washington Before 1887   *04.1216*

Canvas, 7⅛ × 11¹¹⁄₁₆ in. (18.1 × 29.7 cm). Signed, lower right: John J. Hammer. Coll. Charles F. Olney, Cleveland, acquired before 1887. Olney Gift, 1904.   *Fig.* 188

HARNETT, WILLIAM MICHAEL. Born in Clonakilty (County Cork, Ireland) in 1848. His family had moved to Philadelphia by 1869. Trained as an engraver; as a painter, self-taught. Active in New York (1869–76), Philadelphia (1876–80), Europe, mostly Munich (1880–86), and New York again, where he died in 1892.

Meerschaum Pipe 1886   *45.31*

Canvas, 17⅝ × 12¾ in. (44.8 × 32.4 cm). Signed, lower right: WMHarnett (WMH in ligature) 1886. Coll. A. F. Mondschein, New York. Purchased from Olney Fund, 1945.   *Fig.* 185

Almost identical in composition with the picture of the same year in Coll. Martin B. Grossman, New York (16½ × 11½ in.; Frankenstein, 1953, p. 171 and pl. 65) but without the newspaper clipping and the nail. Other differences occur in the cracks and other marks.

Exh.: "Still Life Paintings, 17th to 19th Century," AMAM, 1945; "Harnett Centennial," New York, Downtown Gallery, 1948; "Paintings and Drawings from Five Centuries" (AMAM), New York, Knoedler Galleries, 1954, no. 62; "Still Life Painting since 1470," Milwaukee Art Institute and Cincinnati Art Museum, 1956, no. 29; "An American University Collection" (AMAM), Kenwood (London County Council), 1962, no. 22.

Lit.: A. Frankenstein, *After the Hunt*, Berkeley-Los Angeles, 1953, p. 72 and p. 171, no. 101.

HARPIGNIES, HENRI JOSEPH. Born in Valenciennes in 1819. Pupil of J. Achard in Paris, Crémieux (Dauphine) and Brussels, 1846–49; 1850–52 and 1863–65 in Italy. Active in Paris, the Nivernais, Saint-Privé (Yonne; after 1878) and the French Mediterranean Coast. Died in Saint-Privé in 1916.

Landscape 1907   *15.54*

Panel (mahogany), 22½ × 15 in. (57.2 × 38.1 cm). Signed, lower left: HJHarpignies 1907. (HJH in ligature). Bequest of Charles Martin Hall, Daytona, Fla., 1914.   *Fig.* 114

HART, GEORGE OVERBURY, CALLED "POP HART." Born in Cairo, Ill., in 1868. Self-taught. Active on Tahiti and Iceland, in Morocco and Mexico, and in New York, where he died in 1933.

The Hero 1927 *47.76*

Panel (hardwood veneer), 9½ × 12⅞ in. (24.1 × 32.7 cm). Signed, lower left: Hart, Mex '27. Coll. Downtown Gallery, New York (1927); Mrs. Malcolm L. McBride, Cleveland. Gift of Mrs. McBride, 1947. *Fig. 203*

HART, JAMES MCDOUGAL. Born in Kilmarnock, Scotland, in 1828, younger brother of William Hart. His family moved to Albany, N.Y., in 1831. Attended the Academy at Düsseldorf, 1850. After his return in 1853 active in Albany and New York (from 1857); member of the National Academy in 1860. Died in Brooklyn in 1901.

Peaceful Homes 1868 *04.1190*

Canvas, 51 × 93½ in. (129.5 × 237.5 cm). Signed, lower left: James M. Hart; a second signature, lower right, same form, partly over-painted. Coll. Charles F. Olney, Cleveland, acquired in 1891/92. Olney Gift, 1904. *Fig. 164*

Finished in 1868 after several years of work (some newspaper reports indicate two, others ten years). The New York *Commercial Advertiser* of Feb. 25, 1867, calls the picture unfinished and, in a description identical with that by Tuckerman (1867), mentions that "down a somewhat stony road, one side of the field, a boy is driving some rather frisky cows," a passage apparently later deleted by the artist (see also the statement above on the partly overpainted first signature). The scene represents Farmington Valley, Connecticut.

Exh.: Cleveland, James F. Ryder's Art Gallery (1892?); "American Artists Discover America," AMAM, 1946, no. 19.

Lit.: H. T. Tuckerman, *Book of the Artists*, New York, 1867 (second ed., 1882), p. 549.

Landscape with Cattle; Evening 1869 *04.1224*

Canvas, mounted on board, semicircular top, 6¹⁵⁄₁₆ × 3¹⁵⁄₁₆ in. (17.6 × 10 cm). Signed, lower left: J. M. Hart. 69. Coll. Charles F. Olney, Cleveland, acquired before 1887. Olney Gift, 1904.

Homeward Path 1882 *04.1191*

Canvas, 15 × 10⅛ in. (38.1 × 25.7 cm). Signed, lower left: James M. Hart 1882. Coll. Charles F. Olney, Cleveland, acquired before 1887. Olney Gift, 1904. *Fig.* 165

Exh.: "American Artists Discover America," AMAM, 1946, no. 20.

HART, WILLIAM. Born in Paisley, Scotland, in 1823, elder brother of James M. Hart. His family moved to Albany, N.Y. in 1831. Traveling portrait and landscape painter (Troy, N.Y., Richmond, Va., Michigan) in the early 1840's. Later active in Albany (from ca. 1847), Scotland (1849–52), New York (from 1854; member of the National Academy, 1858) and Brooklyn; first President of the Brooklyn Academy of Design, 1865. Died in Mt. Vernon, N.Y., in 1894.

Beside the Brook Before 1887 *04.1192*

Canvas, 5½ × 10¼ in. (14 × 26 cm). Signed, lower right: W. HART. Coll. Charles F. Olney, Cleveland, acquired before 1887. Olney Gift, 1904. *Fig.* 167

Exh.: "American Artists Discover America," AMAM, 1946, no. 21.

Farmington Valley, Connecticut 1866 *04.1193*

Canvas, 8¾ × 16⅜ in. (22.2 × 41.6 cm). Signed, lower left: WM. HART 66. Coll. Charles F. Olney, Cleveland, acquired before 1887. Olney Gift, 1904. *Fig.* 166

Exh.: "American Artists Discover America," AMAM, 1946, no. 22.

Coming Storm, Lake Cayuga (N.Y.) Before 1887 *04.620*

Canvas, 7 × 12¼ in. (17.8 × 31.1 cm). Signed, lower left: W. HART. Coll. Charles F. Olney, Cleveland, acquired before 1887. Olney Gift, 1904.

The picture was sold to Mr. Olney by A. D. Shattuck to whom Hart had given it in exchange for one painted by Shattuck.

Bit of Nature Before 1892 *04.425*

Canvas, 8½ × 10½ in. (21.6 × 26.7 cm). Canvas stamped: Goupil & Co. Artists Colourmen Broadway, New York; and on top of this: Robt Fullerton Art Dealer. Coll. Charles F. Olney, Cleveland, bought in 1892. Olney Gift, 1904. *Fig.* 168

HEEM, JAN DAVIDSZ DE. Born in Utrecht in 1606. Pupil of his father David (I) de Heem. Ca. 1626–31 active in Leyden; by 1635/36 master in the Antwerp guild. After another stay in Utrecht (ca. 1669–72) back in Antwerp, where he died in 1683 or 1684.

Still Life *54.21*

Canvas, 17¾ × 24⅛₆ in. (45.1 × 61.1 cm). Signed, upper center: JD de Heem fc. Coll. Hermitage, Leningrad (no. 3728); Dr. Leyendecker, Berlin; Eugene L. Garbáty, Berlin and New York. Purchased from Mrs. F. F. Prentiss Fund, 1954. *Fig.* 58

Possibly either one of the two paintings mentioned in G. F. Waagen, *Die Gemäldesammlung in der kaiserlichen Eremitage zu St. Petersburg* . . ., Munich, 1864, p. 364 f., as being in the Winter Palace: "Ein Frühstück, bezeichnet. Ein warmes and fleissiges Bild seiner früheren Zeit. Ein anderes, ebenfalls gutes Bild ähnlicher Art." The picture may have been transferred from the Winter Palace to the Hermitage in 1922; no. 3727, a picture by Cornelis de Heem, was transferred to the Hermitage from the Academy Collection in that year.

The same Chinese bowl with exactly the same arrangement of fruit, the same short roemer on the wooden box, the same arrangement on the pewter tray and the same lobster appear in a different composition on an oriental rug in a large painting in the Coll. Emile Wolf in New York which is signed and dated 1645 (Exh. Brussels, 1965, no. 105).

Exh.: Worcester, Mass., Art Museum, 1948; "Glass Vessels in Dutch Painting of the 17th Century," Corning Museum of Glass, Corning, N.Y., 1952, no. 3; "An American University Collection" (AMAM), Kenwood (London County Council), 1962, no. 23, "Treasures from the Allen Memorial Art Museum," Minneapolis Institute of Arts, 1966.

Lit.: Cat. Exh. "Le siècle de Rubens," Brussels, 1965, in text to no. 105 (as at "Aberdeen College").

HEEMSKERCK, MAERTEN VAN. Born in Heemskerk (North Holland) in 1498. Pupil of Jan Scorel in Haarlem, ca. 1527. In Italy, mostly Rome, 1532–35. Afterwards active in Haarlem until his death in 1574.

Samson Slaying the Philistines   Brown monochrome   *49.81*

Panel (oak), 18½ × 5⅝ in. (47 × 14.3 cm). Coll. Lord Kinnaird, Rossie Priory, Inchture, Perthshire, Scotland, sale in London (Christie's), June 21, 1946, in lot no. 36; Grete Ring, London; F. Kleinberger & Co., New York. Purchased from Charles F. Olney Fund, 1949.

Fig. 33

Together with no. 49.82, part of an ensemble of twelve panels (three of them signed) which was kept together until sold from Lord Kinnaird's Collection (as "The Twelve Labours of Hercules"). Of the other ten, four are in the Rijksmuseum, Amsterdam (nos. 1128-A 3-6), two in the Coll. Dr. H. Wetzlar, Amsterdam (Cat. 1952, no. 44), and four in the Yale University Art Gallery (given by Chester D. Tripp of Chicago, 1960; see *Yale Art Gallery Bulletin*, XXVI, Dec. 1961, 7 and 48). According to Erwin Panofsky (*in litteris*, 1950), a Hercules-Samson parallel is established in pairs: (1) Hercules carrying the Column of Heaven (Yale) and (2) Samson carrying the Gates of Gaza (Wetzlar Coll.); (3) Hercules conquering Antaeus (Yale) and (4) Samson conquering the Philistines (Oberlin); (5) Hercules conquering Hydra (Yale) and (6) Samson conquering the Lion (Amsterdam); (7) Hercules destroying Nessus (Amsterdam; there as Pholos) and (8) Samson pulling down the Palace (Amsterdam). The Hercules scenes can also be seen in terms of the Four Elements (Panofsky): (1)=Air; (3)=Earth; (5)=Fire; (7)=Water (Nessus as Ferryman; Pholos' death at the hand of Hercules is very rarely represented; many ancient representations of the Slaying of Nessus show Hercules clubbing rather than shooting him). The other deities involved in the ensemble can also be related to the Four Elements: Jupiter (Oberlin 49.82)= Air; Pluto (Wetzlar Coll.)=Fire; Saturn (Yale)=Earth; Neptune (Amsterdam)=Water. The original function of the series remains unexplained; paneling of a scholar's study? The date is hard to determine but it may not be far from that of Heemskerck's return from Rome in 1535. The memory of Roman sarcophagi is very vivid.

Exh.: "Paintings and Drawings from Five Centuries" (AMAM), New York, Knoedler Galleries, 1954, no. 29.

Lit.: *Catalogue of Paintings, Rijksmuseum Amsterdam*, 1960, p. 126.

Jupiter   Brown monochrome   *49.82*

Panel (oak), 18½ × 5⅝ in. (47 × 14.3 cm).
See no. 49.81 for all further details.   *Fig. 33*

Exh.: "Paintings and Drawings from Five Centuries" (AMAM), New York, Knoedler Galleries, 1954, no. 30.

HENRI, ROBERT. Real name Robert Henry Cozad. Born in Cincinnati in 1865. Studied at the Pennsylvania Academy in Philadelphia, 1886–88; in Paris, 1888–90. Taught in Philadelphia, 1891–95; after another stay in Paris, settled in New York in 1899, taught at the Chase School, 1903–08, and founded his own, 1909. Member, National Academy, 1906; one of "The Eight," 1908. Died in New York in 1929.

The Gypsy Girl   *00.32*

Canvas, 24 × 20⅛ in. (61 × 51.1 cm). Signed, lower right: Robert Henri. Inscribed on back of the canvas: Spanish gipsy girl Robert Henri Madrid. Purchased by the Oberlin Art Association after 1915.

Fig. 196

The inscription on the back makes it appear certain that Henri painted this picture in Madrid; whether the additional mark "99 H" indicates that it was painted in 1899 is not entirely clear but it seems possible that Henri was in Madrid in that year before settling in New York. (A picture called "Spain," painted in 1902, was exhibited in the Brooklyn Museum in 1943/44, no. 2 [The Eight].) However, the style of the Oberlin picture would seem to point to its having been painted during the artist's stay in Madrid in 1906; cf. *Gypsy with Guitar* of the Chrysler Coll. (Exh. "Robert Henri, Fifty Paintings," New York, Hirschl and Adler Galleries, 1958, no. 16).

Exh.: William Macbeth Gallery, New York, date uncertain (label on frame: "Paintings by American Artists William Macbeth 450 Fifth Avenue New York, Spanish Gipsy Girl, Robert Henri N. A."; the latter initials prove a date after 1906 for the exhibition).

HOBBEMA, MEINDERT. Born in Amsterdam in 1638. Pupil of Jacob van Ruisdael; active in Amsterdam from 1658 (first dated picture) to at least 1689 but only sporadically after 1668, when he accepted a job as gauger of wine casks for the city of Amsterdam. Died at Amsterdam in 1709.

A Pond in a Forest   1668   *44.52*

Panel (oak), 23⅝ × 33¼ in. (60 × 84.5 cm). Signed and dated, lower right: M. Hobbema 1668. Coll. Michael Zachary, 1825 (bought from John Smith, who had imported it into England); Frederick Perkins, London, 1835; George Perkins, sale in London (Christie's), June 14, 1890, no. 7 (engraved by P. Teyssonier); H. M. W. Oppenheim, London, sale June 13, 1913, no. 53; Edward Drummond Libbey, Toledo (1914); Knoedler Galleries, New York; Mrs. Dudley P. Allen (Prentiss), Cleveland, acquired in 1916. Prentiss Bequest, 1944.   *Fig. 69*

Extraordinarily well preserved. Before 1944, the date was misread as 1664 or 1669 (the date 1644 given by Graves, 1921, is a misprint).

Exh.: "Paintings and Drawings from Five Centuries" (AMAM),

Knoedler Galleries, New York, 1954, no. 47; "Dutch Painting: The Golden Age," New York—Toledo—Toronto, 1954–55, no. 18; "Trends in Painting, 1600–1800," Albright Art Gallery, Buffalo, 1957, p. 32.
Lit.: John Smith, *Catalogue Raisonné* . . . VI, 1835, p. 133, no. 62; G. Waagen, *Art Treasures in Great Britain*, London, 1854, II, p. 336; C. Hofstede de Groot, *Catalogue Raisonné* . . . IV, 1912, p. 423, no. 218; W. R. Valentiner, "The Hobbema from the Oppenheim Collection," *Art in America*, II, 1914, pp. 165 f.; A. Graves, *Art Sales*, II, 1921, pp. 32 f.; G. Broulhiet, *Meindert Hobbema*, Paris, 1938, p. 435, no. 438; W. Stechow, *Dutch Landscape Painting of the Seventeenth Century* (*National Gallery of Art, Kress Foundation Studies in the History of European Art*, I), London, 1966, p. 78.

HOFER, CARL.   Born in Karlsruhe in 1878. Studied at the Karlsruhe Academy, 1896–1901. 1903–08 in Rome, 1908–13 in Paris. Settled in Berlin in 1913; Professor at the Academy, 1919–33, and at the Hochschule für bildende Künste, 1945, until his death in 1955.

The Repast   1932   *46.30*
Canvas, 31 × 39 in. (78.7 × 99.1 cm). Signed, lower right: CH32 (in ligature). Coll. J. B. Neumann, sale New York, April 11, 1940, no. 69; Nierendorf Gallery, New York. Purchased from C. F. Olney Fund, 1946.   *Fig. 138*

Exh.: "Five Expressionists," AMAM, 1946, no. 13.

HOGARTH, WILLIAM.   Born in London in 1697. Trained as a goldsmith and engraver, started painting ca. 1728. Visited Paris in 1743 and 1748. Active in London, where he died in 1764. Founder of the new Academy at St. Martin's Lane, author of "The Analysis of Beauty" (1753).

Portrait of Theodore Jacobsen   1742   *42.127*
Canvas, 35¾ × 27¾ in. (90.9 × 70.5 cm). Signed, lower right: W. Hogarth pinx. 1742. Further inscriptions: In front at the top, left of center: "Theodore Jacobson, Esq."; lower left, across the top of

the paper: ". . . Elevation of a Triangular House by Theodore Jacobson, Esq."; on the back, copied from the original canvas when relined ca. 80 years ago: "Portrait of Jacobson the Architect with a plan of Longford Castle, Wilts, by W. Hogarth 1742." Coll. (?) Earl of Radnor, Longford Castle near Salisbury, Wiltshire; William Davies, London (1817), but not in sale June 9, 1821; George Watson Taylor, London and Earlestoke Park, Wiltshire, sale London, July 24, 1832, no. 45 (bought by Woodin); Henry Ralph Willet, Merly House, Canford, Dorset, sale in London, July 10, 1869, no. 52 (bought in); sale in London, Jan. 12, 1942, no. 161 (from the collection of a lady to whose father the picture had been bequeathed by H. R. Willet); M. Knoedler & Co., New York. Purchased from R. T. Miller, Jr. Fund, 1942.   *Fig.* 85

The sitter, son of a Hamburg alderman, was a wealthy London merchant, architect, and governor of the Foundling Hospital for which he drew up plans approved in 1742 (executed 1742–52, building destroyed in 1928). He died in London in 1772. Hogarth, too, was a governor of the Hospital and painted its founder, Captain Coram, in 1740. Under the ground plan which the sitter is holding in his hands one can clearly distinguish the elevation, with a classical façade, of the same building (revealed by cleaning, 1955). The ground plan is not identical with that of Longford Castle as was formerly surmised (see also the inscription on the back) but corresponds exactly to "A Plan of a Triangular House designed by Theodore Jacobsen Esqr.," engraved by P. Fourdrinier (Colvin, 1954; Oxford, Bodleian Library, Gough Maps 30, fol. 75). Although this design may have been inspired by Longford Castle there is no record of any activity by Jacobsen for that building. It is possible that the tradition according to which the present picture was once in the collection of the Earl of Radnor was based on a confusion of the two plans; however it is a fact that Jacobsen was a friend of Sir Jacob Bouverie, ancestor of the Earls of Radnor, owner of Longford Castle at that time and a governor of the Foundling Hospital together with Jacobsen in 1739.

The ring on the sitter's left hand is undoubtedly the one presented to Jacobsen by the East India Company in 1729 (Colvin 1954).

Exh.: "Paintings, Watercolors, Drawings and Prints by William

Hogarth," Smith College Museum, Northampton, Mass., 1944; "Three Centuries of British Art," Art Institute, Milwaukee, Wis., 1946; "Great Portraits by Famous Painters," Institute of Arts, Minneapolis, Minn., 1952, no. 18; "Paintings and Drawings from Five Centuries" (AMAM), Knoedler Galleries, New York, 1954, no. 52; "The Century of Mozart," Nelson Gallery and Atkins Museum of Fine Arts, Kansas City, Mo., 1956, no. 54; "Masterworks from American University Museums," European Tour, sponsored by the College Art Association, 1956/57, Cat. Malmö no. 25, Utrecht no. 22, Lyons no. 17; "Art Museum of the Month," Art Gallery, Grands Rapids, Mich., 1962; "An American University Collection" (AMAM), Kenwood (London County Council), 1962, no. 24; "Treasures from the Allen Memorial Art Museum," Minneapolis Institute of Arts, 1966; "William Hogarth," Museum of Fine Arts, Richmond, Va., 1967, no. 25.

Lit.: J. Nichols and G. Steevens, *The Genuine Works of William Hogarth*, London, 1817, III, p. 178; J. B. Nichols (ed.), *Anecdotes of William Hogarth Written by Himself*, London, 1833, p. 386; A. Dobson and Sir Walter Armstrong, *William Hogarth*, London, 1902, p. 182; A. Dobson, *William Hogarth*, London, 1907, p. 215; L. N. Simpson (and C. Hussey), "The Architect of the Foundling Hospital," *Country Life*, March 1927, p. 621; W. Stechow, " 'Theodore Jacobsen' by William Hogarth," *Art Quarterly*, VI, 1943, pp. 70 f.; R. B. Beckett, "Famous Hogarths in America," *Art in America*, XXXVI, 1948, pp. 159 ff. (173); R. B. Beckett, *Hogarth*, London, 1949, p. 15 and p. 56, no. 135; H. M. Colvin, *A Bibliographical Dictionary of English Architects, 1660–1840*, Cambridge, Mass., 1954, p. 313.

HOPPNER, JOHN.   Born in Whitechapel (London) in 1758. Began his studies at the Royal Academy in 1775, became Portrait Painter to the Prince of Wales in 1793. Full member of the Royal Academy, 1795. Died in London in 1810.

Mrs. Frances Henrietta Jerningham (later Lady Stafford)
1800   *59.118*

Canvas, 30 × 24¾ in. (76.2 × 62.9 cm). Coll. Sir William Jerningham, 6th Baronet (1800); Sir George William Jerningham (after

1826 Baron Stafford); Barons Stafford, Costessey Hall, Norfolk; Ethel Tod Humphreys, New York, sold in New York, Nov. 10, 1956, no. 415; M. Knoedler & Co., New York. Anonymous gift, 1959. *Fig. 88*

The sitter, youngest daughter of Edward Sulyarde of Haughley Park, Suffolk, married George William Jerningham in 1799; she died in 1832.

Painted in June 1800, when George William Jerningham wrote to his sister: "Fanny is sitting for her picture to Hoppner, for my father, at half-length, 30 guineas," a passage once (McKay-Roberts 1909) erroneously connected with the portrait of the same sitter as Hebe (painted in 1805).

Lit.: Egerton Castle (ed.), *The Jerningham Letters*, 1896, I, p. 188; W. McKay and W. Roberts, *John Hoppner, R. A.*, London, 1909, p. 138 (with erroneous identification, see above; the present one acknowledged by Roberts in letter to former owner, London, Feb. 27, 1925).

HUMPHREYS, RALPH. Born in Youngstown, Ohio, in 1933. Active in Youngstown, Paris, and since 1956 in New York.

Portland 1, 1957 1957 *64.45*

Canvas, 33 × 48 in. (83.8 × 121.9 cm). Gift of Mr. and Mrs. André Emmerich, New York, 1964.

ISRAELS, JOZEF. Born in Groningen in 1824. Studied at the Academy of Design in Groningen and from 1840 with J. A. Kruseman and J. W. Pieneman in Amsterdam. 1845–47 and 1853 in Paris and Barbizon. After 1847 active in Amsterdam and Zandvoort. From 1871 resident of The Hague, where he died in 1911.

Mother and Son—Twilight *19.10*

Canvas, 18 × 24 in. (45.7 × 61 cm). Signed, lower left: Jozef Israels. Coll. Peter A. Schemm, Philadelphia, sold in New York (American

Art Association) on March 14–17, 1911, no. 260; A. Augustus
Healy, Brooklyn. Gift of A. A. Healy, 1919.   *Fig.* 104

Probably a work of the 1890's or even later.

ITALIAN (Florentine), ca. 1330–40.

Crucifix from a Rood Screen   *42.129*

Panel (softwood like fir, gesso ground containing linen), 94¼×
69½ in. (239.4×176.5 cm). Coll. Graf Wilczek, Castle Kreuzenstein near Vienna; E. & A. Silberman Galleries, New York (1936).
Purchased from R. T. Miller, Jr. Fund, 1942.   *Fig* 1.

The inclined surface of the halo is formed by an added semicircular block. In spite of extensive damage in detail, the large
work has preserved its original character reasonably well.

Offner (1956) has convincingly attributed this Crucifix to the
workshop of his "Master of the Corsi Crucifix," so named for two
crosses (in the Corsi Collection and in the Accademia, Florence),
which show him as a close follower of the Sta. Cecilia Master, active
ca. 1325. A very similar, somewhat smaller Crucifix (178×145 cm)
from the same workshop was recently acquired by the Staats-
galerie in Stuttgart (Beye 1967).

Exh.: Gallery of Medieval Art, Brooklyn Museum of Art, 1936,
no. 117; Centennial Exposition, Dallas, Texas, Museum, 1936,
no. 19; "Six Centuries of Italian Painting," Rochester, N.Y.,
Memorial Art Gallery, 1939.

Lit.: R. Offner, *A Critical and Historical Corpus of Florentine
Painting*, Section III, vol. VI, New York, 1956, p. 26 and pls. VI
and VIa; P. Beye, "Ein unbekanntes Florentiner Kruzifix," *Pantheon*, XXV, 1967, pp. 5ff.

ITALIAN (Florentine), late 15th century.

The Archangel Raphael Guiding Tobias   *53.234*

Panel (poplar), round, the panel diam. 21½ in. (54.6 cm), painted surface 18⅜ in. (46.7 cm). Coll. Michael Dreicer, New York (1917); Baroness René de Kerchove, New York. Gift of Baroness de Kerchove, 1953.　　　　　　　　　　　　　　　　　　*Fig.* 12

Cut down to tondo form.

The work of a minor eclectic in which features from Jacopo del Sellajo, Botticini and Antonio Pollaiuolo (for Tobias cf. the Apollo of the London *Daphne*) are combined. The subject (votive panel for safe return) is characteristic of Florence. The traditional attribution to Francesco Granacci (O. Sirén in Exh. Cat. 1917) cannot be maintained. Instead of the usual semi-naturalistic fish dangling from a string Tobias carries under his arm a heraldic fish (note tail and fins; the long nose suggests a dolphin) apparently copied from the Pazzi coat-of-arms (cf. arms above door on Pazzi Chapel, Florence). It is possible that this indicates a Pazzi commission.

Exh.: "Loan Exhibition of Italian Primitives," New York, Kleinberger Galleries, 1917, no. 36.

ITALIAN (Lombard), ca. 1500.

Adoration of the Child with Portrait of Donor　　　*43.240*

Panel (probably poplar, thin gesso and paint on back) 14 × 10½ in. (35.5 × 26.6 cm). Coll. Sir Edgar Speyer; Paul Drey, New York. Purchased from A. Augustus Healy Fund, 1943.　　　　　*Fig.* 13

Well-preserved with only a small scar along the edges of the Virgin's robe. X-ray shows that the present donor was painted over a portrait of a young boy or possibly girl with a slightly larger head, hair differently arranged, no cap and wearing a garment with open curving neckline. None of these details indicates a material difference in date.

A note on the back in an eighteenth-century hand records the transfer by legacy of the painting from aunt to nephew. The date 1758 can be clearly read but not the family name of either party.

In the Speyer collection the painting was listed as a Francesco Cossa, an attribution that cannot be retained in view of the Lombard character of the Virgin and the very Lombard features of the original donor. Lombard School has been suggested in conversation by both Denis Mahon and Creighton Gilbert. Judging by the drawing of the hands and other details the artist was trained as a miniature painter which may explain a figure style somewhat earlier than the landscape which must be dated ca. 1500. It strongly resembles that of the Pseudo-Boccaccino portrait in a private collection, Milan (Exh. *Kunstschätze der Lombardei*, Kunsthaus, Zürich, 1948–49, p. 255, no. 706, fig. 89).

ITALIAN (Neapolitan), first quarter 16th century.

Madonna del Suffragio   *61.80*

Panel (hardwood like poplar), 58¾×20¼ in. (149.3×51.4 cm). Coll. Piero Tozzi, New York; F. Kleinberger, New York (1924); Dr. Paul Fiala, New York (1938); Contini-Bonacossi, Florence; Samuel H. Kress (1948). Kress Study Collection, 1961.   *Fig. 22*

Panel cut down on both sides removing part of a small figure of a kneeling nun at lower left and all but the hands of another figure at lower right, as well as narrow strips of landscape on both sides. Well preserved; minor areas of retouching in the drapery.

First published by Giacomo de Nicola (1924), as the central part of a triptych, "apparently . . . from Sorrento." The lateral panels show an *Adoration of the Child* and a *Visitation*. They were still together when owned by F. Kleinberger. Their records state that the panels came from a private collection in Naples. In 1938 the *Madonna* and *Adoration* were sold together. The *Adoration* appeared in a sale from a New York private collection at Parke-Bernet, New York, March 5, 1952, no. 70, and again in a sale at the same gallery on October 12, 1963 where it passed from the estate of G. Butler Sherwell to Coll. Michel, New York. The whereabouts of the *Visitation* is uncertain. All three panels are clearly by the same hand.

De Nicola attributed the paintings to Cristoforo Scacco under whose name the *Madonna del Suffragio* came to the Allen Art Museum. F. Zeri (1949 and 1954) rejects the attribution of the three panels to Scacco. In a letter of January 28, 1964 in the files of the Kress Foundation, he tentatively suggests the name of Vincenzo de Rogata, "a strange and obscure painter, who is known only through a triptych in the Museum of the Cathedral at Salerno, in which Scacco's influence is obvious." The attribution to Scacco no longer seems tenable. The Neapolitan follower appears less attracted to the Antoniazzo Romano elements in the painting of Scacco and more to those that come from the Paduan-Venetian school. The pomegranate motif developed into a vase form seen on the Virgin's mantle is found in Italian and Spanish brocades of the 16th century (Otto von Falke, *Decorative Silks*, New York, 1936, p. 49 and figs. 495, 496; Jaques and Fleming, *Encyclopedia of Textiles*, New York, 1958, pp. 69, 81, 127, pl. VI. Cf. also van Marle, *Italian Schools of Painting*, The Hague, XV, p. 366, fig. 224). The unusual subject in which milk from the Virgin's breasts is directed toward souls in Purgatory is found largely in the Neapolitan area and in Spain (van Marle, *op. cit.* XV, figs. 150, 222, 231, 233; C. R. Post, *A History of Spanish Painting*, X, 1950, p. 262).

Lit.: G. de Nicola, "A Triptych by Cristoforo Scacco," *Burlington Magazine*, XLIV, 1924, pp. 284–289; F. Zeri, "Un trittico di Cristoforo Scacco," *Bollettino d'arte*, XXXIX, 1949, pp. 338–340 (p. 340 n. 4); F. Zeri, "Two Early Cinquecento Problems in South Italy," *Burlington Magazine*, XCVI, 1954, pp. 147–150 (p. 150 n. 9); W. Stechow, "The Samuel H. Kress Study Collection, Catalogue," *AMAM Bulletin*, XIX, 1961–62, pp. 20 ff., no. 3.

ITALIAN (North), last half 15th century.

Madonna of Humility   *43.7*

Panel, 12½ × 9¾ in. (31.8 × 24.8 cm). Gift of Robert Lehman, New York, 1943.

Condition very poor; panel is warped and vermiculated. A large repair covers Virgin's left shoulder and halo above it. Small losses occur along all edges. Larger losses in the background above her head and to her right.

By a provincial master working in the vicinity of Venice, Padua and Verona under the influence of the Vivarini and possibly Domenico Morone to whose name it was once assigned.

ITALIAN (Sienese), ca. 1300.

Madonna with Child and St. Francis   45.9

Panel (hardwood like poplar), 27 × 20¼ in. (68.6 × 51.4 cm). Coll. Paul Drey, New York. Purchased from the R. T. Miller, Jr. Fund, 1945.   *Fig.* 3

A vertical split left of the center, as well as minor paint and gold losses throughout, have been repaired. The picture was apparently left unfinished; green underpainting in the flesh parts.

The design of this panel and that of a picture from the circle of Cimabue in the Louvre seems to be based on a common source, perhaps a work of either Cimabue or (more probably) Duccio about 1285 (Meiss 1955); for the insertion of St. Francis in the gold ground compare that of the *Stigmatization* in the Louvre painting. Stylistically, the Oberlin panel is very closely related to the early Duccio.

Lit.: E. B. Garrison, *Italian Romanesque Panel Painting*, Florence, 1949, p. 60, no. 98; M. Meiss, "Nuovi dipinti e vecchi problemi," *Rivista d'arte*, XXX, 1955, pp. 107 ff. (111).

ITALIAN (Sienese), ca. 1350.

Madonna and Child Enthroned with Bishop Saint and Donor
47.1

Panel (poplar), 22 × 10½ in. (55.9 × 26.7 cm). Coll. Prince Urusow (Ourousoff), Vienna; Philip Lehman, New York. Gift of Philip Lehman, 1947.   *Fig.* 4

The heads of the Madonna and the Child are overpainted.

This is the center piece of a tabernacle of a special devotional type, on which see Garrison (1943–45). The attribution of the panel has varied, partly because of insufficient realization of the distortion caused by the overpainting of the faces of the Madonna and Child. The Lehman Catalogue (1928) quotes the opinions of de Nicola ("late follower of Duccio"), Offner (do., "ca. 1360, possibly earlier"), van Marle ("possibly an early work of the Master of the Madonna in the Cathedral of Massa Maritima," whom he had identified with Segna in 1924), and Berenson ("Giovanni di Niccolò restored by Neroccio"; if this is not a misprint for Neruccio it may reflect the feeling that the restored heads are somewhat in the quattrocento rather than trecento manner). Garrison (1943–45) calls the picture Sienese, first half 14th century. Influences of Simone Martini in addition to Duccesque features are undeniable; the relatively simple type of halo occurs in Simone's Avignon circle (e. g., Matteo Giovanetti), and it may be significant that the devotional type to which the picture belongs is found in the North earlier than in the South. Coloristically, the work is closer to Martini than to Duccio.

Lit.: R. van Marle, *The Development of the Italian Schools of Painting*, II, The Hague, 1924, p. 153; Robert Lehman, *The Philip Lehman Collection, New York, Paintings*, Paris, 1928, no. XXXVII; E. B. Garrison, Jr., "A New Devotional Panel Type in Fourteenth-Century Italy," *Marsyas*, III, 1943–45, pp. 15 ff. (39).

ITALIAN (Sienese?), ca. 1450.

Madonna of Humility   47.*III*
In the roundels above, the *Annunciation*.
Panel (poplar), 31 × 21 in. (78.7 × 53.3 cm), within frame, 27½ × 17⅝ in. (69.9 × 44 cm). Coll. Philip Lehman, New York (1920). Gift of Robert Lehman, New York, 1947.

The heads of Mary and the Child are new, as is the light blue of the mantle; this makes it very difficult to arrive at a satisfactory attribution of the rest of the panel. It has been given to Sassetta (van Marle, see Lehman Catalogue, 1928), to Pellegrino da Mariano (tentatively; Berenson, *ibid.*), and to an unidentified follower of Sassetta (Perkins 1920; Pope-Hennessy 1939). The authenticated altarpiece of 1450 by Pellegrino (*Dedalo*, XI, 1930–31, p. 629) is not very closely related to the present panel. The heavily patterned floor occurs in paintings tentatively attributed to him (*ibid.*, p. 631) but also elsewhere in Central and Southern Italy.

Lit.: F. Mason Perkins, "Some Sienese Paintings in American Collections, Part Three," *Art in America*, IX, 1920, pp. 6 ff. (18 ff.); Robert Lehman, *The Philip Lehman Collection, New York*, Paris, 1928, no. XLI ("Follower of Sassetta, circa 1470"); J. Pope-Hennessy, *Sassetta*, London, 1939, pp. 180 and 200, note 107.

ITALIAN (Veronese), 1581. Probably Battista Angolo del Moro.

A Vision of the Holy Family near Verona   1581   *61.83*

Canvas, 34⅞ × 43¼ in. (88.8 × 109.8 cm). Inscribed on a cartellino, center below: VERONA / Fatta nel monasterio / Santo Angolo / A 1581. Coll. Durlacher Bros., New York; Samuel H. Kress, 1948. Kress Study Collection, 1961.   *Fig.* 28

Painted as a *trompe l'œil* in imitation of a scene with the *Holy Family* being revealed under, and seen through a picture with an evening view of Verona seen from the north, with shepherds and a resting traveler in front. Sant' Angelo in Monte, north of Verona outside Porta San Giorgio (see the map in Luigi Simeoni, *Verona*, 1948, p. 35) "sul colle Castel San Pietro, dov' è la serra di fiori del giardino Zeiner" (Vittorio Fainelli in *Madonna Verona*, IV, 1910, p. 51), has vanished. The vision here alluded to remains to be identified. The little St. John with his lamb can be discerned below and slightly to the left of the central tree. Mr. Terence Mullaly of London (*in litteris*, 1967) attributes this picture to Battista Angolo del Moro, active second half 16th century, with special reference to his *Madonna in Glory with Saints* in San Fermo Maggiore, the large chiaroscuro fresco with a scene from the life of St. Stephen in Santo Stefano, and the frescoes on the façade of Casa Bentegodi, all in Verona, as well as to drawings such as Inv. No. 260 in the Leipzig Museum and No. 1375/1863 in the Stockholm Museum (Exh. "Konstens Venedig," 1962–63, no. 260). Mr. Mullaly noted the play upon words in the inscription: Angolo, the artist's family name, for Angelo, the monastery.

Lit.: W. Stechow, "The Samuel H. Kress Study Collection, Catalogue," *AMAM Bulletin*, XIX, 1961–62, pp. 30 ff., no. 6.

ITALIAN, mid 17th century.

The Crowning with Thorns 04.424

Canvas, 29⁹⁄₁₆ × 24⅝ in. (75.2 × 62.5 cm). Coll. Charles F. Olney, Cleveland, acquired before 1887. Olney Gift, 1904. *Fig.* 45

Catalogued as Murillo by Olney; a 19th century label on the stretcher ascribes it, even more adventurously, to Domenico Alfani. Most probably by a painter from either Genoa or Naples.
Exh.: "Art Loan Exhibition," Cleveland, 1894, no. 19.

ITALIAN, late 17th century.

Mercury Lulling Argus into Sleep 04.402

Canvas, 62¼ × 45½ in. (158.1 × 115.6 cm). Spurious signature, lower right: Rosa. Coll. Charles F. Olney, Cleveland, acquired before 1887. Olney Gift, 1904. *Fig.* 48

The attribution to Salvator Rosa is out of the question; the signature, though old, does not correspond to authentic ones. The picture was tentatively assigned to Carl Loth (1632–98) by several scholars but its quality remains below Loth's level. Stylistically, there are ties with Loth, Langetti and Saiter; the sharp shadow on Mercury is actually reminiscent of comparable compositions by Rosa.

ITALIAN (Venetian), ca. 1780.

Landscape (Capriccio) 61.87

Canvas, 16½ × 22⅛ in. (41.9 × 56.5 cm). Coll. Samuel H. Kress, 1933. Kress Study Collection, 1961. *Fig.* 76

Two figures in the right foreground, and two in the left middleground, which had been added later, were removed in a recent cleaning.
The companion piece, a *Landscape with a Ruined Arch*, is still in the Kress Collection; its figures are likewise of later date (reproduced by Stechow, 1961, p. 50).

The painter, whose style is strongly influenced by that of Francesco Guardi, remains to be identified; he may also have had ties with Giuseppe Zais.

Lit.: W. Stechow, "The Samuel H. Kress Study Collection, Catalogue," *AMAM Bulletin*, XIX, 1961–62, pp. 48 ff., no. 10.

JACOPO DEL CASENTINO. Born in the Casentino Valley, active there and in Florence. One of the founders of the guild of St. Luke in Florence in 1339. Died in 1349 or 1358. Father of Francesco Landini.

Crucifixion *40.37*

On the right, St. Anthony with the Pig.

Panel (hardwood like poplar), 17¾ × 7¼ in. (45.1 × 18.4 cm). Coll. Baron Jakob von Schenck, Flechtingen near Magdeburg (1853); private coll. in France (1936); Schaeffer Galleries, New York. Purchased from R. T. Miller, Jr. Fund, 1940. *Fig.* 2

Right (sinister) wing of a small diptych; an upper gable (rising to the right), presumably with the Madonna of the Annunciation, removed. Some flaking of pigment; the face of St. John is restored.

As Offner (1957) has shown, this is the sinister wing of a tabernacle the dexter wing of which, showing the *Nativity* and *The Three Quick and the Three Dead*, remained in the von Schenck Coll. (see above) until the second world war (now lost). A triptych with almost identical composition of the wings is in Berlin (Offner III, II, II, pp. 126 ff. and III, VII, p. 105). It shows the Enthroned Madonna in the center, suggesting that the present work had a similar center part; Offner (1957) tentatively identified this with a panel in Berlin (formerly Bonn, Offner III, II, II, p. 122 and pl. L), which however is only 32 cm wide. From the middle period of the artist.

Exh.: "Cornerstones for a College Art Collection," AMAM, 1939, no. 22; "Italian Panels and Manuscripts from the 13th and 14th Centuries, in Honor of Richard Offner," Hartford, Conn., Wadsworth Atheneum, 1965, no. 3.

Lit.: R. Offner, *A Corpus of Florentine Painting*, III, II, II, New York, 1930, p. 262, and III, VII, 1957, pp. 119 ff.

JACQUE, CHARLES. Born in Paris in 1813. Self-taught as a painter. Active as illustrator in London, 1836–38, and in Paris. From 1848 closely allied with J. F. Millet and Th. Rousseau in Barbizon. Active mostly in Paris, where he died in 1894.

Sheep at the Entrance to a Forest   Before 1874   *44.56*

Canvas, 27⅜ × 39½ in. (69.5 × 100.3 cm). Signed, lower left: Ch. Jacque; on the back certified as original by the artist, March 15, 1874. Coll. E. Chouanard, Paris; Charles A. Dana, New York, sale New York, Feb. 24–26, 1898, no. 587; F. A. Bell, St. Louis; M. Knoedler & Co., New York; bought from them in 1914 by Mrs. F. F. Prentiss, Cleveland. Prentiss Bequest, 1944.   *Fig.* 105

JAWLENSKY, ALEXEJ. Born in Kuslovo (Gouv. Twer) in 1867. Student of A. Rjepin in St. Petersburg. Settled in Munich in 1896; cofounder of the *Neue Künstlervereinigung* (1909). Moved to Ascona, Switzerland, in 1914, to Wiesbaden in 1921. Co-founder of *Die Blauen Vier* in 1924. Died in Wiesbaden in 1941.

Head of a Woman   *55.23*

Cardboard, 21 × 19¼ in. (53.3 × 48.9 cm). Signed, lower right: a. jawlensky. Coll. Fernand Graindorge, Liége (1954); Theodore Schempp, New York. Purchased from R. T. Miller, Jr. Fund, 1955.

Fig. 118

Painted ca. 1912. The sitter was formerly wrongly identified with Mme. Sakaroff.

Exh.: "Collection Fernand Graindorge," Basel, Kunsthalle, 1954, no. 51; "An American University Collection" (AMAM), Kenwood (London County Council), 1962, no. 25.

Lit.: Clemens Weiler, *Alexej Jawlensky*, Cologne, 1959, p. 233, no. 100.

JEFFERSON, JOSEPH. Born in Philadelphia in 1829. Famous as actor, ca. 1833–1904. Exhibited at Philadelphia in 1868 and at the National Academy in New York in 1890; had a one-man show in Washington, 1899. Died in Palm Beach in 1905.

Rip van Winkle's Nook in the Catskills   Before 1887   *04.1194*

Canvas, 9⅞×16 in. (25.1×40.6 cm). Signed, lower left: JF. Coll. Charles F. Olney, Cleveland, acquired before 1887. Olney Gift, 1904.   *Fig. 190*

Jefferson was famous for his impersonation of Rip van Winkle; see also the plaster group by J. Rogers (p. 212).

Exh.: "American Artists Discover America," AMAM, 1946, no. 27.

The Old Mill by the Sea   1895   *04.411*

Canvas, 13¾×21½ in. (34.9×54.6 cm). Signed: J. Jefferson 95. Coll. Charles F. Olney, Cleveland, given to him by the artist in 1897. Olney Gift, 1904.   *Fig. 191*

Exh.: "American Artists Discover America," AMAM, 1946, no. 26.

JEWETT, WILLIAM, see WALDO and JEWETT.

JIMÉNEZ (XIMÉNEZ), MIGUEL. Active in Saragossa and surroundings, 1466–1503/05. Follower of Bermejo.

Man of Sorrows   *58.58*

Panel (softwood like pine), 18⅞×12¾ in. (47.9×34.4 cm). Coll. Elisabeth Lotte Franzos, Vienna and Washington. Franzos Bequest, 1958.   *Fig. 18*

In the original frame.

As José Gudiol first pointed out (orally, 1961), a work characteristic of Jiménez' style. Most closely related is the Pietà, signed and dated 1470, in the Lanckorónski Coll. (C. R. Post, *A History of Spanish Painting*, VIII, I, Cambridge, Mass., 1941, p. 77); for the angel see also *St. Quiteria* in Huesca (Post, p. 116), and for Christ, the *Dead Christ* in Salvatierra (Post, p. 100). For the iconography see E. Panofsky, "Imago Pietatis," *Festschrift für Max J. Friedländer*, Leipzig, 1927, pp. 261 ff.

JORDAENS, JACOB. Born in Antwerp in 1593. Pupil (1607) and son-in-law of Adam van Noort. Master in Antwerp in 1615; dean of the guild in 1621. Active in Antwerp, where he died in 1678.

An Oracle

64.35

Panel, transferred to masonite, 23×35¾ in. (58.4×90.8 cm). Probably Coll. Michiel Wauters, Antwerp, 1679, acquired from Jordaens' estate; Arthur Holford, London, sale Nov. 28, 1963, no. 72; F. Mont, New York. Purchased from Mrs. F. F. Prentiss Fund, 1964.

Fig. 53

The core of the composition, in its first state (ca. 41×54 cm), was the modello for a tapestry (of which versions exist in the Boston Museum and in the Palazzo Reale in Turin), which is inscribed "Achilles puer a matre adducitur ad oraculum" and was one of two pieces designed by Jordaens before 1643 in supplementation of Rubens' series of eight tapestries from the life of Achilles. Its subject, for which no antique source exists, was probably suggested by a passage in Natale Conti's *Mythologiae*. After serving its purpose, the modello was added to on all sides and transformed by Jordaens into a different representation of an oracle, probably Tiresias' prophecy on the young Heracles before Alcmene as reported in Theocritus' *Herakliskos* (Stechow 1965). A drawing with "An Offering in a Pagan Temple" was in the Prince de Ligne sale, Vienna, Nov. 4 ff., 1794 (M. Rooses, *Jacob Jordaens, His Life and Works*, London, 1908, p. 260).

Lit.: J. Denucé, *Inventare von Kunstsammlungen zu Antwerpen im 16. und 17. Jahrhundert*, Antwerp, 1932, p. 303; W. Stechow, "A Modello by Jacob Jordaens," *Nederlands Kunsthistorisch Jaarboek*, XVI, 1965, pp. 67 ff. (reprinted in *AMAM Bulletin*, XXIII, 1965–66, pp. 5 ff.).

KELDER, C. Dutch portrait painter of the late seventeenth century, probably active in Deventer, about whose life nothing is known. His style recalls C. Netscher and M. van Musscher.

Portrait of a Gentleman 1684   *04.1219*

Canvas, 29¼ × 23¾ in. (74.3 × 60.4 cm). Signed, left center: C. Kelder pinxit 1684. Coll. Charles F. Olney, Cleveland, bought in New York in 1890. Olney Gift, 1904.

Companion piece of no. 04.1220.
A portrait of a lady by the same artist, dated 1689, is or was in Coll. Coenen, Oosterhof near Rhenen. Some other works are known through prints only.

Portrait of a Lady 1684   *04.1220*

Canvas, 29¼ × 23¾ in. (74.3 × 80.5 cm). Signed, lower right: C. Kelder.fe. 1684. Coll. Charles F. Olney, Cleveland, bought in New York in 1890. Olney Gift, 1904.

Companion piece of no. 04.1219.

KELLER, HENRY. Born aboard ship in 1869 as his parents immigrated from Germany. Studied at the Cleveland Institute of Art 1887–88, in Karlsruhe, at the Art Students League in New York (1891) and the Cincinnati School of Art, in Düsseldorf (1899) and Munich (1900 under H. Zügel). Taught at the Cleveland Institute of Art, 1902–1945. Traveled extensively in Europe and in the Western Hemisphere. Died in San Diego, Cal., in 1949.

Head of Mozart, after Munkacsy 1894   *04.1215*

Canvas, 22⅛ × 18 in. (56.2 × 45.7 cm). Signed, lower right: H. KELLER 94 AFTER MUNKACSY. Coll. Charles F. Olney, Cleveland, acquired as gift of the Cleveland Art Loan Exhibition, 1894. Olney Gift, 1904.

Partial copy after Mihaly de Munkacsy's *Last Hours of Mozart* (exhibited at the Art Loan Exhibition, Cleveland, 1894, no. 160), painted in 1880 and now in the Detroit Institute of Arts.

KELLY, WILLIAM.

Tally-Ho! (Delaware Water Gap)   Before 1887   *04.1217*

Panel (mahogany), 1⅞ × 4⁷⁄₁₆ in. (4.8 × 11.3 cm). Coll. Charles F. Olney, Cleveland, acquired before 1887. Olney Gift, 1904.

The attribution is Olney's. There were two American lithographers by that name, both living in Philadelphia in 1860: William F. Kelly, born ca. 1833 in Pennsylvania, and William J. Kelly, born ca. 1838. That the sketch was made by a professional lithographer is quite possible.

KENSETT, JOHN FREDERICK.   Born in Cheshire, Conn., in 1816. Son and pupil of the engraver, Thomas Kensett, later pupil of his uncle, Alfred Daggett in New Haven. Studied painting in Europe, 1840–47. Settled in New York early in 1848; member of the National Academy in 1849. Traveled widely in the United States. Died in New York in 1872.

The Temple of Neptune, Paestum   *04.432*

Canvas, 9⅜ × 14⁵⁄₁₆ in. (23.8 × 36.3 cm). Coll. Charles F. Olney, Cleveland, acquired before 1887. Olney Gift, 1904.   *Fig.* 160

Exh.: "American Artists Discover America," AMAM, 1946, no. 30; "Major Works in Minor Scale," American Federation of Arts circulating exhibition, 1959, no. 34.

Mt. Mansfield from Malletts Bay, Lake Champlain   *55.54*

Canvas, 9¼ × 18¹³⁄₁₆ in. (23.5 × 46.5 cm). On a label on back: "Art Exhibition—April, 1893. Landscape, J. F. Kensett. Maryland Society Sons of the Revolution . . . Owner Mrs. J. S. Gilman, value 200." On another label, on the stretcher: "M. Mansfield from Mallets Bay Lake Champlain, 701." Gift of John G. D. Paul, Baltimore, 1955.   *Fig.* 161

Painted ca. 1860

KIRCHNER, ERNST LUDWIG.   Born in Aschaffenburg in 1880. Studied architecture in Dresden, 1901–05. Co-founder of "Die

Brücke," 1905. Active in Berlin (1911–15) and in Davos-Frauenkirch, Switzerland, where he died in 1938.

Self Portrait as Soldier   1915   *50.29*

Canvas, 27¼ × 24 in. (69.2 × 61 cm). Signed, lower right: ELKirchner. Coll. Städtische Galerie, Dresden, ca. 1916–19; L. Schames, Frankfurt, 1919; Städtische Galerie, Frankfurt, on loan to the Städelsche Kunstinstitut, 1919–37, Inv. No. S. G. 299 (not among the pictures sold at auction in Lucerne in 1939); Kurt Feldhaeusser, Berlin (until 1943) and Kirchberg in Württemberg (1943–45); E. Weyhe, New York, 1950. Purchased from Charles F. Olney Fund, 1950.   *Fig.* 124

Painted in 1915 at Halle (Saale), where the artist was on garrison duty.

Exh.: "Ernst Ludwig Kirchner," New York, Curt Valentin Gallery, 1952, no. 8; "In the Flat and Round," Cincinnati, Ohio, Modern Art Association, 1952; "Paintings and Drawings from Five Centuries" (AMAM), New York, Knoedler Galleries, 1954, no. 70; "War and Aftermath," Busch-Reisinger Museum, Harvard University, Cambridge, Mass., 1957; "Ernst Ludwig Kirchner, German Expressionist," North Carolina Museum of Art, Raleigh, 1958, no. 23; "What is Modern Art?," Toledo, Ohio, Museum of Art, 1960; "The Logic of Modern Art," Nelson Gallery and Atkins Museum, Kansas City, Missouri, 1961, no. 9; "An American University Collection" (AMAM), Kenwood (London County Council), 1962, no. 26; "Treasures from the Allen Memorial Art Museum," Minneapolis Institute of Arts, 1966.

Lit.: S. Schwabacher, "Moderne Bilder im Städel-Neubau," *Jahrbuch der jungen Kunst*, 1923, pp. 360 ff. (363); P. Selz, "Kirchner's Self-Portrait as a Soldier in Relation to Earlier Self-Portraits," *AMAM Bulletin*, XIV, 1956–57, pp. 91 ff; B. S. Myers, *The German Expressionists*, New York, 1957, p. 132; P. Selz, *German Expressionist Painting*, Los Angeles, 1957, pp. 299 f.; W. Grohmann, *E. L. Kirchner*, Stuttgart, 1958 (English ed., New York, 1961), p. 68; Manuel Gasser, *Self-Portraits from the Fifteenth Century to the Present Day*, New York, 1961, pp. 264 ff.; G. Tolzien, s.v. *Kirchner* in *Kindlers Malerei-Lexikon*, III, Zürich, 1966, pp. 601 and 602 (color repr.).

KLEE, PAUL. Born in Münchenbuchsee (near Bern) in 1879. Studied in Munich, 1898–1901. In Italy, 1901–02. Active in Bern 1903–06, and Munich 1906–20; taught at the Bauhaus in Weimar and Dessau 1920–30, and at the State Academy in Düsseldorf 1930–33. After 1933 again active in Bern. Died at Muralto in 1940.

Flower Gardens in Taora   1918   *53.222*

Gouache on two sheets of paper mounted side by side and framed with black painted line. Left sheet: 6⅜ × 4⁷⁄₁₆ in. (16 × 11.3 cm); right sheet: 6¼ × 5¼ in. (15.9 × 13.3 cm); whole page: 7⅜ × 10¾ in. (18.7 × 27.3 cm). Left sheet, signed, upper left: Klee; right sheet, signed, upper left: K. Inscribed, lower left: "1918, 77. Blumengärten von Taora." Sale in Stuttgart (Stuttgarter Kunstkabinett), April 6–8, 1949; sale in Bern (Gutekunst and Klipstein), Dec. 3, 1949, no. 146; Coll. Clifford Odets, New York; Curt Valentin Galleries, New York. Purchased from Friends of Art Fund, 1953.

Fig. 130

Exh.: "Paul Klee," New York, Curt Valentin Galleries, 1953, no. 4; "Paintings and Drawings from Five Centuries" (AMAM), New York, Knoedler Galleries, 1954, no. 72; "In Memory of Curt Valentin, 1902–1954," New York, Curt Valentin Galleries, 1954, no. 12; "Drawings and Water Colors from the Oberlin Collection," Ann Arbor, University of Michigan Museum of Art, 1956; "Masterworks from American University Collections," European Tour, sponsored by the College Art Association, 1956–1957, Cat. Malmö no. 29; Cat. Utrecht no. 26; Cat. Lyons no. 21; "Community Angels Build," Grand Rapids, Michigan, Art Gallery, 1959–60, no. 12; "An American University Collection" (AMAM), Kenwood (London County Council), 1962, no. 41.

Lit.: R. Reiff, "Paul Klee," *AMAM Bulletin*, XI, 1953–54, pp. 137 ff.

Die Paukenorgel ("Kettledrum-Organ")   1930   *44.21*

Paper board, 12½ × 16½ in. (31.8 × 41.9 cm). Signed, lower left: Klee. On stretcher dated: 1930. Coll. Buchholz Galleries, New York. Purchased from R. T. Miller, Jr. Fund, 1944.   *Fig.* 131

Oeuvre catalogue Klee 1930, no. 212 (see Exh. Cat. 1956). Most closely related to *Plastik einer Blumenvase*, likewise of 1930 (color repr. in *Paul Klee*, ed. Klee-Gesellschaft Bern, I, 1949, pl. XIII).

Exh.: "Paintings and Drawings from Five Centuries" (AMAM), New York, Knoedler Galleries, 1954, no. 75; "Paul Klee," Bern Kunstmuseum, 1956, no. 602; "Paul Klee," Hamburg, Kunsthalle, 1956–57, no. 265; "Music and Art," Minneapolis, University of Minnesota Gallery, and Grand Rapids, Michigan, Art Gallery, 1958, unnumbered; "Paul Klee in Review," Denver, Colorado, Art Museum, 1963, no. 32.

Lit. Will Grohmann, *Paul Klee*, New York, 1954, p. 398, no. 112.

KLINE, FRANZ (JOSEF). Born in Wilkes-Barre, Pa., in 1910; studied at Girard College, Boston University and Heatherley School, London. Taught at Black Mountain College, Pratt Institute, Philadelphia Museum and Cooper Union. From 1939 active in New York, where he died in 1962.

Untitled 19   *64.1*

Paper, collage, 18⅟₁₆ × 23¹⁵⁄₁₆ in. (45.9 × 60.8 cm). Signed, lower right: K (in circle). Priv. coll., Provincetown, Mass.; Leo Castelli Gallery, New York. Purchased from Mrs. F. F. Prentiss Fund, 1964.

Fig. 208

Probably painted in 1958.

KOKOSCHKA, OSKAR. Born in Pöchlarn (on the Danube) in 1886. Pupil of W. Löffler in Vienna. Active in Vienna, Dresden (Professor at the Academy, 1920–24), Prague (Professor at the Academy, 1934–38), and since 1938 in London, later also in Salzburg. Extensive travels throughout Europe, Asia, Africa, U.S.A., 1924–31 and later. Dramatist and poet.

Sposalizio (Double Portrait)   *58.51*

Canvas, 41⅛ × 24¾ in. (140.5 × 62.9 cm). Signed, lower left: O K. Coll. Dr. Hans Reichel, Vienna; Elisabeth Lotte Franzos, Vienna and Washington. Franzos Bequest, 1958.   *Fig. 123*

Said to be a portrait of Emil Alphonse Rheinhardt, author of biographical books (1889–1945), and his fiancée, an assistant to Professor Max Dvořák in Vienna. Painted late in 1911 or early in 1912. A drawing for the woman is reproduced in Stefan (1913); a drawn portrait of the man, later than the painting (May 29, 1912), is mentioned by Wingler (1956) as being illustrated in *O. Kokoschka, Handzeichnungen*, Berlin, 1935, pl. 45.

Exh.: "Sonderbund," Cologne, 1912 (May), no. 359; "Oscar Kokoschka," Dresden, Galerie Arnold, 1925, no. 10 (dated 1910); "Oskar Kokoschka," Vienna, Österreichisches Museum für Kunst und Industrie, 1937, no. 8 (dated 1913); "Kokoschka," New York, Buchholz Gallery, 1941, no. 10 (dated 1912); "Oskar Kokoschka: a Retrospective Exhibition," Boston, Institute of Contemporary Art—New York, Museum of Modern Art—Phillips Memorial Gallery, Washington—St. Louis, City Art Museum—San Francisco, M. H. de Young Memorial Museum, 1948, no. 20; "Oskar Kokoschka," Munich, Haus der Kunst, no. 28—Vienna, Künstlerhaus—The Hague, Gemeente Museum, 1958, no. 21; "Signposts of Twentieth Century Art," Dallas, Texas, Museum for Contemporary Arts, 1959, p. 16; "German Expressionism," Columbus, Ohio, Gallery of Fine Arts, 1961, no. 42; "Kokoschka," London, Tate Gallery, 1962, no. 34; "Oskar Kokoschka," Zürich, Kunsthaus, 1966, no. 24; "Oskar Kokoschka. Das Portrait," Karlsruhe, Badischer Kunstverein, 1966, no. 18.

Lit.: Paul Stefan, *Oskar Kokoschka, Dramen und Bilder*, Leipzig, 1913, ill.; Edith Hoffmann, *Kokoschka, Life and Work*, London, 1947, p. 113, no. 71 and p. 300; J. S. Plaut, *Oskar Kokoschka*, New York, 1948, pp. 15, 23, 82; H. M. Wingler, *Oskar Kokoschka*, Salzburg, 1956 (English ed., New York, 1958), p. 301, no. 67.

KROLL, LEON. Born in New York City in 1884. Studied at the Art Students League in New York and with J. P. Laurens in Paris. Taught at the National Academy of Design in New York, 1911–18. Elected member of the National Academy in 1927. Active in New York City.

Still Life with Lemon Tree   1918   *42.25*

Canvas, 23 × 19½ in. (58.4 × 49.5 cm). Signed, lower right: Kroll

1918. Coll. Mrs. Malcolm L. McBride, Cleveland. Gift of Mrs. McBride, 1942. *Fig. 198*

LARGILLIERE, NICOLAS DE, COPY AFTER. Born in Paris in 1656. Trained by A. Goubau in Antwerp where he became a master in the guild in 1672. 1674–78 in London, assistant to P. Lely. Active in Paris from 1678 until his death in 1746. Member of the Academy from 1686.

Lady Holding a Pink   *59.119*

Canvas, oval, 35 × 42¾ in. (88.9 × 108.6 cm). Coll. James Speyer, New York, sale April 10, 1942, no. 22. Anonymous gift, 1959.

Copy after the presumable original last recorded in the exhibition of 100 portraits of women of the 18th century held in Paris in 1909, no. 73, and reproduced in L. Vaillat and R. Dell, *Cent portraits de femmes des écoles anglaises et françaises*, Paris, 1910, no. 73, the size of which was given (obviously wrongly) as 110 × 225 cm. That picture came from the Coll. Vicomte G. de Chabert (sale Paris, June 5, 1909, no. 6) and was supposed to represent Madame de Parabère; its provenance was erroneously appropriated for the present copy in the 1942 sale catalogue (with the addition of Coll. Ducrey, Paris, after Chabert). Either the presumed original or the present copy was at one time in Coll. Basil Dighton in New York.

LÁSZLÓ DE LOMBOS, FÜLÖP ELEK (PHILIP ALEXIUS). Born in Budapest in 1869. Studied at the academies of Budapest and Munich (1890–91); subsequently, one year in Paris with J. Lefebvre and B. Constant. Active mainly in Budapest and London; 1908 and 1932 in the U.S.A. President of the Royal Society of British Artists, 1930 ff. Died in London in 1937.

Portrait of Mrs. F. F. Prentiss 1932   *46.24*

Canvas, 35 × 29 in. (88.9 × 73.7 cm). Signed, lower right: de Laszlo N. Y. 1932. Gift of John A. Hadden, 1946.   *Facing p. vii*

The sitter (1865–1944) was one of the main patrons of the AMAM; see the Introduction to this catalogue.

LAUFMAN, SIDNEY. Born in Cleveland in 1891. Studied at the Art Institute of Chicago and the Art Students League in New York. Active in Paris, New York and Woodstock, N.Y.

French Landscape *35.62*

Canvas, 13 × 16¼ in. (33 × 41.3 cm). Signed, lower left: Sidney Laufman. Coll. Mrs. Malcolm L. McBride, Cleveland. Gift of Mrs. McBride, 1935.

Painted in Paris, probably ca. 1930

LAWSON, ERNEST. Born in San Francisco in 1873. Studied in New York 1890 and Paris 1893. Active mostly in New York from 1898; one of "The Eight," 1908; member of the National Academy in 1917. Taught at Colorado Springs 1926 and at the Kansas City Art Institute 1928. Died in Florida in 1939.

Harlem River *19.20*

Canvas, 20 × 24 in. (50.8 × 61 cm). Signed, lower left: E. Lawson. Coll. A. Augustus Healy, Brooklyn. Gift of A. A. Healy, 1919.

Fig. 197

Painted ca. 1910/15. Stylistically similar views of Harlem River are at the Phillips Memorial Gallery, Washington (dated 1913), the Newark Museum, the Engineer's Club, New York, and elsewhere (see the reproductions in F. Newlin Price, *Ernest Lawson, Canadian-American*, New York, 1930).

LÉGER, FERNAND. Born in Argentan (Orne) in 1881. Studied in Paris under J. L. Gérôme and G. Ferrier, 1902–05. Exhibited at the Salon des Indépendants from 1910. Extensive travels after 1931; in the U.S.A., 1942–45. Active mostly in Paris. Died in Gif-sur-Yette in 1955.

Composition 1941   *44.22*

Opaque watercolor on paper, 23⅛ × 29 in. (58.7 × 73.7 cm). Signed, lower right: F. L. 41. Coll. Theodore Schempp, New York (acquired from the artist). Purchased from R. T. Miller, Jr. Fund, 1944.   *Fig. 142*

Exh.: "Fernand Léger," Indianapolis, John Herron Museum of Art, 1950.

LEVERE, EUGÈNE.

Country Road   *04.403*

Canvas, 10 × 14 in. (25.4 × 35.6 cm). Signed, lower right: Eug Levere. Coll. Charles F. Olney, Cleveland, acquired in 1890. Olney Gift, 1904.

Nothing is known to us about the life of this artist of considerable skill. The present picture shows intimate connection with the style of Corot in the 1860's.

LIGOZZI, JACOPO. Born in Verona in 1547. From ca. 1575 (certainly by 1577) court painter to Grandduke Francesco I. of Tuscany in Florence; remained in the service of three of Francesco's successors until his death in 1626.

Portable Altar in Carrying Case 1608   *58.1*

The scene of *Christ on the Mount of Olives Supported by an Angel* is inserted in a wooden tabernacle flanked by two lapis lazuli columns with gilded Corinthian capitals; underneath, the *Sacrifice of Isaac* painted on lapis set in a cartouche; on the broken pediment, two angel putti of lead with gilded wings, holding gilded wreaths. Inlays of mother-of-pearl, agate, lapis, and other semiprecious stones. Crowning object (probably a *Resurrected Christ*) missing. The wooden carrying case, with two doors and two brass handles, shows a rich floral and vinal design around a cartouche with the monogram of Christ, crowned by two cherubs and the Dove. The main scene on copper, 10½ × 6¼ in. (26.7 × 15.9 cm).

Signed, lower left: Jacopo Ligozzi. F. 1608. Altar: 23 × 13¼ × 3¼ in. (58.4 × 33.7 × 8.3 cm). Case: 26⁹⁄₁₆ × 16½ × 5½ in. (67.5 × 41.9 × 14 cm). Coll. Bauer, Vienna; F. Kleinberger & Co., New York. Purchased from R. T. Miller, Jr. Fund, 1958. *Fig.* 43

A closely related drawing with the Angel and Christ is in the Berlin-Dahlem Print Room (no. 15515; with later inscription "Jacopo Ligozzio Veronese"). The subject of the *Angel Supporting Christ on the Mount of Olives* is rather rare; in *formal* organization, the closest parallel is the *Dead Christ Supported by an Angel over the Tomb* painted by Otto van Veen for St. Waudru in Mons, ca. 1593/94 (see J. Müller Hofstede in *Bulletin des Musées Royaux des Beaux-Arts*, Brussels, VI, 1957, pp. 134 ff.).

Lit.: N. Bacci, "Jacopo Ligozzi e la sua posizione nella pittura fiorentina," *Proporzioni*, IV, 1963, pp. 46 ff. (84); N. Bacci, "A Portable Altar by Ligozzi," *AMAM Bulletin*, XX, 1962–63, pp. 47 ff.

LORRAIN, CLAUDE GELLÉE CALLED LORRAIN, FOLLOW-ER OF. Born in Chamagne (Dép. Vosges) in 1600. Went to Rome where he worked for Agostino Tassi possibly as early as 1616; also active in Naples sometime before 1625. After extensive travels and a short stay in Nancy (1625–27) he returned to Rome, where he remained active until his death in 1682. Member of the Accademia di San Luca, 1633.

A Harbor Scene 45.33

Canvas, 39⅝ × 53 in. (100.7 × 134.6 cm). Coll. Yorke (English ambassador to The Hague), 1752; Prince Paul of Württemberg, sale London, July 1, 1848, no. 88 (to Fuller); Hugh A. J. Munro of Novar (1865), sale London, July 13, 1923, no. 129 (to Knoedler); M. Knoedler & Co., London, who sold it in 1931 to Sir Ronald Lindsay (Röthlisberger 1961); M. Knoedler & Co., New York. Purchased from R. T. Miller, Jr. Fund, 1945. *Fig.* 70

Twice engraved by Thomas Major: (1) 1752, signed Major (Coll. Yorke); (2) signed Jorma (no owner given).

A somewhat smaller copy is in the Galleria di San Luca in Rome, catalogued as "Turner?" (Röthlisberger LV 19,6 as probably an English copy after the present picture).

The picture, accepted as an original by John Smith (1837) but not mentioned in Waagen's account of the Munro Collection, is a variation on the *Harbor* in Windsor (Röthlisberger LV 19: ca. 1637), from which however no single part has been copied outright, not even the very similar architecture on the right. The arrangement of the small figures, well back from the frontal plane, suggests the hand of an able late seventeenth-century follower who combined features of the later Claude with those of the time of the Windsor picture. Röthlisberger's dating as "possibly early 18th century" lacks support.

Mrs. Mark Patterson (*Claude Lorrain* . . ., Paris, 1884, p. 236) wrongly identified the original of the engraving of 1752 (the present picture) with the one at Windsor.

Exh.: "Le paysage français de Poussin à Corot," Paris, Palais des Beaux-Arts, 1925, no. 122; "Ideal Home," London, Olympia, 1930, no. 29; "French Painting, Classic to Romantic," Dallas Museum of Fine Arts, 1942; Akron, Ohio, Art Institute, 1953 (always as Claude).

Lit.: John Smith, *A Catalogue Raisonné* . . ., VIII, London, 1837, p. 347, no. 321; *Catalogue of Paintings . . . Munro*, 1865, no. 21; G. Redford, *History of Art Sales*, London, 1888, I, p. 270; M. Chamot, "Old Masters at Knoedler's," *Country Life*, May 3, 1924, p. 714; *Pantheon*, Nov. 1928, pp. 567 ff.; *Studio*, CII, August 1931, opp. p. 102 (color plate); M. Röthlisberger, *Claude Lorrain: The Paintings*, New Haven, 1961, I, p. 137, no. LV 19,5, and II, fig. 385.

MAGNASCO, ALESSANDRO. Born in Genoa in 1667. Pupil of his father Stefano, later (ca. 1680–82) of Filippo Abbiati in Milan. 1705–11 in Genoa and Florence, 1711–35 in Milan. He then returned to Genoa where he died in 1749.

Landscape with Washerwomen   *43.238*

Canvas, 41 × 56 in. (104.1 × 142.2 cm). Coll. Sir Walter Lawrence (?); Jacob M. Heimann, New York; David M. Koetser, New York. Purchased from A. A. Healy Fund, 1943.   *Fig. 74*

Probably a work of the early middle period of the master, whose chronology is extremely difficult to establish. The subject of the washerwomen appears often in Magnasco's work; a characteristic late example is found in the Vienna Museum (Geiger 1949, pl. 66).

Exh.: "Alessandro Magnasco," Speed Art Museum, Louisville, and University of Michigan Museum of Art, Ann Arbor, 1967, no. 40.

Lit.: B. Geiger, *Magnasco*, Bergamo, 1949, p. 124 (Geiger's listing of another painting as being in the Oberlin Museum is erroneous).

MANDER, KAREL VAN (?). Born in Meulebeke near Courtrai in 1548. Pupil of Lukas de Heere in Ghent until 1568 and of Pieter Vlerick in Courtrai and Tournai from 1568–69. 1573–77 in Italy, afterwards active in Krems and Vienna, back in Flanders (Courtrai, Bruges) 1581–83. Emigrated to Haarlem in 1583; after 1604 in Amsterdam, where he died in 1606. Painter, poet, and—before all—theoretician and historiographer of art.

Rustic Landscape   *59.43*

Panel (oak), 14 × 18¹¹⁄₁₆ in. (35.6 × 47.5 cm). Coll. Julius Weitzner, New York. Purchased from Friends of Art Fund, 1959.   *Fig. 34*

Acquired with a tentative attribution to Abraham Bloemaert which is out of the question. Although doubts remain, there are good reasons to consider it a work by van Mander of the 1590's; it is less comparable to the painted landscapes around 1600, which are more loose and panorama-like, than to some drawings in which the same closer view, thick tree trunks and rustic figures occur (*Kermesse* of 1591, Masson Coll., École des Beaux-Arts, Paris; *Sermon of John the Baptist* of 1597, Albertina, Vienna; both illustrated in E. Valentiner, *Karel van Mander als Maler*, Strassburg, 1930, figs. 28 and 22).

Exh.: "Seventeenth Century Painters of Haarlem," Allentown (Pa.) Art Museum, 1965, no. 48.

MARIOTTO DI NARDO. Florentine painter, active between 1394 and 1424, when he made his will. Worked under the strong influence of the Gerini (Niccolò di Pietro and Lorenzo di Niccolò) and Lorenzo Monaco.

Adoration of the Magi *43.118*

Panel (poplar; gesso ground containing linen), 12⅜ × 20⅝ in. (31.4 × 52.5 cm). Coll. Marchese Franzoni, Genoa; N. Acquavella, New York. Purchased from R. T. Miller, Jr. Fund, 1943. *Fig.* 7

Very well preserved.

As Eisenberg (1951) has shown, this panel formed part of the same predella to which an *Adoration of the Shepherds*, now in the Count Lanckoroński Coll., originally belonged (later added to above and below, producing the shape of a birth salver). A mature work of the artist, datable ca. 1410–1420.

Exh.: New York, N. Acquavella, 1940, no. 19; "Paintings of the Adoration of the Magi," Zanesville, Ohio, Art Institute, 1948; "Medieval Art," Ackland Art Center, Chapel Hill, N.C., 1961, no. 5.

Lit.: M. J. Eisenberg, "A Partial Reconstruction of a Predella by Mariotto di Nardo," *AMAM Bulletin*, IX, 1951–52, pp. 9 ff. (cf. *Burlington Magazine*, XCIV, 1952, p. 85).

MARIS, JACOBUS HENDRICUS. Born in The Hague in 1837, elder brother of the painters Matthijs and Willem Maris. Pupil of J. A. B. Stroebel 1849 and Hubertus van Hove 1852, also attended the Academy of Design in The Hague. 1853–57 study at the Antwerp Academy. 1865 pupil of Ernest Hébert in Paris. Returned to The Hague in 1871, active there until his death (in Carlsbad) in 1899.

The Bridge *42.83*

Canvas, 28⅜ × 36 in. (72.1 × 91.4 cm). Signed, lower right: J. Maris. Gift of Mrs. J. W. Simpson, East Craftsbury, Vermont, 1942. *Fig.* 101

Several versions of this motif, supposedly a site near Rijswijk, exist. A quick oil sketch on panel (undated, 22 × 28 cm) is in the Rijksmuseum in Amsterdam (no. 1518 A 16). The elaborate version in the John G. Johnson Collection in Philadelphia (no. 1030) is dated 1872 and measures 31½ × 57 inches; another, very similar and likewise dated 1872, was in the Collection Mrs. E. B. Greenshields in Montreal (reproduced in her book, *Landscape Painting and Modern Dutch Artists*, New York, 1906, pl. XXX). Still another version is in the Frick Collection in New York, Cat. 1949, I, p. 119 f., no. 54 (43⅝ × 53⅝ in.), said to have been painted in 1885. An etching of the same motif (in reverse) is most closely related to the Johnson and Greenshields pictures. On additional versions see the Frick Cat. of 1949. The windmill on the left and the washerwoman on the right seem to occur only in the Oberlin picture, which can tentatively be dated in the 1880's.

MASTER OF GROSSGMAIN, CIRCLE OF. A Salzburg painter, named for the altarpiece he did in 1499 for the pilgrimage church of Grossgmain near Reichenhall. Related to, but not identical with, Rueland Frueauf (active in Salzburg and Passau, 1476–1507).

St. Augustine *50.12*

Panel (fir), 26¾ × 17⅞ in. (67.9 × 45.4 cm). Coll. C. Benedict, Paris. Gift of Mrs. Charles E. Monroe, 1950. *Fig.* 17

Somewhat abraded but without significant restoration. Closely related to two panels by the Master of Grossgmain, now in Vienna, with the single figures of St. Ambrosius (dated 1498) and St. Augustine, but apparently not by the same hand. A St. Jerome (dated 1498) in the Thyssen Coll., Lugano, may belong to the same series as the Vienna panels but seems to be by a different hand again (see L. von Baldass, *Conrad Laib und die beiden Rueland Frueauf*, Vienna, 1946, figs. 113–115). The head of the Oberlin Augustine is reminiscent of that of the *Standing Christ* in the Grossgmain Church (probably from the Grossgmain altar proper). The blue vision of the Trinity is an iconographical rarity.

Exh.: "Paintings and Drawings from Five Centuries" (AMAM), New York, Knoedler Galleries, 1954, no. 22.

MASTER OF THE STERZING ALTARPIECE. Active at Ulm in the 1450's; named for his share in the altarpiece the sculptured parts of which were executed by Hans Multscher in 1456–58 for the Town Hall in Sterzing (Vipiteno) in Southern Tyrol.

St. Mary Magdalen

41.75

On linen spread on a panel (spruce?), 19⅞ × 15⅛ in. (50.5 × 38.4 cm). Coll. W. C. Escher, Zürich (sold ca. 1933); Henry Schniewind, New York (1936); Richard Ederheimer, New York (1936); Schaeffer Galleries, New York. Purchased from R. T. Miller, Jr. Fund, 1941.   *Fig.* 15

Unusually well preserved. The panel, together with a companion piece representing St. Martha, probably formed the inner sides of a pair of predella wings, or the top parts ("panhandles") of an altarpiece, possibly the one once in Heiligkreuzthal, parts of which are now in the Stuttgart and Karlsruhe Museums (Stechow 1951). The companion piece was lost sight of ca. 1933; it was reported to have been acquired for the collection of Marschall Göring. Both panels have been cut down in size, and their reverse sides sawn off, reducing the thickness of the present panel to ca. 3 mm. Their probable date is ca. 1450.

Exh.: "European Art 1450–1500," Brooklyn Museum, 1936, no. 36; Germanic Museum, Harvard University, Cambridge, Mass., 1936; "A Selection of Paintings by the Old Masters," New York, R. Ederheimer, 1936, no. 11; "Paintings of Women from the 15th to the 20th century," Toronto Art Gallery, 1938, no. 3; "Early German Paintings," New York, Schaeffer Galleries, 1939, no. 16; "German Painting of the Fifteenth Century," New York, Durlacher Bros., 1947, no. 8; "Paintings from College and University Collections," AMAM, 1953, no. 12; "Paintings and Drawings from Five Centuries" (AMAM), New York, Knoedler Galleries, 1954, no. 19.

Lit.: C. L. Kuhn, *A Catalogue of Paintings . . . in American Collections*, Cambridge, Mass., 1936, p. 59, no. 225; H. S. Francis, "The Lovers, A Swabian Gothic Picture of Secular Life in the Fifteenth Century," *Gazette des Beaux-Arts*, ser. 6, XXIV, 1943, pp. 343 ff. (351); Thieme-Becker XXXVII, 1950, p. 317; E. Buchner,

"Allgemeines Lexikon . . . Band 37: Meister mit Notnamen . . .,"
Zeitschrift für Kunst, IV, 1950, pp. 308 ff. (319); W. Stechow,
"Notes on the Master of the Sterzing Altarpiece," *AMAM Bulletin*, VIII, 1950–51, pp. 87 ff.; A. Stange, *Deutsche Malerei der Gotik*, VIII, Berlin, 1957, pp. 8 f.; B. Bushart, "Studien zur altschwäbischen Malerei," *Zeitschrift für Kunstgeschichte*, XXII, 1959, pp. 133 ff. (136); H. Th. Musper, *Gotische Malerei nördlich der Alpen*, Cologne, 1961, p. 90.

MATISSE, HENRI.   Born in Le Cateau (Nord) in 1869. Pupil of
G. Moreau in Paris, 1892–97. Exhibited with the *Indépendants* from 1901,
in the Salon d'Automne from 1903. Active in Paris (conducted an Art
School, 1908–11), St. Tropez, Issy and Nice; traveled in Morocco, Tahiti,
Spain, Russia, and America. Died in Nice in 1954. Sculptor, writer on art.

Young Girl Seated (La Biche)   1936   *59.120*

Canvas, 24 × 19¾ in. (61 × 50.2 cm). Signed, lower left: Henri
Matisse 36. Coll. Mr. and Mrs. Joseph Bissett, New York. Gift of
Mr. and Mrs. Bissett (life interest retained), 1959.   *Fig.* 140

Lit.: G. Besson, *Matisse* (*Collection des Maîtres*), Paris, 1943,
pl. 19 (as "Jeune Fille Assise"; label with date 18-1-36 covers lower
right corner; the works for this booklet were selected by the artist);
M. Raynal, *History of Modern Painting: Matisse, Munch,
Rouault*, Geneva, 1950, p. 57, with color plate (as "Girl on Red
Background," owned by the artist).

MAUVE, ANTON.   Born in Zaandam in 1838. Pupil of P. F. van Os
and W. Verschuur in Haarlem. Active in Haarlem 1858–68, The Hague
1872–85, and Laren 1886–88. Died in Arnhem in 1888.

"The Pensioner" (White Horse)   *19.8*

Paper (mounted on mahogany), 12¼ × 16½ in. (31.1 × 41.9 cm).
Signed, lower right: A. Mauve. Coll. Joseph Jefferson, sale New
York, April 27, 1906, no. 11 (bought by F. S. Flower); Mrs. Hilda
C. Flower, sale (Ch. S. Smith a.o.), New York, April 24, 1919,
no. 24; A. Augustus Healy, Brooklyn. Gift of A. A. Healy, 1919.
                                                           Fig. 102

The title "The Pensioner" goes back to the former owner of the picture, the painter Joseph Jefferson (see this cat., pp. 88–9).

MAYS, PAUL KIRTLAND. Born in Cheswick, Pa., in 1887. Attended Oberlin Academy 1904–05. Pupil of Charles Hawthorne, W. M. Chase and Henry Keller. Painted murals under the Federal Works Agency in Los Angeles (Paramount and Grauman Theatres), at the White House, Washington, D.C., at the University of Pennsylvania, and the Bryn Athyn (Pa.) Library. Died in Carmel, Calif., in 1961.

Harvesters (Buck's County, Pennsylvania)   *38.5*

Tempera and oil on plywood, 27×39 in. (68.6×99 cm). Signed, lower right: Paul Mays 1940. Gift of an anonymous donor, 1937.

Fig. 202

Painted in the middle 1930's and retouched by the artist in 1940.

MEZA, GUILLERMO. Born in Mexico City in 1919. Pupil and assistant of Santos Balmori until 1937. Active in Mexico City from 1938.

Nopalera 1946   *47.29*

Paper, 19⅝×25¾ in. (49.8×65.4 cm). Signed, lower right: G. Meza . . . (illegible) 1946. Coll. La Galleria de Arte Mexicana, Mexico City. Purchased from Charles F. Olney Fund, 1947.

Fig. 213

MICHEL, GEORGES. Born in Paris in 1763; pupil of N. A. Taunay. Active in Paris until his death in 1843. Exhibited at the Salon, 1796–1814.

Landscape   *19.14*

Paper glued to canvas, 19¼×23¾ in. (48.9×60.3 cm). Coll. Catholina Lambert, Belle Vista Castle, Paterson, N.J., sale New York, Feb. 21–24, 1916, no. 37 (bought by Healy); A. Augustus Healy, Brooklyn. Gift of A. A. Healy, 1919.   *Fig. 91*

Probably painted after 1830; a very similar painting (*L'Orage*) is in the Museum in Strasbourg.

MIRÓ, JOÁN. Born in Barcelona in 1893. 1907–15 studied at Barcelona; active there until 1919. Moved to Paris in 1919. Left France 1940; active chiefly in Spain from then on; since 1956 in Palma de Mallorca. In the United States, 1947, 1959, 1961. Writer.

Woman, Bird and Serpent in Front of the Sun   1944   *62.42*

Canvas, 21 × 15⅛ in. (52.5 × 37.8 cm). Signed, on the back: Miró 1944. Coll. Pierre Matisse Gallery, New York; Gordon Bunshaft, New York; Mr. and Mrs. Joseph Bissett, New York. Bissett Gift, 1962 (life interest retained).   *Fig.* 144

A closely related *Woman and Bird before the Moon*, painted in the same year, is illustrated in J. Lassaigne, *Miró* (Skira ed.), 1963, p. 85.

Lit.: Jacques Dupin, *Joán Miró, Life and Work*, New York, 1962, no. 616, p. 547.

The Spokesman of the Birds Plunges into the Night   1954
58.178

Cardboard, 13¾ × 39½ in. (34.4 × 98.8 cm). Signed, lower left of center: Miró. Inscribed on the back, "L'oiseau porte-parole sombre dans la nuit. Miró 1954." Coll. Mr. and Mrs. Joseph Bissett, New York. Bissett Gift, 1958 (life interest retained).   *Fig.* 145

Lit.: Jacques Dupin, *Joán Miró, Life and Work*, New York, 1962, p. 564, no. 847 (as "The Spokesman of the Birds Founders in the Night," painted on December 17, 1953; no owner given).

MODIGLIANI, AMEDEO. Born in Leghorn, Italy, in 1884. Began painting in 1898 under instruction of local painter, G. Micheli. 1906 in Paris; became member of the Société des Indépendants in 1907. 1909–14, concentrated mainly on sculpture. Died in Paris in 1920.

Head of a Man *56.25*

Canvas, 21 × 16¾ in. (52.5 × 41.9 cm). Signed, upper right: Modi-gliani. Coll. Mr. and Mrs. Joseph Bissett, New York. Bissett Gift, 1956 (life interest retained). *Fig.* 125

The man portrayed here is a Spanish painter who frequented the Montparnasse cafés. His name is unknown. Painted in Paris, ca. 1915–16.

Exh.: "Modigliani," Cleveland Museum of Art—Museum of Modern Art, New York, 1951; AMAM, April 1953.

Lit.: J. T. Soby, *Modigliani*, New York, 1951, p. 51.

Nude with Coral Necklace 1917 *55.59*

Canvas, 25¾ × 39¾ in. (64.4 × 99.4 cm). Signed, upper right: Modigliani. Coll. Leopold Zborowski, Paris (ca. 1917); Francis Carco, Paris, sale March 2, 1925, no. 64; Galérie Bing, Paris (1925); Félix Fénéon, Paris, sale May 30, 1947, p. 51; Mr. and Mrs. Joseph Bissett, New York. Bissett Gift, 1955 (life interest retained).

Fig. 126

Exh.: Galérie Bing, Paris, 1925; "Italienische Maler," Kunst-haus, Zürich, 1927, no. 99; "Modigliani," Cleveland Museum of Art—Museum of Modern Art, New York, 1951; "Amedeo Modig-liani," Fine Arts Associates, New York, 1954, no. 10; "Amedeo Modigliani," Arts Club of Chicago—Milwaukee Art Center—Con-temporary Arts Center, Cincinnati, 1959, no. 16; "The Art of Modigliani," Atlanta Art Association, Atlanta, Ga., 1960, no. 16; "Modigliani," Tate Gallery (Arts Council), London—Royal Scottish Academy, Edinburgh, 1963, no. 36.

Lit.: F. Carco, *Le nu dans la peinture moderne*, Paris, 1924, pl. XIX; Waldemar George, "Modigliani," *L'Amour de l'art*, VI, 1925, pp. 383 ff. (388); A. Pfannstiel, *Modigliani*, Paris, 1929, catalogue présumé, p. 23; P. Descargues, *Modigliani*, Paris, 1951, and 1954, pl. 22–23; J. T. Soby, *Modigliani*, New York, 1951, p. 52; G. Jedlicka, *Modigliani*, Erlenbach-Zürich, 1953, pl. 37; A. Pfannstiel, *Modigliani et son oeuvre*, Paris, 1956, cat. rais. p. 102, no. 143, as "Nu au collier (un oeil clos)"; Ambrogio Caroni, *Amedeo Modigliani*, Milan, 1958, p. 61, no. 119.

MOELLER, LOUIS CHARLES. Born in New York in 1855. Student at the Cooper Institute and the National Academy of Design in New York, later studied for six years with W. von Diez and F. Duveneck in Munich. Member, National Academy, 1895. Active in New York City and Wakefield, N.Y. Died in Weehawken, N.J., in 1930.

The Old Armchair *04.583*

Canvas, 17½ × 20 in. (44.5 × 50.8 cm). Signed, lower right: Louis Moeller. Coll. Charles F. Olney, Cleveland, acquired in New York in 1891. Olney Gift, 1904.

Canvas stamped: Rob't Fullerton/Art Dealer.

MOLA, PIER FRANCESCO. Born in Coldrerio (Tessino) in 1612. Studied in Bologna and Venice. Active in Lucca, Coldrerio and Rome (after about 1645). Member of the Accademia di San Luca in 1655. Died in Rome in 1666.

Mercury Putting Argus to Sleep *61.85*

Canvas, 23⅛ × 39⅛ in. (58.7 × 99.4 cm). Coll. Armando Sabatello, Rome; Ars Antiqua, New York; Samuel H. Kress (1950). Kress Study Collection, 1961. *Fig.* 44

Probably painted ca. 1640–50; compare the *Hagar* of the Colonna Gallery and the *Endymion* of the Capitoline Gallery, both in Rome, thus dated by W. Arslan in *Bolletino d'arte*, VIII, 1928/29, pp. 59 f. Inferior variant at Brown University, Providence. A later picture by Mola with the same subject, probably about 1660/65, is in the Berlin Museum (no. 383).

Exh.: "An American University Collection" (AMAM), Kenwood (London County Council), 1962, no. 27; "Art in Italy, 1600–1700," Detroit Institute of Arts, 1965, no. 18; "Treasures from the Allen Memorial Art Museum," Minneapolis Institute of Arts, 1966.

Lit.: W. Stechow, "The Samuel H. Kress Study Collection, Catalogue," *AMAM Bulletin*, XIX, 1961–62, p. 39, no. 8; B. N[icolson] in *Burlington Magazine*, CIV, 1962, p. 310; D. Mahon, "Stock-Taking in *Seicento* Studies," *Apollo*, LXXXII, 1965, pp. 378 ff. (386).

MOLL, CARL. Born in Vienna in 1861. Pupil of C. Griepenkerl and E. Schindler. Co-founder and member of the Vienna *Sezession*, 1897–1905; later more closely related in style to the groups around G. Klimt and O. Kokoschka. Died in Vienna in 1945.

Spring in Kahlenbergerdorf   *58.52*
Panel (softwood like pine), 13⅞ × 14³⁄₁₆ in. (35.2 × 36 cm). Signed, lower right: C. Moll. Coll. Elisabeth Lotte Franzos, Vienna and Washington. Franzos Bequest, 1958.   *Fig.* 115

River Landscape 1909   *58.53*
Panel (hardwood), 9¾ × 13½ in. (24.8 × 34.3 cm). Signed, lower left: CM (in ligature) 1909. Coll. Elisabeth Lotte Franzos, Vienna and Washington. Franzos Bequest, 1958.

MOMPER, JOOS (JOSSE) DE. Born in Antwerp in 1564. Pupil of his father Bartholomeus. Member of the Antwerp guild in 1581, dean in 1611. Active in Antwerp until his death in 1635.

Mountainous Landscape   *48.321*
Panel (oak), 19¹¹⁄₁₆ × 36⁹⁄₁₆ in. (50 × 92.9 cm). Probably Coll. Prof. Wedewer, Wiesbaden; sale Meurer (Wiesbaden) a. o., Berlin, Feb. 26, 1918, no. 27; Dr. K. Lilienfeld, Leipzig (1927) and New York. Purchased from R. T. Miller, Jr. Fund, 1948.   *Fig.* 50

The oak panel has been shaved to a very thin veneer and mounted on masonite. Very slight losses in the paint.

The same landscape motif appears in several other paintings by (or from the workshop of) de Momper: 1. Chicago, Art Institute, no. 35.157 (Burkam 1950, p. 12); 2. Dresden Museum, no. 868 (*ibid.*); 3. Grunewald Castle near Berlin, Cat. 1964, no. 133; 4. Abels Galleries, Cologne, 1956 (octagonal, 19 × 19 cm). The right side and right center alone occur in a panel of the Museum Wuyts-van Campen-Caroly at Lier, Belgium.

As no dated paintings by de Momper exist the question of his development remains wide open but it is reasonable to assume that the present picture belongs in his middle period, ca. 1610–20. The figures are probably by a different, as yet unidentified hand.

Exh.: "Joos de Momper, 1564–1635," Chemnitz, Kunsthütte, 1927, no. 29; "Picture of the Month," Akron, Ohio, Art Institute, 1958.

Lit.: K. Zoege von Manteuffel, "Chemnitz: Joos de Momper Ausstellung in der Kunsthütte," *Zeitschrift für bildende Kunst*, LXI, 1927–28, section *Kunstchronik und Kunstliteratur*, pp. 90 f. (91; dated "not earlier than ca. 1630"); F. M. Burkam, "Joos de Momper's 'Mountain Landscape,' " *AMAM Bulletin*, VIII, 1950–51, pp. 5 ff.; W. Stechow, "A Landscape by Paul Bril," *AMAM Bulletin*, XII, 1954–55, pp. 23 ff. (26); H. Börsch-Supan, *Die Gemälde im Jagdschloss Grunewald*, Berlin, 1964, p. 102.

MONET, CLAUDE OSCAR.

Born in Paris in 1840; moved to Le Havre, 1845. Pupil of E. Boudin in Le Havre, 1855, and active there intermittently between 1860 and 1882. In Paris first from 1856 to 1860, then from 1862. Afterwards active in Argenteuil, Vétheuil 1878–83, London 1871 and 1901–03, and Giverny where he died in 1926.

Garden of the Princess, Louvre   48.296

Canvas, 36⅛ × 24⅜ in. (91.8 × 61.9 cm). Signed, lower right: Claude Monet. Coll. Latouche, Paris (1867); Frederic Bonner, New York, sale Jan. 24, 1912, no. 36; Durand-Ruel Galleries, New York; Horace Havemeyer, New York, Cat. H. O. Havemeyer Coll. 1931, p. 421; M. Knoedler & Co., New York. Purchased from R. T. Miller, Jr. Fund, 1948.   *Fig.* 95

As Cooper and Richardson (1957) have pointed out, and as Isaacson (1966–67) has convincingly demonstrated, the present picture and the undated oblong version of the same motif in the Gemeentemuseum in The Hague were most probably painted, not in 1866 (as generally assumed) but in spring, 1867; at that time (April) Monet wrote to Bazille that he and Renoir were painting views of Paris. The date 1866 on the similar *Saint-Germain l'Auxerrois* in the Berlin Nationalgalerie was added later, and the picture was most probably likewise painted in 1867 (J. Isaacson

1966–67); other works of 1867 are very closely related to these paintings (e.g., *Beach at Sainte Adresse*, Chicago Art Institute).

It is reported that Daumier saw the present picture in Latouche's shop and urged the owner to take the "horror" out of his window (Rewald 1946).

Exh.: "Claude Monet," Paris, Galerie des Beaux-Arts, 1952, no. 5; "Claude Monet," Zürich, Kunsthaus, 1952, no. 9; "Claude Monet," The Hague, Gemeentemuseum, 1952, no. 6; "Paintings and Drawings from Five Centuries" (AMAM), New York, Knoedler Galleries, 1954, no. 59; "Two Sides of the Medal," Detroit Institute of Arts, 1954, no. 44; "Claude Monet," St. Louis City Museum and Minneapolis Institute of Arts, 1957, no. 3; "Paintings by Claude Monet," Palm Beach, Florida, Society of the Four Arts, 1958, no. 1; "An American University Collection" (AMAM), Kenwood (London County Council), 1962, no. 28; "Treasures from the Allen Memorial Art Museum," Minneapolis Institute of Arts, 1966.

Lit.: G. Grappe, *Claude Monet*, Berlin, n. d., p. 32; G. Geffroy, *Claude Monet, sa vie, son oeuvre*, Paris, 1922, p. 262; F. Fels, *Claude Monet*, Paris, 1925, p. 18; J. Wilhelm, *Les Peintres des paysages parisiens*, Paris, 1944, pl. 46; J. Rewald, *The History of Impressionism*, New York, 1946, p. 131; J. Leymarie, *Impressionism*, Lausanne, 1955, I, p. 34; D. Cooper and J. Richardson, Catalogue of the Exhibition of Paintings by Claude Monet, London, Tate Gallery, 1957, p. 41; M. Salinger, *Claude Monet*, New York, 1957, pl. 18; W. C. Seitz, *Claude Monet*, London, 1960, p. 68; J. Isaacson, "Monet's Views of Paris," *AMAM Bulletin*, XXIV, 1966–67, pp. 5 ff.

Wisteria   *60.5*

Canvas, 59⅛ × 78⅞ in. (151.2 × 200.3 cm). Signed, lower left, with estate stamp: Claude Monet. Coll. Michel Monet, Paris; Paul Rosenberg & Co., New York. Purchased from R. T. Miller, Jr. Fund, 1960.   *Fig. 127*

Closely related to several pictures with the same subject. One of these is now in the Gemeentemuseum, The Hague (ex Coll. G. David Thompson, Pittsburgh, exh. Düsseldorf, 1960–61, no.

152), and is usually dated 1920–25. W. Seitz (Exh. Cat. New York 1960) has proposed a date of ca. 1918–20 for the present picture; this date has also been suggested for two other similar versions, likewise once with P. Rosenberg & Co.; however, the somewhat later date appears more likely, although the present state of research offers no firm criteria for it. See also the undated painting of the same subject and the same size, Exhibition "Claude Monet, Letzte Werke," Beyeler Gallery, Basel, 1962, no. 11.

Exh.: "Claude Monet," St. Louis City Art Museum and Minneapolis Institute of Arts, 1957, no. 92; "Claude Monet: Seasons and Moments," New York, Museum of Modern Art, and Los Angeles County Museum, 1960, no. 113; "Impressionism and its Roots," Iowa City, University of Iowa Gallery of Art, 1964, no. 38; "Man and his World," Universal and International Exhibition, Montreal, Quebec, 1967.

Lit.: L. Degand and D. Rouart, *Claude Monet*, Paris-Cleveland, 1958, p. 104.

MONTICELLI, ADOLPHE JOSEPH THOMAS. Born in Marseilles in 1824. Pupil of A. R. Aubert. Active in Paris, 1847–49 and 1856–70, and in Marseilles, 1849–56 and after 1871. Died in Marseilles in 1886.

Autumn Landscape   *40.25*

Panel (mahogany), 15½ × 23½ in. (39.4 × 59.7 cm). Signed, lower right: Monticelli. Coll. Daniel Cotter (acquired from the artist); James S. Inglis, New York, sale March 9–10, 1910, no. 97 (bought by J. R. Andrews); J. R. Andrews, New York, sale Jan. 28, 1916, no. 127 (bought by A. A. Healy); A. Augustus Healy, Brooklyn, N.Y. Gift of Mrs. A. A. Healy, 1940.   *Fig.* 96

Related in style to *L'Allée ombreuse* of 1871 (Exh. Monticelli, Rotterdam—Amsterdam, 1959, no. 63, and Exh. "A. J. T. Monticelli, La belle époque, 1871–1880," London, A. Tooth & Sons, 1965, no. 3), and, particularly in composition, to a picture of exactly the same size in the Pushkin Museum, Moscow (Exh. "Chefs-d'œuvre de la peinture française dans les musées de Leningrad et de Moscou," Paris, 1965/66, no. 66).

Study in Color *44.58*

Panel (hardwood like walnut), 13⅞ × 7¾ in. (35.2 × 19.7 cm). Signed, lower right: Monticelli. Coll. Henry Clay Angell, Boston (1906); Mrs. F. F. Prentiss, Cleveland. Prentiss Bequest, 1944.

Fig. 97

Study for or variant of the right section of the *Réception dans un Parc* (panel 33½ × 50 cm), Coll. Georges Martin (1938; ex coll. Georges Haviland, sale Paris, June 2–3, 1932, no. 54), reproduced and dated 1872 in J. Robiquet, *La femme dans la peinture française du XV. au XX. siècle*, Paris, 1938, p. 191.

Exh.: Boston Museum of Fine Arts, 1906 (no. 571.06).

MORAN, EDWARD. Born in Bolton, Lancashire, in 1829. After the family had moved to Maryland in 1844 he studied in Philadelphia with Paul Weber and James Hamilton. Went to London for further study in 1862. Active in Philadelphia 1857–72 and subsequently in New York, where he died in 1901.

Ruins of Aspinwall Castle *04.428*

Board, 4⅟₁₆ × 4 in. (11.7 × 10.2 cm). Signed, lower left: E. M. On the back, remains of an inscription: "Taken at the bottom . . . of . . . deeper . . ." Coll. Charles F. Olney, Cleveland, acquired before 1887. Olney Gift, 1904. *Fig.* 179

The title of the picture goes back to Olney and appears to be reliable. The mansion of the famous builder of the Panama Railway and collector of paintings, William H. Aspinwall, was situated near Fort Wadsworth on Staten Island, New York; the fire which destroyed it, probably before 1880, left little more than a tower standing. The picture was probably painted soon after the fire, and certainly before 1887, by which time it was in Olney's collection.

Exh.: "American Artists Discover America," AMAM, 1946, no. 34.

MULLER, CHARLES LOUIS. Active in New York in the 1880's.

The Antiquarian   *04.261*

Canvas, 12½ × 5⁹⁄₁₆ in. (31.8 × 14.1 cm). Coll. Charles F. Olney, Cleveland, acquired in 1890. Olney Gift, 1904.

The inscription on the back: "PAINTED by Chas. Muller 1893" must contain an error regarding the date since Olney acquired the picture in 1890.

For the artist see under Brooks, p. 25. He is known as the painter of a *Dollar Bill*, signed "C. Muller" (A. Frankenstein, *After the Hunt*, Berkeley—Los Angeles, 1953, p. 149).

NATTIER, JEAN MARC. Born in Paris in 1685. Probably pupil of Jean Jouvenet; member of the Academy in 1718. Active in Amsterdam (1717) and in Paris, where he became one of the favorite portraitists of the court and died in 1766.

Portrait of a Lady   *63.35*

Canvas, 21½ × 18 in. (54.6 × 45.7 cm). Purchased in Paris for Coll. Mrs. Helen B. Tolles, Miami Shores, Florida. Gift of Mrs. Tolles, 1963.   *Fig. 83*

X rays show several re-workings of the garments.

As was first shown in a seminar paper by Pamela Thompson (1964), this is probably a portrait of "Madame Victoire," daughter of Louis XV (born in 1733), rather than of her sister, "Madame Adélaïde," with whom the sitter was formerly identified; see her portrait (as "Water") in the Museum of São Paulo as against that of Adélaïde (as "Air"), both reproduced by P. M. Bardi, *The Arts in Brazil: A New Museum at São Paulo*, Milan, 1956, p. 206. The unsigned picture was painted ca. 1755, possibly by an assistant of Nattier but certainly retouched by him.

NERI DI BICCI. Born in Florence in 1419. Pupil of his father, Bicci di Lorenzo. Very productive painter of frescoes and altarpieces, and

116

influential teacher. Kept a diary on his artistic activities, 1453–75. Died after 1491.

Altar Wing with Five Saints   61.78

Panel (hardwood like poplar), 48⅝×32¼ in. (123.5×81.9 cm). Church of SS. Annunziata, Florence (until 1688); Coll. Vatican Gallery, Rome, before ca. 1870 (?); Coll. Giulio Sterbini, Rome (?); Newman, Florence (?); Contini-Bonacossi, Florence; Samuel H. Kress (1933). Kress Study Collection, 1961.   *Fig.* 8

Represented are: in the lower row, St. John the Baptist, St. Margaret, St. James Major; in the upper row, St. Bernard and St. Matthew. Generally well preserved; cleaned in 1961.

Left (dexter) wing of an altarpiece commissioned by Jacopo di Giovanni di Matteo Villani for the Villani di Stoldo family chapel in the left transept of SS. Annunziata, Florence, between ca. 1444 (the approximate date when the chapel became Villani property) and 1453 (when the artist started his "Libro di Ricordanze," in which the altar is not mentioned); the patron saints of his wife Margareta and their six sons are all represented on the two wings. A seventeenth-century drawing shows the altarpiece *in situ* (Casalini 1962). The hypothesis (*ibid.* and Parronchi, 1964) that the altarpiece was transferred from the high altar of the same church in 1449, in which case its painter would be the otherwise unknown Ventura di Moro, has little to recommend it, the less so as the patronage of the apse chapel belonged to the Falconieri, not the Villani. The center part with the Madonna is lost; the right (sinister) wing, also with five saints (Francis, Philip, Catherine; Jerome, Albertus Magnus?) is in the Accademia in Florence (no. 3470, formerly as by Paolo di Stefano; ill. in *AMAM Bulletin*, 1961–62, p. 11; see also U. Procacci, *The Gallery of the Accademia of Florence*, 1951, p. 35). An early work, probably from the middle of the 1440's, very close in style to the artist's father and teacher, Bicci di Lorenzo.

Exh.: "Italian Paintings from the Collection of Samuel H. Kress," Seattle, Wash. (Cat. 1933, p. 14) through Charlotte, N. C., 1935; National Gallery, Washington, 1941–52.

Lit.: P. Tonini, *Il Santuario della SS. Annunziata di Firenze,*

Florence, 1876, p. 132; B. Berenson, *Pitture italiane del rinascimento*, Milan, 1936, p. 333 ("studio of Bicci di Lorenzo but early work by Neri"); W. and E. Paatz, *Die Kirchen von Florenz*, I, Frankfurt, 1940, p. 129; *Preliminary Catalogue, National Gallery*, *Washington*, 1941, no. 235 (*Book of Illustrations*, p. 154); W. Cohn, "Notizie storiche intorno ad alcune tavole fiorentine del trecento e quattrocento," *Rivista d'arte*, XXXI, 1958, pp. 41 ff. (61 ff.); W. Stechow, "The Samuel H. Kress Study Collection Catalogue," *AMAM Bulletin*, XIX, 1961–62, pp. 9 ff. (wrong provenience); W. Stechow, "Neri di Bicci: A Correction," *AMAM Bulletin*, XIX, 1961–62, p. 102; E. M. Casalini, "Per una tavola di T. Gaddi già all' Annunziata," *Studi storici sull'Ordine dei Servi di Maria*, XII, 1962, pp. 57 ff.; B. Berenson, *Italian Pictures of the Renaissance, Florentine School* (Phaidon Edition), 1963, I, p. 156 (Neri di Bicci, soon after 1444); A. Parronchi, *Studi su la dolce prospettiva*, Milan, 1964, note on pp. 131 ff.; F. R. Shapley, *Paintings from the Samuel H. Kress Collection: Italian Schools XIII–XV Century*, I, London, 1966, pp. 112 f.

OROZCO, JOSÉ CLEMENTE. Born in Zapotlán (Est. de Jalisco, Mexico) in 1883. Studied at the National Academy, 1908–14. In the U.S.A. in 1917–18, 1927–34, and 1940. Painted mural decorations in Mexico and the U.S.A. Died in Mexico City in 1949.

Mexican House 1929   *43.273*

Canvas, 16½ × 20½ in. (41.9 × 52.1 cm). Signed, lower right: J C · Orozco. Coll. Mrs. Malcolm L. McBride, Cleveland (1934). Gift of Mrs. McBride, 1943.   *Fig.* 211

Exh.: "Paintings and Drawings by J. C. Orozco," New York, Art Students League, 1929, no. 1 (as "Adobe Walls"); "J. C. Orozco," La Porte, Indiana, Civic Auditorium, 1934, no. 26.

Lit.: Alma Reed, *José Clemente Orozco*, New York, 1932 (unpaginated reproduction, under "Paintings"); Justino Fernandez, *José Clemente Orozco, Forma e Idea*, Mexico, 1942, pp. 166 and 170; Nancy Coe, *The History of the Collecting of European Paintings and Drawings in the City of Cleveland* (Oberlin Master's Thesis, typewritten), 1955, II, p. 137, no. 26.

OROZCO ROMERO, CARLOS. Born in Guadalajara (Mexico) in 1898. Studied in France and Spain. Active in Guadalajara and Mexico City. Wood carver.

Head 1932 *45.139*

Canvas, 14 × 11 in. (35.6 × 27.9 cm). Signed, lower left: C. OROZCO / ROMERO. / 1932. Coll. Mrs. Malcolm L. McBride, Cleveland. Gift of Mrs. McBride, 1945.

Lit.: Nancy Coe, *The History of the Collecting of European Paintings and Drawings in the City of Cleveland* (Oberlin Master's Thesis, typewritten), 1955, II, p. 138, no. 30.

PARTON, ARTHUR. Born in Hudson, N.Y., in 1842. Pupil of W. T. Richards; traveled to Paris and London 1870, and Scotland 1871. Member of the National Academy in 1884. Died in Yonkers, N.Y., in 1914.

Autumn on the Ausable River 1871 *04.1197*

Canvas, 8⅛ × 12 in. (20.6 × 30.5 cm). Signed, lower left: Arthur Parton 1871. Coll. Charles F. Olney, Cleveland, acquired before 1887. Olney Gift, 1904. *Fig.* 169

Exh.: "Art Loan Exhibition," Cleveland, 1894, Letter D (p. 110).

PERLMUTTER, JACK. Born in New York in 1920. Active in Washington; Professor at the Corcoran Gallery School of Art.

Still Life Before 1958 *58.59*

Canvas, 6¹⁄₁₆ × 8 in. (15.4 × 20.3 cm). Signed, lower left: J. P. Coll. Elisabeth Lotte Franzos, Washington. Franzos Bequest, 1958.

PICASSO, PABLO. Born Pablo Ruiz-Picasso in 1881. Attended the Provincial Art School at Barcelona and the Academy in Madrid (1897). First visit to Paris in 1900; took up residence there in 1904. Since 1945 chiefly active in Southern France.

Glass of Absinthe   1911   *47.36*

Canvas, 15⅛ × 18¼ in. (38.4 × 46.4 cm). Signed on back of canvas: Picasso. Coll. Ambroise Vollard, Paris; Galerie Pierre, Paris; Walter P. Chrysler, Jr., New York (1937–44); Theodore Schempp, New York. Purchased from Mrs. F. F. Prentiss Fund, 1947.   *Fig.* 120

Painted in Paris in spring, 1911.

Exh.: "Picasso, 1901–1934," New York, Valentine Gallery, 1936, no. 34; "Walter P. Chrysler, Jr., Collection," Arts Club, Chicago, 1937, no. 20; "Walter P. Chrysler, Jr., Collection," Detroit Institute of Arts, 1937, no. 7; "Seven Centuries of Painting," San Francisco, M. H. de Young Memorial Museum, 1939–40, no. 194; "Collection of Walter P. Chrysler, Jr.," Virginia Museum of Fine Arts and Philadelphia Museum of Art, 1941, no. 168; "Paintings and Drawings from Five Centuries" (AMAM), New York, Knoedler Galleries, 1954, no. 68; "Masterworks from American University Museums," European Tour, sponsored by the College Art Association, 1956–57, Cat. Malmö no. 38, Utrecht no. 38, Lyons no. 30; "Picasso, An American Tribute," New York, Saidenberg Gallery, 1962, no. 6; "Pablo Picasso Exhibition—Japan 1964," Tokyo, National Museum of Modern Art—Kyoto, National Museum of Modern Art—Nagoya, Prefectural Museum of Art, 1964, no. 19; "700 Years of Spanish Art," Jacksonville, Fla., Cummer Gallery of Art, 1965, no. 49; "Treasures from the Allen Memorial Art Museum," Minneapolis Institute of Arts, 1966.

Lit.: C. Zervos, *Pablo Picasso*, II, Paris, 1942, no. 261; Ellen Johnson, "On the Role of the Object in Analytic Cubism," *AMAM Bulletin*, XIII, 1955–56, pp. 11 ff.; *Picasso: in Commemoration of Pablo Picasso Exhibition in Japan, 1964*, Tokyo, 1964, no. 8 (color pl.).

Woman in a Peplos   1923   *44.24*

Gouache on paper board, 8³⁄₁₆ × 6¹³⁄₁₆ in. (20.8 × 17.3 cm). Signed, lower left: Picasso 1er Janvier 23. Coll. Paul Gallimard, Paris; M. Knoedler & Co., New York. Purchased from R. T. Miller, Jr. Fund, 1944.   *Fig.* 132

Exh.: "Current Painting Styles and Their Sources," Des Moines, Iowa, Art Center, 1958; "Picasso, an American Tribute: The

Classical Period of Picasso's Art," New York, Duveen Brothers Gallery, 1962, no. 26; "Pablo Picasso Exhibition—Japan, 1964," Tokyo, National Museum of Modern Art—Kyoto, National Museum of Modern Art—Nagoya, Prefectural Museum of Art, 1964, no. 34 (erroneously dated 1922).

Lit.: A. H. Barr, *Picasso, Fifty Years of His Art*, New York, 1946, p. 283; C. Zervos, *Pablo Picasso*, VI, Paris, 1954, no. 1401 (erroneously dated 1921); *Picasso: in Commemoration of Pablo Picasso Exhibition in Japan in 1964*, Tokyo, 1964, no. 17 (color plate; erroneously dated 1922).

Chair and Owl 1947   *57.113*

Canvas, 29 × 23 in. (73.7 × 58.4 cm). Signed, lower left: Picasso. Coll. Pierre Matisse Gallery, New York; from there acquired in 1947 by Mr. and Mrs. Joseph Bissett. Bissett Gift, 1957 (life interest retained).   *Fig.* 143

Painted in 1947 and given by Picasso to be sold for the benefit of Benjamin Peret, French surrealist poet, stranded in Mexico during the war. Jacqueline (Mrs. André) Breton brought it to the U.S.A. in 1947.

Not listed by Zervos but closely related to other representations of the same subject (1947) and particularly to the drawing, Zervos (*Pablo Picasso*, XV, Paris, 1965) no. 25, dated Jan. 13, 1947.

PINTORICCHIO, BERNARDINO, CIRCLE OF. Real name Bernardino di Betto. Born probably in Perugia ca. 1454. Trained there presumably by Fiorenzo di Lorenzo. Became a member of the guild in 1481 but worked extensively with Pietro Perugino in Rome from the same year on. Active in Perugia, Rome, Orvieto, Spello and Siena, where he died in 1513.

The Mystic Marriage of St. Catherine   *44.51*

Panel (poplar), diam. 24½ in. (62.2 cm). Coll. Baron Lazzaroni, Paris (not in sale Baron M. A. Lazzaroni, Rome, Dec. 10, 1894); J. P. Labey and G. Hall, New York (1916); from them acquired in 1919 by Mrs. F. F. Prentiss, Cleveland. Prentiss Bequest, 1944.

Fig 21

In the background, scenes from the Saint's martyrdom.

At the time of acquisition by Mrs. Prentiss, restoration had prettified the faces of Madonna and Child in Pintoricchio's manner, and added innumerable decorative details in the mantle of the Madonna and in the haloes. The present state of the picture is satisfactory but makes an attribution to Pintoricchio himself (Berenson 1932; as work of his "ripest maturity" in certificate of 1916) very improbable. The somewhat harsh details are related to Pintoricchio's Siena Library frescoes of 1504–08; many tondi from Pintoricchio's school exist. The dress of the Christ Child is nearly identical with that in the Madonna of the former J. R. Thompson Coll., Chicago, sold in New York, Jan. 15, 1944, no. 36 (R. van Marle, *The Development of the Italian Schools of Painting*, XIV, p. 254); the Christ Child of the Oberlin picture probably had the same sandals on originally. Cf. also the Christ Child of the tondo with the *Holy Family with St. John* in Siena (Enzo Carli, *Il Pintoricchio*, Milan, 1960, pl. 146), a late work by Pintoricchio which may have influenced the painter of the present tondo.

Lit.: B. Berenson, *Italian Pictures of the Renaissance*, Oxford, 1932, p. 459.

PIPPIN, HORACE. Born in Philadelphia in 1888. Self-taught. Active in Philadelphia, where he died in 1946.

Harmonizing 1944 *64.26*

Canvas, 24 × 30 in. (61 × 76.2 cm). Signed, lower right: H. Pippin 1944. Coll. Downtown Gallery, New York; Mr. and Mrs. Joseph Bissett, New York. Bissett Gift, 1964 (life interest retained).

Fig. 205

Exh.: "Three Pennsylvania Self-taught Artists: Edward Hicks, John Kane, Horace Pippin," Carnegie Institute, Pittsburgh, and Corcoran Gallery of Art, Washington, D.C., 1966–67, p. 110.

PISSARRO, CAMILLE. Born in St. Thomas (West Indies) in 1831. Studied drawing with M. Savary in Paris, 1843. 1847/55 in St. Thomas, 1855 in Paris; after 1857 active in Montmorency, 1867–82 (with interruptions) in Pontoise, after 1883 in Eragny-Bazincourt (Oise) and in Paris, where he died in 1903.

Pont Neuf, Paris 1901 *41.49*

Canvas, 17¾ × 14¾ in. (45.1 × 37.5 cm). Signed, lower right: C. Pissarro. 1901. Coll. J. Helft, Paris (1939); S. Salz, New York. Purchased from R. T. Miller, Jr. Fund, 1941. *Fig.* 113

Similar versions in upright format are in Coll. Joseph S. Gruss, New York (dated 1901; Pissarro-Venturi no. 1179), and in the Museum of Fine Arts in Budapest (dated 1902; Pissarro-Venturi no. 1211).

Exh.: "Impressionist Painting," Pittsfield, Mass., Berkshire Museum, 1946; "French Impressionism," Columbia, South Carolina, Museum of Art, 1960, no. 25; "C. Pissarro," New York, Wildenstein & Co., 1965, pl. 79 (caption exchanged with no. 78).

Lit.: L. R. Pissarro and L. Venturi, *Camille Pissarro*, Paris, 1939, I, p. 244, no. 1177; *Tavlan och Tiden*, Radions Konstserie, Stockholm, 1956 (color reproduction).

POONS, LARRY. Born in Tokyo in 1937. Studied at the New England Conservatory of Music in Boston, 1955–57, and the Boston Museum School of Fine Arts, 1958. Active in New York.

Away Out on the Mountain 1965 *65.25*

Acrylic emulsion on canvas, 72 × 144 in. (182.3 × 365.8 cm). Coll. Green Gallery, New York. Purchased from the Ruth C. Roush Fund for Contemporary Art, 1965. *Fig.* 210

Exh.: "Three Young Americans," AMAM, 1965, no. 3; "VIII. São Paulo Biennal, United States of America," São Paulo, Brazil, 1965—Washington, National Collection of Fine Arts, Smithsonian Institution, 1966, no. 39; "Obelisk Without an Eye," Minneapolis, Walker Art Center, 1966; "Sound, Light, Silence: Art that Performs," Nelson Gallery—Atkins Museum, Kansas City, Mo., 1966, unnumbered.

Lit.: Ellen H. Johnson, "Three Young Americans: Hinman, Poons, and Williams," *AMAM Bulletin*, XXII, 1964–65, pp. 83 ff.

(reprinted under the title "Three New, Cool, Bright Imagists" in *Art News*, LXIV, Summer 1965, pp. 42 ff.).

POPE, JOHN.   Born in Gardner, Maine, in 1820. Studied in Boston from ca. 1836; exhibited at the Athenaeum, 1843 ff. In Rome and Paris in the mid-fifties. After 1857 active in New York, where he died in 1880. Associate member of the National Academy, 1859.

View near Great Barrington, Mass.   *04.1091*

Board, 10³⁄₁₆ × 16³⁄₁₆ in. (25.9 × 41.1 cm). Signed, lower left: J. Pope. Coll. Charles F. Olney, Cleveland, acquired before 1887. Olney Gift, 1904.

Inscribed on the back by a later hand: "Stockbridge Mass J Pope."

PORTOCARRERO, RENÉ.   Born in Havana in 1912; mostly self-taught. Active as painter, illustrator, stage designer and writer in Havana. Visited New York in 1945.

Senales No. 2   *56.7*

Tempera and ink on paper, 14¹⁵⁄₁₆ × 10¹⁵⁄₁₆ in. (38 × 27.8 cm). Signed, lower right: Portocarrero 1952. Gift of Joseph Cantor, Indianapolis (through Smithsonian Institution), 1956.

PYNE, R. L.   Active in New York, 1856–60. Exhibited landscapes with views of the Catskills and Berkshires at the National Academy.

On the Bronx   Before 1887   *04.1198*

Canvas, 14 × 20⅛ in. (35.6 × 51.1 cm). Signed, lower right: R. L. Pyne. Coll. Charles F. Olney, Cleveland, acquired before 1887. Olney Gift, 1904.   *Fig. 163*

Exh.: "American Artists Discover America," AMAM, 1946, no. 37.

RAPHAEL, COPY AFTER. Born in Urbino in 1483, son and pupil of Giovanni Santi. Active in Perugia, Florence (1504–08), and Rome, where he died in 1520.

Madonna di Loreto   *00.31*

Canvas, 47×35 in. (119.4×88.9 cm). Found in an antique shop in Boston and given to the College by Frederick B. Allen, 1900.

One of about thirty copies of the Madonna which was painted probably in 1509 (the date which appears with the signature on the ruined version owned by the Demidoff-San Donato Family at Nizhni-Tagil, Russia) and for which drawings exist in the British Museum in London and the Lille Museum. A picture identified by some with Raphel's original is in the Paul Getty Coll. and was exhibited at the Metropolitan Museum in New York, June–December, 1966. The present picture is considerably later than the copies in the Louvre and in the Naples Museum; the prepared canvas on which it was painted suggests ca. 1825–50, as does the style.

Exh.: "Portraits of the Madonna," Akron, Ohio, Art Institute, 1961.

Lit.: Louis E. Lord, "Raphael's Madonna of the Veil," *Oberlin Alumni Magazine*, XXII, 1925, no. 3, pp. 5 ff.

RAY, MAN. Born in Philadelphia in 1890. Studied at the National Academy in New York; member of the dada group in Paris, 1921. Returned to the U.S. in 1940. Active in Hollywood, Calif. Sculptor, printmaker and photographer.

Bird from Nowhere 1934   *63.25*

Canvas (mounted on aluminum), 15⅛×18⅛ in. (38.4×46 cm). Signed, lower right: Man Ray 1934. Coll. Marcel Duchamp (and Mary Reynolds), Paris (acquired from the artist); Mrs. Katharine Kuh, New York (1957/58). Gift of Mrs. Kuh, 1963.   *Fig. 204*

RENOIR, PIERRE AUGUSTE. Born in Limoges in 1841. Moved to Paris in 1845. Painter of porcelain, fans etc., 1854 ff.; pupil of

C. Gleyre in 1862. Sent pictures to the Salon from 1864. Extensive travels in France and abroad (Algeria, Italy, Spain, Netherlands, England, Germany) after 1879. Most of his last twenty years were spent in Provence. Died in Cagnes in 1919.

Landscape at Cagnes (Renoir's Garden)   *42.119*

Canvas, 11½ × 17⅜ in. (29.2 × 44.1 cm). Signed, lower right: Renoir. Coll. Alexandre Farra, Paris (acquired from the Renoir family); C. H. Worcester, Chicago (after 1939); Theodore Schempp, New York. Purchased from A. Augustus Healy Fund, 1942.

Fig. 117

The motif is from the garden of Renoir's villa "Les Collettes" at Cagnes, where he settled about 1907. It occurs in a similar form in a picture of comparable size said to have been painted in 1914 (Exh. "XIX. and XX. Century French Painting," London, Lefevre Gallery, Feb. 1962, no. 16). For a roughly comparable painting, also assigned the date 1914, see Jean Renoir, *Renoir, My Father*, Boston-Toronto, 1962, fourth plate after p. 374; the treatment of the trees and foliage already appeared in similar form in the *Garden at Les Collettes* of 1909 in the Gangnat Coll., Paris (Denis Rouart, *Renoir*, Ed. Skira, Cleveland, 1954, p. 95). The date traditionally assigned the picture (1905) appears to be too early.

Exh.: "Impressionist Painting," Pittsfield, Mass., Berkshire Museum, 1946; "Paintings and Drawings from Five Centuries" (AMAM), New York, Knoedler Galleries, 1954, no. 65; "Art since 1889," Albuquerque, University of New Mexico Art Gallery, 1964, no. 96; "La Peinture Française: Collections Américaines," Bordeaux Museum, 1966, no. 77.

REYNOLDS, SIR JOSHUA. Born in Plympton-Earl's (Devonshire) in 1723. Pupil of Thomas Hudson in London (1741–43). Active in Plymouth and London until 1749; in Rome, 1749–1752. After this, active in London, where he died in 1792. First President of the Royal Academy, 1768–90; Painter to the King, 1784; writer.

The Strawberry Girl   *44·53*

Canvas, 30¼ × 25⅛ in. (76.8 × 63.8 cm). Coll. Lady George Gordon; bequeathed by her to Major (later Colonel) Copley Wray (1884); T. Agnew & Sons, London (1899); George Jay Gould, Georgian Court, Lakewood, New Jersey (1900); Duveen Brothers, New York; Mrs. F. F. Prentiss, Cleveland. Prentiss Bequest, 1944.

Fig. 87

Replica, by Reynolds' own hand but not in prime condition, of the picture in the Wallace Collection in London (no. 40), which may have been painted in 1775. The first version of this subject, slightly different from the Wallace Coll. and Oberlin ones, is in the Coll. of Lord Lansdowne; it was first exhibited in 1773 (engraved in mezzotint by T. Watson, 1774). Other replicas of the composition are (or were) in the collections of Lord Normanton and of Col. Brocklehurst, Ranksborough, Oakham; see further the list in Algernon Graves, *Art Sales*, London, III, 1921, pp. 6 ff.

The tradition that the model for the picture was Reynolds' niece, Theophila (Offée, Offy) Palmer, cannot be substantiated.

Exh.: "Works of Sir Joshua Reynolds," Grosvenor Gallery, London, 1884, no. 86; "English Masterpieces of the XVIII. Century," Detroit Institute of Arts, 1926, no. 33; "Old and New England," Rhode Island School of Design, Providence, 1945, no. 92; "Sir Joshua Reynolds and his American Contemporaries," Columbus, Ohio, Gallery of Fine Arts, 1958, no. 13; "The Artist Looks at Children," Milwaukee, Wis., Art Center, 1959, no. 4.

Lit.: A. Graves and W. V. Cronin, *A History of the Works of Sir Joshua Reynolds*, London, III, 1899, p. 1215; Sir Walter Armstrong, *Sir Joshua Reynolds*, London, 1900, p. 242; *Harper's Bazaar*, March 3, 1900, p. 178 (reproduction showing the picture hanging in the drawing room at Georgian Court); E. K. Waterhouse, *Reynolds*, London, 1941, p. 63.

RIBERA, JUSEPE DE. Born in Játiva near Valencia in 1591. Possibly pupil of Francisco Ribalta in Valencia. Traveled in Italy and settled for good in Naples in 1616; by 1626 he was a member of the Accademia di San Luca in Rome. Died in Naples in 1652.

Blind Old Beggar *55.9*

Canvas, 49 × 40⅟₁₆ in. (124.5 × 101.7 cm). Signed, lower left: Jusepe de Ribera español 163– (last digit illegible). Coll. Dr. Carvalho, Villandry, France, sold at Tours, Nov. 19, 1953, no. 76; Rosenberg & Stiebel, New York. Purchased from R. T. Miller, Jr. Fund, 1955.

Fig. 73

On the (generally good) preservation see the article by R. Buck (1957). The subject of the old beggar guided by a young boy had become popular in Spain through the picaresque novel *Lazarillo de Tormes*, published anonymously in 1554. Ribera's picture, certainly painted in Naples, may have been commissioned by a Spaniard but the book may have been equally popular in Spanish-governed Naples. In any case the artist's interpretation of the subject differs from the sarcastic one of the novel. The motif of the blind beggar alone occurs with different connotations in other works by Ribera; the model of the Oberlin picture is the same as in the *Blind Philosopher* (by some considered an allegory of *Touch*) in the Prado, Madrid (no. 1112, dated 1632).

The last digit of the date, tentatively read as a 7 or 8 by Angulo (1957), is undecipherable; from the point of view of style, a somewhat earlier date in the 1630's is indicated, but probably a little later than the above mentioned Prado picture of 1632. The tentative characterization of the picture as "on the borderline" with regard to attribution to Ribera himself (Angulo 1957) does not seem to be justified.

Exh.: "Paintings and Graphics by Jusepe de Ribera," AMAM, 1957, no. 2; "Treasures in America," Virginia Museum of Fine Arts, Richmond, 1961, p. 60; "El Greco to Goya," John Herron Museum of Art, Indianapolis, Indiana, and Rhode Island School of Design, Providence, 1963, no. 66; "Treasures from the Allen Memorial Art Museum," Minneapolis Institute of Arts, 1966.

Lit.: J. Milicua, review of Elizabeth du Gué Trapier, *Ribera*, in *Archivo Español de Arte*, LII, 1952, pp. 296 ff. (297, as workshop piece, but this designation retracted by the author *in litteris*, Sept. 1959); P. Rogers, "The Blind Man and His Boy," *AMAM Bulletin*, XIV, 1956–57, pp. 49 ff.; D. Angulo, "The Blind Old Beggar by Ribera," *ibid.*, pp. 59 ff.; R. D. Buck, "Oberlin's Ribera: A Case

History," *ibid.*, pp. 62 ff.; A. Gaya Nuño, *La pintura española fuera de España*, Madrid, 1958, p. 280, no. 2329; A. Gaya Nuño, "Peinture Picaresque," *L'Oeil*, VII, no. 84, Dec. 1961, pp. 53 ff. (54); H. Wethey, "Spanish Painting at Indianapolis and Providence," *Burlington Magazine*, CV, 1963, pp. 207 f. (208).

ROSIERSE, JOHANNES. Born in Dordrecht in 1818. Pupil of Michiel Versteeg and Johannes Boshamer (1836). Active in Dordrecht where he died in 1901.

The Bird's Nest   Before 1887   *04.1225*

Canvas, 14¼ × 10⅞ in. (36.2 × 27.6 cm). On a label attached to the stretcher a certificate of authenticity (in Dutch) by the artist, made out in Dordrecht (no date). Coll. Charles F. Olney, Cleveland, acquired before 1887. Olney Gift, 1904.

Candlelight scenes in the tradition of Gerard Dou and Godfried Schalcken were a specialty of the artist; cf. the *Interior of a Peasant House* in the Dordrecht Museum, reproduced in P. A. Scheen, *Honderd Jaren Nederlandsche Schilder-en Teekenkunst*, The Hague, 1946, fig. 109.

Exh.: "Art Loan Exhibition," Cleveland, 1894, Letter H (p. 110).

ROSSITER, THOMAS PRITCHARD. Born in New Haven, Conn., in 1818. Pupil of N. Jocelyn, studied in London and Paris in 1840. Traveled in Italy, Switzerland and Germany, 1841–46. Lived in New York, 1846–51; in Europe again, 1855–56. Active in Hudson Highlands after 1860. Died in Cold Springs, N.Y., in 1871.

The Inlet   *04.1200*

Canvas, 9 × 12⅛ in. (22.9 × 30.8 cm). Signed, lower left: PTR. On the back an exhibition label (no. 83) with caption: "Rossiter, T. P. (dec'd)." Coll. Charles F. Olney, Cleveland, acquired before 1887. Olney Gift, 1904.   *Fig.* 162

Probably painted at Hudson Highlands after 1860.

Exh.: "American Artists Discover America," AMAM, 1946, no. 39 (as "Hudson Highlands").

ROUAULT, GEORGES. Born in Paris in 1871. Studied and practiced stained glass painting, 1885–89; later pupil of E. Delaunay and Gustave Moreau (1892–94). Director of the Musée Gustave Moreau, 1902. Member of the "Fauves," 1904–07. Active in Paris, where he died in 1958.

Nocturne (Gethsemane)   *41.48*

Canvas, 17½ × 23½ in. (44.5 × 59.7 cm). Signed, lower right: GRouault. Coll. Theodore Schempp, New York. Purchased from R. T. Miller, Jr. Fund, 1941.   *Fig.* 137

Painted in 1915 and thoroughly re-worked in 1939. Closely related to the *Landscape with Figures* of 1939 in Coll. L. Venturi (Exhibition Georges Rouault, Boston—Washington—San Francisco, 1940–41, no. 78) and to the *Autumn* of 1938, ex Vollard Coll. (Pierre Courthion, *Georges Rouault*, New York, 1961, fig. 338).

Exh.: "Modern Religious Paintings," New York, Durand-Ruel Galleries, 1946; "Paintings and Drawings from Five Centuries" (AMAM), New York, Knoedler Galleries, 1954, no. 71; "Paintings, Drawings, Prints and Sculpture from American College and University Museums," Chapel Hill, N.C., Ackland Museum of the University of North Carolina, 1958, no. 94.

Three Clowns   *56.22*

Cardboard, 13½ × 8½ in. (34.3 × 31.6 cm). Label on the back: P[ierre] M[atisse] 1938. Coll. Pierre Matisse, New York; from him acquired in 1938 for Coll. Mr. and Mrs. Joseph Bissett, New York. Bissett Gift (life interest retained), 1956.   *Fig.* 136

Perhaps a preliminary sketch for the large *Wounded Clown* of ca. 1933 in a private collection in Paris, which was used as cartoon for a tapestry (Exh. Georges Rouault, Boston—Washington—San Francisco, 1940–41, no. 22, ill.) and which is reproduced in L. Venturi, *Rouault*, Skira ed., Paris, 1959, p. 94. The large version dated 1939 (71 × 46 in.), also in a private collection, illustrated in J. T. Soby, *Georges Rouault* (Exh. Cat. New York, Museum of Modern Art), 1945, p. 92, no. 81, retains decisive features of the composition of 1933, whereas the corresponding parts in the present sketch seem to antecede them; the motif of the *wounded* clown has not yet been incorporated.

ROUSSEAU, (PIERRE ÉTIENNE) THÉODORE. Born in Paris in 1812. Studied with A. Pau de Saint-Martin, C. Rémond (1827–28) and G. Lethière (1828–29). Exhibited at the Salon, from 1831–37, and from 1849. Active mainly in Paris and in Barbizon (first in 1836–37), where he settled permanently a few years later and died in 1867.

The Source   *66.7*

Paper on panel (oak), 9½ × 13½ in. (24.1 × 34.3 cm). Signed, lower right: T H. R. . . (remainder of name illegible). Private Coll., France (1958); Hazlitt Gallery, London; E. V. Thaw & Co., New York. Purchased from Friends of Art and General Acquisitions Funds, 1966.   *Fig.* 90

Painted in the Auvergne, ca. 1830; compare *The Torrent* in the National Museum in Buenos Aires (Exh. "Barbizon Revisited," San Francisco—Toledo—Cleveland—Boston, 1962–63, no. 84), which shows the same typically early form of signature.

Exh.: "Some Paintings of the Barbizon School," London, Hazlitt Gallery, 1959, no. 5; "Théodore Rousseau," *ibid.*, 1961, no. 7.

RUBENS, PETER PAUL. Born in Siegen, Westphalia, in 1577. In Antwerp after 1587; pupil of Tobias Verhaeght, Adam van Noort and Otto van Veen. Member of the painters' guild in 1598. From 1600–08 in the service of Vincenzo Gonzaga of Mantua, many travels and commissions in Genoa and Rome as well as in Spain (1603). Returned to Antwerp in 1608, court painter to Archduke Albrecht and Infante Isabella in 1609. In Paris 1622 and 1625 in connection with work for Marie de' Medici. 1628 in Spain, 1629–30 in England, active as painter and diplomat. From 1635 until his death in 1640 mostly active at his castle "Het Steen" near Antwerp.

The Finding of Erichthonius   *44.96*

Canvas, 43¼ × 40½ in. (110 × 103 cm). Coll. Duc de Richelieu (1676); Morel, sale in Paris announced for April 19, held on May 3, 1786, no. 34, bought by Vicomte de Chamgrand; his sale in Paris, March 20, 1787, no. 30; R. A. C. Godwin-Austen, sale George Smith a. o., London (Christie's), May 27, 1882, no. 98 (erroneously as from the Orléans Gallery, sold to Lesser); Archibald Coats, Woodside, Paisley, sale London (Christie's) July 3, 1914, no. 126; unidentified sale in London, 1939; A. F. Mondschein, New York. Purchased from R. T. Miller, Jr. Fund, 1944.   *Fig.* 52

Generally well preserved; some retouching in and around the head of the old woman.

For pentimenti see below.

The subject is basically from Ovid, Metamorphoses, II, 552 ff.; it had been represented by Rubens in an earlier picture (ca. 1615), now in the Liechtenstein Gallery, Vaduz. In both cases, he added the old nurse for the sake of contrast to the young girls. The present fragment is the only known remaining part of the large picture (probably 164 × 233 cm) which was still intact when in the Richelieu and Morel collections (Burchard 1953). This complete composition is known through a considerable number of copies, not only in its final state (with the right leg of the now completely invisible girl withdrawn to the left) but also in a former state in which the girl's leg was stretched out to the right under the basket. An earlier state yet can be reconstructed on the basis of the still traceable piece of an antique cornice under the basket. This state differed little from the modello for the picture now in the collection of the Duke of Rutland at Belvoir Castle (42 × 51 cm), of which many copies exist. A preliminary oil sketch is in the National Museum, Stockholm (31 × 33 cm).

The Oberlin fragment existed as such by 1786; it was listed as "une jardinière," for the baby Erichthonius was overpainted with flowers. The standing sister, now half visible on the left, was painted out, as were the remains of the basin on the right and the right hand of the girl touching the basket. In the cleaning after the sale of 1939, carried out by Sebastian Isepp, only the latter two minor areas remained covered.

One other part of the original canvas, the head of the standing girl, was identified by Ludwig Burchard in the Coll. Harold Petri at Antwerp in 1924; it was sold in Amsterdam on Nov. 30, 1926, no. 98 (as "Hélène Fourment"; round, diam. 43 cm) and has not been seen since.

Exh.: "Nicolas Poussin, Peter Paul Rubens," Cincinnati Art Museum, 1948, no. 12; "A Loan Exhibition of Rubens," New York, Wildenstein & Co., 1951, no. 32; "Paintings and Drawings from Five Centuries" (AMAM), New York, Knoedler Galleries, 1954, no. 40; "The Venetian Tradition," Cleveland Museum of Art, 1956–57, no. 40; "The Human Image," Museum of Fine Arts, Houston, Texas, 1958, no. 39; "An American University Collection" (AMAM), Kenwood (London County Council), 1962, no. 29; "Treasures from the Allen Memorial Art Museum," Minneapolis Institute of Arts, 1966.

Lit.: Roger de Piles, *Le cabinet de Monseigneur le Duc de Richelieu*, Paris, 1677 (as "Ericton ou la Curiosité des filles de Cécrops"; reprinted in *Recueil de divers ouvrages sur la peinture et le coloris*, Paris, 1775, pp. 348 f.); M. Rooses, "Les Rubens de la Galérie du Duc de Richelieu," *Bulletin-Rubens*, V, 1897, pp. 138 ff.; W. Stechow, "Two Seventeenth Century Flemish Masterpieces . . .," *Art Quarterly*, VII, 1944, p. 296; W. R. Valentiner, "Rubens' Paintings in America," *Art Quarterly*, IX, 1946, p. 167, no. 132; J. Goris and J. S. Held, *Rubens in America*, New York, 1947, p. 37, no. 71; E. Larsen, *P. P. Rubens*, Antwerp, 1952, p. 219, no. 102; L. Burchard, "Rubens' 'Daughters of Cecrops,' " *AMAM Bulletin*, XI, 1953–54, pp. 4 ff.; D. and E. Panofsky, *Pandora's Box*, New York, 1956, p. 20 n. 16; W. Stechow, "The Finding of Erichthonius: An Ancient Theme in Baroque Art," *Studies in Western Art (Acts of the XX. International Congress of the History of Art)*, Princeton, 1963, III, pp. 27 ff. (33); B. Teyssèdre, "Une collection française de Rubens au XVIIe siècle: le cabinet du duc de Richelieu décrit par Roger de Piles (1676–1681)," *Gazette des Beaux-Arts*, 6. ser., LXII, 1963, pp. 241 ff. (269 and 293; without knowledge of the Oberlin picture); B. Teyssèdre, *ibid.*, 6. ser. LXIV, 1964, p. 68 (addendum to previous article); W. Stechow, article "Erichthonius" in *Reallexikon zur deutschen Kunstgeschichte*, V, Stuttgart, 1965, col. 1243.

RUBIN, REUVEN. Born in Romania in 1893; studied briefly in Paris at the École des Beaux-Arts and Académie Julian. After extensive travel worked in Palestine, 1922–40; in New York, 1940–47; since then, again active in Palestine. Sculptor, stage designer, poet.

White Roses 1943   *46.78*

Canvas, 26 × 20 in. (66 × 50.8 cm). Signed, lower right: rubin. On the stretcher inscribed: 1943 RUBIN—WHITE ROSES 1943. Coll. Vladimir Horowitz, New York. Gift of Vladimir Horowitz, 1946.

RUSSIAN, 16th century (?).

The Nativity   *55.52*

Linen on panel; panel, 20⅞ × 15¹³⁄₁₆ in. (53.2 × 40.2 cm); painted surface, 16¾ × 13 in. (42.5 × 33 cm). Coll. Jacques Zolonitzky, Paris, 1931; La Vieille Russie, Inc., New York. Purchased from R. T. Miller, Jr. Fund, 1955.   *Fig. 20*

Reasonably well preserved.

Muratoff (1931), who stresses the non-Russian elements in the iconography of the panel, connects it closely with Byzantine proto-types and dates it in the late fourteenth century or even earlier. However, as Miss Der Nersessian has shown (1966), the style of the panel most clearly reflects the style of Russian (Novgorod?) icons of the late fifteenth century such as the *Entombment* in the Tretiakov Gallery in Moscow. The reversal of the common position of the Magi, the Bath and the Annunciation to the Shepherds is due to the process of tracing a model similar to the fifteenth-century icon of the Tretiakov Gallery (Der Nersessian 1966). The late date of the panel is also supported by the depiction of one of the Magi as a Moor; it does not belong in Russian art proper and did not become popular in Western art before the fifteenth century.

Exh.: "Dedication Exhibition," Museum of Art, University of Georgia, Athens, 1958, no. 87; "College Collections," Kresge Art Center, Michigan State University, East Lansing, 1959, no. 67; "Russian Icons," New York, A la Vieille Russie, 1962, no. 3.

Lit.: P. Muratoff, *Thirty-Five Russian Primitives: Jacques Zolonitzky's Collection*, Paris, 1931, pp. 37 ff.; S. Der Nersessian, "A Russian Icon of the Nativity," *AMAM Bulletin*, XXIII, 1965–66, pp. 123 ff.

RYLAARSDAM, JAN. Born in Nieuwkoop, Holland, in 1911; studied with A. G. Hulshoff-Pol. Lives in Hilversum.

Two Midinettes *59.123*

Canvas, 38¾ × 22⅞ in. (98.4 × 58.1 cm). Signed, lower left: J Rylaarsdam. Anonymous Gift, 1959.

SANTI DI TITO, see TITO.

SCHAUFFLER, MARGARET REYNOLDS. Born in Cleveland in 1896. Studied at Oberlin College, Cleveland School of Art and Western Reserve University; also with H. H. Breckenridge, W. Forrest and Abel Warshawsky. Taught at Oberlin College, 1923–61; at Ashland College since 1962.

Fisherman's Wharf 1946 *47.46*

Canvas board, 9½ × 12½ in. (24.1 × 31.8 cm). Signed, lower right: M. R. Schauffler '46. Purchased from Charles F. Olney Fund, 1947.

SCHMIDT-ROTTLUFF, KARL. Born Karl Schmidt in Rottluff near Chemnitz (now Karl-Marx-Stadt) in 1884. Studied architecture in Dresden, 1905–06; co-founder of "Die Brücke," 1905. Active in Dresden until 1911, since then mostly in Berlin, where he became Professor at the Hochschule für bildende Künste in 1947.

Parkway 1911 *64.38*

Canvas, 30¼ × 33¼ in. (76.8 × 84.5 cm). Signed, lower right: S. Rottluff 1911. Inscribed on the back across the top stretcher:

Schmidt-Rottluff, Parkweg, Ölgem[älde]. Coll. W. R. Valentiner, Berlin and Detroit. Gift of (estate of) W. R. Valentiner, 1964.

Fig. 119

Exh.: "Expressionist Paintings from the Detroit Institute of Arts," AMAM, 1951; AMAM, 1951–64.

Lit.: Will Grohmann, *Karl Schmidt-Rottluff*, Stuttgart, 1956, pp. 256 and 284.

SCHÖNFELD, JOHANN HEINRICH, COPY AFTER?

Born in Biberach am Riss in 1609. Pupil of J. Sichelbein in Memmingen. After working in Stuttgart and Basel he spent several years in Rome (1633 ff.) and Naples. Active in Dresden (1647), Ulm (1652), and from 1652 in Augsburg, where he died in 1682/83.

Thunderstorm in a Village   *04.444*

Canvas, 15⅜ × 18½ in. (39.1 × 47 cm). Signed lower right: J. H. Schönfeld. 1660. Coll. Charles F. Olney, Cleveland, acquired in 1899. Olney gift, 1904.

The quality of the picture is too low for Schönfeld but it is possible that its signature was copied, together with the painting itself, from a lost original in the 18th or 19th century.

SCHWITTERS, KURT. Born in Hannover in 1887. Studied at the Dresden Academy 1908–14, and at the Berlin Academy 1914. Active in Hannover 1915–37, in Lysaker near Oslo 1937–40, in London 1941–45 and in Little Langdale near Ambleside, Westmorland, where he died in 1948. Writer and poet.

Grey and Yellow   1947   *55.6*

Collage, 8¼ × 6⅝ in. (21 × 16.8 cm). Signed on mount: Kurt Schwitters 1947 Grey and Yellow. Coll. Sidney Janis Gallery, New York. Purchased from Friends of Art Fund, 1955.   *Fig.* 149

Exh.: "Drawings and Watercolors from the Oberlin Collection," Ann Arbor, University of Michigan Museum of Art, 1956; "Kurt Schwitters," Circulating Exhibition through Museum of Modern Art, New York, 1962–63.

SHACKLETON, CHARLES. Born in Mineral Point, Wisconsin, in 1856. Pupil of F. C. Gottwald in Cleveland; later studied in Italy. Active in Cleveland, Silver Mine, Conn., and Provincetown, Mass. Died in New Canaan, Conn., in 1920.

A Glimpse of the Atlantic   Painted ca. 1918–19   *37.38*

Canvas, 16 × 20 in. (40.6 × 50.8 cm). Label with title and name of artist on stretcher. Coll. Mrs. Malcolm L. McBride, Cleveland (purchased at the Memorial Show, 1921). Gift of Mrs. McBride, 1937.

A very similar view of the beach is illustrated in the *Bulletin of the Cleveland Museum of Art*, VIII, 1921, p. 146.

Exh.: "Charles Shackleton Memorial Exhibition," Cleveland Museum of Art, 1921.

SHATTUCK, AARON DRAPER. Born in Francestown, New Hampshire, in 1832. Pupil of Alexander Ransom in Boston in 1851 and of the National Academy in New York in 1852. Member of the National Academy in 1861. After 1868 resided on a farm near Granby, Connecticut, where he died in 1928.

The Hudson River   Before 1887   *04.588*

Canvas, 6⅛ × 12 in. (15.6 × 30.5 cm). Signed, lower left: A. D. S. Coll. Charles F. Olney, Cleveland, acquired before 1887. Olney Gift, 1904.   *Fig.* 181

Exh.: "American Artists Discover America," AMAM, 1946, no. 41.

SISLEY, ALFRED.   Born in Paris in 1839. Studied with C. Gleyre, 1860–63; exhibited at the Salon from 1866. Later active at Sèvres 1875–79, in England 1874 and 1897, and after 1880 at Moret-sur-Loing, where he died in 1899.

The Loing Canal at Moret   Painted ca. 1892   *60.99*

Canvas, 23¾ × 28¾ in. (60.3 × 73 cm). Signed, lower right: Sisley. Coll. Kojiro Matsukata, Paris; Mr. and Mrs. Joseph Bissett, New York. Gift of Mr. and Mrs. Bissett, 1960 (life interest retained).

Fig. 108

Lit.: François Daulte, *Alfred Sisley, Catalogue de l'œuvre peint*, Lausanne, 1959, no. 804.

Bristol Channel, Evening   1897   *52.88*

Canvas, 21½ × 25¾ in. (54.6 × 65.4 cm). Signed, lower left: Sisley 97. Coll. Atelier Alfred Sisley, sale Paris, May 1, 1899, no. 24; François Depeaux, Rouen, sale Paris, April 25, 1901; Durand-Ruel, Paris; François Depeaux, Rouen, sale Paris, May 31, 1906, no. 236; A. Beurdeley, Paris, sale May 6, 1920, no. 115 (as "Canal Saint-Georges, Irlande"); S. Sevadjian, Paris, sale June 1, 1927, no. 42; Norbert Schimmel, New York. Gift of Norbert Schimmel, 1952.   *Fig.* 109

A preparatory drawing, dated July 1897, is in the Musée du Petit Palais, Paris. A painting with the same motif and of the same size, called *La Falaise de Penarth, Le Soir — Temps orageux*, is in the University of New Brunswick, Fredericton, Canada (Daulte 1959, no. 867). Cf. also the *English Coast* of the same year in the Hannover Landesmuseum, no. P.N.M. 576 (not in Daulte) and Daulte no. 865 (both with the same motif from the other side, and of the same size).

Exh.: "Alfred Sisley," Paris, Galéries Georges Petit, 1917, no. 20; "An American University Collection" (AMAM), Kenwood (London County Council), 1962, no. 30.

Lit.: François Daulte, *Alfred Sisley, Catalogue de l'œuvre peint*, Lausanne, 1959, no. 868.

SONNTAG, WILLIAM LOUIS. Born in East Liberty (now part of Pittsburgh) in 1822. Studied and worked in Cincinnati from ca. 1842 until 1855/56, when he went to Italy (mostly Florence) for one year. After his return active in New York (member of the National Academy in 1861), where he died in 1900.

Coming Storm in the Adirondacks   Before 1887   *04.1202*

Canvas, 16⅛ × 24³⁄₁₆ in. (44 × 61.4 cm). Signed, lower left: W. L. Sonntag. Coll. Charles F. Olney, Cleveland, acquired before 1887. Olney Gift, 1904.   *Fig.* 176

> *Exh.*: "American Artists Discover America," AMAM, 1946, no. 42.

Autumn on the Androscoggin   Before 1887   *04.1095*

Canvas, 9⅛ × 14¹⁄₁₆ in. (23.2 × 35.7 cm). Signed, lower left: W. L. Sonntag. Coll. Charles F. Olney, Cleveland, acquired before 1887. Olney Gift, 1904.   *Fig.* 175

> *Exh.*: "American Artists Discover America," AMAM, 1946, no. 43.

SPANISH, first half 16th century.

The Last Supper   *55.27*

Panel (fir), 57⅝ × 65½ in. (146.4 × 166.4 cm). Coll. Mrs. Gerrish Milliken, New York (acquired by her mother in southern France, near the Spanish border, ca. 1915). Gift of Mrs. Gerrish Milliken, 1955.   *Fig.* 41

> Reasonably well preserved, a few retouchings.
> As Mrs. Delphine F. Derby first pointed out (*in litteris*, 1959), the picture belongs to the close circle, perhaps the workshop, of Juan de Borgoña, who was active in Toledo and Avila ca. 1494/5–1536. The profile of the seated apostle farthest to the left is a close, if less inspired variation of the angel of the *Annunciation* in the Chapel of Saint Catalina, San Salvador, Toledo, and the head of Christ is

indebted to that of Mary in the same work (given to "Juan de Borgoña or an intimately related painter" by C. R. Post, *A History of Spanish Painting*, IX, I, Cambridge, Mass., 1947, p. 221). The types of other apostles are generally related to those of Juan de Borgoña (see his *Last Supper* in the Sacristy of the Cathedral in Toledo, Post, 1947, p. 213) but again on a more modest level. José Gudiol (orally, 1961) is inclined to locate the panel in Palencia and dates it ca. 1525.

Saint James Major   47.31

Panel (oak), 32 × 20¾ in. (83.3 × 52.7 cm). Coll. George Grey Barnard, New York (not in cat. 1941); French & Co., New York. Purchased from Charles F. Olney Fund, 1947.   *Fig.* 40

Inscribed on the orphreys of the cope: QUI CONCEPTUS EST DE SP[IRIT]U S[ANCTO]. The scroll on top with the inscription "Santiago" is of a later date.

The picture is part of a series of the Twelve Apostles on individual panels (*Apostolado*) which were still together in the Barnard Collection. Four of them (SS. Jude, John, Thomas and James Minor) are now in the J. B. Speed Museum, Louisville, Kentucky, and two (SS. Peter and Paul) in the Museum at Denver, Colorado. Only one other panel of the series (St. Jude) carries a corresponding inscription from the Creed.

Post's (1947) attribution of the series to his "Mambrillas Master," the author of a retable at the parish church of Mambrillas de Lara near Burgos, is convincing.

Lit.: C. R. Post, *A History of Spanish Painting*, IX, II, Cambridge, Mass., 1947, p. 630.

SPANISH, 16th century.

The Fountain of Life   52.13

Panel (pine), 73 × 45½ in. (185.5 × 115.5 cm). Signed, upper left, with a monogram which contains the letters B, E, L, A, S, C, O and should almost certainly be read as Belasco. With the greatest probability, the picture once in the Chapel of St. Jerome, Cathedral of Palencia (ca. 1780) and seized by a French general in 1812; in the Paris art trade in 1863; Coll. Fernand Schutz, Paris (1913); Mrs. Ogden L. Mills, New York, sold New York, Jan. 23, 1952, no. 96 (as by Lancelot Blondeel).—Purchased from the R. T. Miller, Jr. Fund, 1952. *Fig.* 42

A cleaning after 1952 revealed an excellent state of preservation; two bottom rows of floor tiling, which had been added later, were then removed and replaced with a strip in neutral brown-grey tones. Very slight paint losses.

The composition is based primarily on Revelation XXI and XXII. Christ with the Lamb enthroned between Mary and St. John in upper tier; angels singing and playing instruments in the middle tier; below, the octagonal fountain with the holy water which flows into it from under Christ's throne and carries a large number of hosts, flanked by representatives of the Victorious Church and the Defeated Synagogue. In the upper cuspidal area, on the left, the coat-of-arms of the Girón family of Castille, and on the right, an as yet unidentified one.

Archaizing Spanish copy after the painting in the Prado in Madrid (no. 1511) or its original, with the addition of the mono-gram, the coats-of-arms, the substitution of legible and pertinent Hebrew inscriptions (from Psalms IV 8–9, CVI 1, and CXI 4–5) for the illegible ones (the older, copied one is still visible underneath the first three lines on the banner held by the high priest).

The name Belasco (Velasco) is frequent in Spain; investigation is at present in progress to determine if Luis de Velasco (active 1555–1606) could be the author of this work. The monogram was once erroneously connected with Lancelot Blondeel.

J. Bruyn has shown (1957) that the Prado picture, once at-tributed to Hubert or Jan van Eyck, is post-Eyckian. He connected it with the violation of a Host committed by Jews of Segovia and its miraculous rescue, as reported by Alonso de Espina, and dated it ca. 1455. However, even if the Prado picture is correctly con-nected with this miracle which took place about forty years earlier (a date reflected by the costumes shown in the pictures), the possi-bility of the utilization of a related early Eyckian composition (be-sides the Ghent Altarpiece) remains open (see also Pächt, 1959). The Spanish origin of the Oberlin picture is practically proved by the combination of pine as support and gypsum as ground, as well as by the signature. A crude, smaller copy of the same composition, dated 1560, is in the Museum of the Cathedral of Segovia; a modern one (Frans Meerts, 1836–96) is in the Musée du Cinquantenaire in Brussels. On others see Ponz (1783) and V. von Loga in *Jahrbuch der preussischen Kunstsammlungen*, XXX, 1909, p. 179.

Exh.: "L'art ancien dans les Flandres," World's Fair, Ghent, 1913, no. 552 (as "attributed to Lancelot Blondeel"); "Paintings and Drawings from Five Centuries" (AMAM), New York, Knoedler Galleries, 1954, no. 33; "Religious Painting, 15th to 19th Centuries," The Brooklyn Museum, 1956, no. 27.

Lit.: Antonio Ponz, *Viaje de España*, XII, Madrid, 1783, pp. 154 ff. (ed. C. M. del Rivero, Madrid, 1947, p. 992); Pedro de Madrazo, "El triunfo de la Iglesia sobre la Sinagoga . . ." *Museo español de antigüedades*, IV, 1875, p. 40; W. H. J. Weale, *Hubert and Jan van Eyck*, London-New York, 1908, p. 165; C. Justi, *Miscellaneen aus drei Jahrhunderten spanischen Kunstlebens*, I, Berlin, 1908, p. 300; L. Maeterlinck, *L'énigme des primitifs français*, Ghent, 1921, p. 48; P. Post, "Der Stifter des Lebensbrunnens der van Eyck," *Jahrbuch der preussischen Kunstsammlungen*, XLIII, 1922, p. 120; L. Maeterlinck, *Une école préeyckienne inconnue*, Paris-Brussels, 1925, text under pl. XXXI, fig. 55; M. Dvořák, *Das Rätsel der Kunst der Brüder van Eyck*, Munich, 1925, p. 128; O. Pächt, "Panofsky's 'Early Netherlandish Painting,' II," *Burlington Magazine*, XCVIII, 1956, pp. 267 ff. (271, n. 15); J. Bruyn, *Van Eyck problemen: De Levensbron, het werk van een leerling van Jan van Eyck*, Utrecht, 1957, p. 41 and passim; J. Bruyn, "A Puzzling Picture at Oberlin," *AMAM Bulletin*, XVI, 1958–59, pp. 4 ff.; O. Pächt, review of J. Bruyn, *De Levensbron . . .*, *Kunstchronik*, XII, 1959, pp. 254 ff.; Rudolf Berliner, "Ein Beitrag zur Ikonographie der Christusdarstellungen," *Das Münster*, XIV, 1961, pp. 89 ff. (99).

STEEN, JAN. Born in Leyden in 1626. Active in Leyden until 1648, The Hague 1649–54, Warmond 1656–60, Haarlem 1661–70 and again in Leyden from 1670, where he died in 1679.

A Merry Company   *57.14*

Panel (oak), 17⅝ × 14⅝ in. (44.8 × 37.2 cm). Signed, lower left: J
Steen (J and S in ligature). Coll. Dukes of Saxe-Coburg-Gotha
(probably acquired by Duke Ernst II, 1745–1804), exhibited in the
Museum Friedenstein in Gotha (Cat. 1883, no. 257; 1890, no. 252)
until ca. 1945; G. Cramer, The Hague. Purchased from the R. T.
Miller, Jr., Mrs. F. F. Prentiss, and Charles F. Olney Funds, 1957.

Fig. 68

    Painted ca. 1667–69. The artist has represented himself in the
third person from the right, framed by the open door.

    Exh.: Museum Friedenstein, Gotha (see above); "An American
University Collection" (AMAM), Kenwood (London County Council), 1962, no. 31; "Great Art from Private Colleges and Univer-
sities," Marquette University Art Collection, Milwaukee, Wis.,
1964.

    Lit.: C. Hofstede de Groot, *A Catalogue Raisonné . . .*, London,
I, 1908, no. 593; W. Stechow, "Jan Steen's *Merry Company*,"
AMAM Bulletin, XV, 1957–58, pp. 91 ff.; M. Bernhard, *Verschol-
lene Werke der Malerei*, Munich, 1965, p. 128.

STOCK(T), VRANCK(E) VAN DER (?). Born, possibly in
Brussels, before 1424. Took over the Brussels workshop of his father, Jan,
in 1444. In 1464, succeeded Roger van der Weyden as painter to the City
of Brussels; active there until his death in 1495. His identification with the
painter of a large *œuvre* including the present picture is uncertain and
based almost exclusively on the painter's close relationship to Roger van
der Weyden.

Kneeling Donor with St. John the Baptist   *42.128*

Panel (oak), 17¾ × 8⅛ in. (45.1 × 20.6 cm). Coll. H. Oppenheimer,
London, sale July 24, 1936, no. 6 (as Aelbert Bouts); Art Trade,
Vienna (1937); E. and A. Silberman Galleries, New York. Pur-
chased from R. T. Miller, Jr. Fund, 1942.   *Fig. 14*

    In the landscape, scenes from the *Temptation of Christ*: Satan
offering Christ the stone; Christ inspired by the Dove of the Holy

Ghost; Christ and Satan on top of the cliff; Christ and Satan on the tower of the temple. These scenes were connected with St. John the Baptist because they occurred immediately after the Baptism of Christ.

Left (dexter) wing of a triptych, the other wing of which, representing the donor's wife with St. Margaret in an interior, is now in the Memorial Art Gallery, Rochester, N.Y. (from sale in London, Christie's, April 9, 1937, no. 88, likewise as Aelbert Bouts; Friedländer 1937, pl. XIII). The center part of the triptych has disappeared, but allowing for some cutting it could have been identical with the *Deposition from the Cross* once in a private collection in Brussels (from Coll. Demandolx-Dedon) and reproduced in the *Mémorial* of the Brussels Exhibition "Cinq Siècles d'Art," 1935, pl. XI (no. 32; 38.5 × 38 cm).

Judging from the costume of the donors, the Oberlin and Rochester panels can hardly have been painted later than ca. 1470.

Exh.: "Paintings and Drawings from Five Centuries" (AMAM), Knoedler Galleries, New York, 1954, no. 21.

Lit.: M. J. Friedländer, *Die altniederländische Malerei*, XIV, Leyden, 1937, p. 87; J. Duverger, s. v. "Stock," Thieme-Becker XXXII, 1938, p. 69.

STONE, BENJAMIN BELLOWS GRANT. Born in Watertown (now Belmont), Mass., in 1829. Pupil of B. Champnay and J. F. Cropsey; exhibited at the National Academy and the Boston Athenaeum. After 1865 active in Catskill, also as a journalist and politician. Died in Catskill in 1906.

A Peep at the Hudson at the Home of Thomas Cole

Before 1896   *04.1205*
Fiber board, 7⅜ × 10½ in. (18.7 × 26.7 cm). Coll. Charles F. Olney, Cleveland; given to him in 1896 by his brother, James Olney, a close friend of the artist. Olney Gift, 1904.   *Fig.* 177

Grisaille. On the reverse inscribed: "On the Cole estate Catskill."

Exh.: "American Artists Discover America," AMAM, 1946, no. 44 (erroneously as acc. no. 04.1025).

SWEERTS, MICHAEL. Born in Brussels in 1624. In Rome from 1646 until at least 1652. 1656 in Brussels, 1659 member of the guild. By 1661 in Amsterdam, where he joined a religious mission to the Orient traveling via Marseilles and Palestine; left the mission in Persia in 1662, died at Goa in 1664.

Self Portrait 41.77

Canvas, 37⁵⁄₁₆ × 28⅞ in. (94.5 × 73.4 cm). Coll. Edward Twopeny, London, sale March 5, 1902, no. 57 (as Terborch); Washington B. Thomas, Boston (1907); Mr. and Mrs. William Tudor Gardiner, Gardiner, Maine (1939); M. Knoedler & Co., New York. Purchased from R. T. Miller, Jr. Fund, 1941. *Fig.* 66

Paint losses at the edges, slight abrasions elsewhere.

Etched in reverse by the artist himself (B. 3); the print is not specifically designated as self portrait (Weigel, Suppl. to Bartsch, ed. of 1922, p. 203, erroneously considered it a portrait of Terborch) but the attitude of the sitter leaves little doubt about that identification which also agrees with the age of the artist and is supported by another probable self portrait of ca. 1661 (Stechow 1951 and Exh. Rotterdam 1958, no. 57). The picture shows the influence of works by Sébastien Bourdon (Gerson 1958), P. Franchois (Exh. Rotterdam, 1958), and B. van der Helst (Martin 1907; Stechow 1951; Exh. Rotterdam and Rome, 1958). It seems to be later than the signed portrait of 1656 in Leningrad and may have been painted during Sweerts' late Brussels or early Amsterdam sojourn (ca. 1658–61); E. Schaar (1959) tentatively identified it with a *Self Portrait* given by Sweerts to the Brussels guild in 1660 according to A. Wauters (*Bulletin des commissions royales d'art et d'archéologie*, XVI, 1877, p. 306). The doubts voiced concerning the authenticity of the picture (Incisa della Rocchetta 1959) seem to be unfounded, particularly in view of its authentication by the etching. The pigments on the palette held by the sitter generally correspond to 17th century usage except that blue and black are lacking; however, there is on the palette one damaged spot which may have contained these colors. (The blue of the sky is painted with azurite.)

Exh.: "Old Masters," Copley Society, Boston, 1903, no. 86; "Paintings, Drawings, Prints from Private Collections in New

145

England," Boston Museum of Fine Arts, 1939, no. 129; "Michael Sweerts en tijdgenoten," Rotterdam, Museum Boymans, 1958, no. 43; "Michael Sweerts e i bamboccianti," Rome, Pal. Venezia, 1958–59, no. 44; "An American University Collection" (AMAM), Kenwood (London County Council), 1962, no. 32.

Lit.: W. Martin, "Michiel Sweerts als schilder . . .," *Oud Holland*, XXV, 1907, pp. 133 ff. (136 and 145, cat. no. 1); A. von Wurzbach, *Niederländisches Künstlerlexikon*, II, Vienna, 1910, p. 684; E. Trautscholdt in Thieme-Becker, XXXII, 1938, p. 348; W. Stechow, "Some Portraits by Michael Sweerts," *Art Quarterly*, XIV, 1951, pp. 206 ff. (211), condensed in *AMAM Bulletin*, IX, 1951–52, pp. 64 f.; R. Kultzen, *Michael Sweerts (1624–1664)*, Hamburg Doctoral Thesis, typewritten 1954, cat. no. 69; H. Gerson in *Het Vaderland*, Nov. 15, 1958, p. 14; M. R. Waddingham, "The Sweerts Exhibition in Rotterdam," *Paragone*, 107, Nov. 1958, pp. 67 ff. (71); E. Schaar, "Michael Sweerts e i bamboccianti," *Kunstchronik*, XII, 1959, pp. 41 ff. (44); G. Incisa della Rocchetta, "La Mostra di Michael Sweerts a Roma," *Arte antica e moderna*, V, 1959, pp. 115 ff. (117); R. Bedö, "Ein Doppelporträt des Michael Sweerts," *Acta Historiae Artium*, VIII, 1962, pp. 107 ff.; B. N[icolson], *Burlington Magazine*, CIV, 1962, p. 310; V. Bloch, "Michael Sweerts und Italien," *Jahrbuch der Staatlichen Kunstsammlungen in Baden-Württemberg*, II, 1965, pp. 155 ff. (169 f.); J. Rosenberg, S. Slive, E. H. ter Kuile, *Dutch Art and Architecture, 1600 to 1800* (The Pelican History of Art), Baltimore, 1966, p. 174.

TADDEO DI BARTOLO, shop of.

Born ca. 1362. Style most directly formed under influence of Bartolo di Fredi. Active in Siena and elsewhere. Died in Siena in 1422.

St. John the Baptist   *44.35*

Panel (hardwood like poplar), 19½ × 14¼ in. (49.5 × 36.2 cm). Coll. Robert Lehman, New York. Gift of Robert Lehman, 1944.

Fig. 6

On the back in 18th–19th cen. handwriting: Taddeo Bartolo . . .

The section above the halo is new and was apparently added when the picture was inserted in its present frame. Few paint and gold losses. Part of a polyptych, from the same hand as a *St. Andrew* in Coll. Tosatti, Siena, for which see Sibilla Symonides, *Taddeo di Bartolo*, Siena, 1965, p. 237, no. LXXXII, listed as "Taddeo di Bartolo and assistants (Gualtieri di Giovanni?), c. 1400–1410." There is indeed some resemblance to the works attributed to Gualtieri di Giovanni by Berenson, *International Studio*, XCVII, 1930, Dec., pp. 67 ff. The pattern of the halo is similar to that of the Oberlin *St. Margaret* (no. 43.246) and to a number of other works by Taddeo di Bartolo and his shop; it is probable that both pictures, in spite of their stylistic differences, were executed in that shop by different assistants.

St. Margaret   *43.246*

Panel (hardwood), 27½ × 10¾ in. (69.9 × 27.3 cm) with frame. Coll. Robert Lehman, New York. Gift of Robert Lehman, 1943.

Fig. 5

Numerous small losses and repairs on face and throat.

Part of a polyptych by a member of the shop of Taddeo di Bartolo rather than by Andrea di Bartolo, to whom it was formerly attributed. Painted ca. 1400–1410. The pattern of the halo is exactly like that of the *Redemptor* in Altenburg (Sibilla Symonides, *Taddeo di Bartolo*, Siena, 1965, p. 236, no. LXXX b); the shape of the hand holding the cross is almost identical with that of St. Francis in a panel in the Pisa Museum (*ibid.*, no. VIII a). See also the preceding number.

TENIERS, DAVID THE YOUNGER (?). Born in Antwerp in 1610, son and pupil of his father, David the Elder. Master in the Antwerp guild, 1632/33. Active in Antwerp until 1651 when he settled in Brussels; court painter to the Archdukes Leopold Wilhelm and Don Juan d'Austria. Founder of an art academy in Antwerp, 1665. Died in Brussels in 1690.

Merrymaking Peasants *59.122*

Canvas, 41⅞ × 45½ in. (106.4 × 115.6 cm). Signed, lower right: D. TENIERS. Coll. Earl of Mayo, sale London, Feb. 22, 1929, no. 19; private coll., Danzig; Schaeffer Galleries, New York; Reynolds, sale New York, Feb. 13, 1958, no. 22. Anonymous gift, 1959.

The picture may be a poorly preserved original by Teniers (certified as an original by W. Martin). However, the possibility of an early *pasticcio* cannot by excluded; while the composition does not seem to exist in an identical version or in print, the picture listed by John Smith, *Catalogue Raisonné . . .*, no. 578 (engraved by Le Bas in 1772) showed a principal group of figures consisting of "three couples dancing, in a ring, to the sound of a fiddle played by a man standing on a tub" (the rest of the description does not fit the present painting).

TERBRUGGHEN, HENDRICK. Born near Deventer in 1588. In Utrecht, where he lived from 1591 on, pupil of Abraham Bloemaert. In Italy, chiefly Rome, from 1604 to 1614. In 1616/17 member of the painters' guild in Utrecht; died there in 1629.

Saint Sebastian Attended by Saint Irene 1625 *53.256*

Canvas, 58¹⁵⁄₁₆ × 47¼ in. (149.5 × 120 cm). Signed, top left: HTBrugghen (HTB in ligature) fecit 1625. Coll. Pieter Fris, Amsterdam, given in payment for a debt to Jan de Waale in 1668; sale Jan de Walé (Waale), Amsterdam, May 12, 1706, no. 43; R. Robert, Nice, 1952; Frederick Mont, New York. Purchased from R. T. Miller, Jr. Fund, 1953. *Fig.* 54

Well preserved but for the severe blanching of the robe of St. Irene on the right which probably showed a combination of plum and blue (ultramarine?) (cf. the similar blanching in the *Democritus* in the Rijksmuseum, Amsterdam, no. 656-A1). A canvas margin which had been rather recently added on three sides (tree trunks and leaves at left, tree trunk and branches at top, bare ground below) was removed in 1953. The subject of Saint Sebastian nursed back to life by the two pious women became a

148

favorite of painters of the early 17th century in Italy, France and the Netherlands. The present picture, one of the principal works of this master, reflects the impact of Caravaggio's *Entombment* and perhaps (Nicolson 1958) of Dürer's *Derision of Job* from the Jabach Altarpiece; the expressive use of the desolate landscape motif in the right distance is almost unique in Terbrugghen's work.

Exh.: "Paintings and Drawings from Five Centuries" (AMAM), New York, Knoedler Galleries, 1954, no. 39; "Inaugural Exhibition," Fort Worth, Texas, Art Center, 1954, no. 98; "Dutch Painting: The Golden Age," New York, Metropolitan Museum—Toledo, Ohio, Museum of Art—Toronto Art Gallery, 1954–55, no. 81; "Great Traditions in Painting from Midwestern Museums," Urbana, University of Illinois Department of Art, 1955, no. 34; "Masterworks from American University Museums," European tour, sponsored by the College Art Association, 1956–57, Cat. Malmö no. 45, Cat. Utrecht no. 45, Cat. Lyons no. 37; "Twenty-fifth Anniversary," Kansas City, William Rockhill Nelson Gallery, 1958, no. 4; "Masterpieces of Art," Seattle World's Fair, 1962, no. 24; "Terbrugghen in America," Dayton, Ohio, Art Institute and Baltimore Museum of Art, 1965, no. 10; "Treasures from the Allen Memorial Art Museum," Minneapolis Institute of Arts, 1966; "The Age of Rembrandt," California Palace of the Legion of Honor, San Francisco—Toledo, Ohio, Museum of Art—Museum of Fine Arts, Boston, 1966–67, no. 11, color pl.

Lit.: W. Stechow, "Terbrugghen's Saint Sebastian," *Burlington Magazine*, XCVI, 1954, pp. 70 ff.; M. E. Houtzager, "Bemerkingen over het werk van Hendrick Terbrugghen," *Nederlands Kunsthistorisch Jaarboek*, VI, 1955, pp. 143 ff.; J. R. Judson, *Gerrit van Honthorst*, The Hague, 1956, p. 87 n. 2, p. 88; J. Leymarie, *Dutch Painting*, New York, 1956, p. 70; C. Virch, "The Crucifixion by Hendrick Terbrugghen," *Metropolitan Museum of Art Bulletin*, XVI, 1958, pp. 217 ff. (225 f.); B. Nicolson, *Hendrick Terbrugghen*, London, 1958, cat. A 54 and *passim*; H. Gerson, review of Nicolson's book, *Kunstchronik*, XII, 1959, pp. 314 f. (315); E. Plietzsch, *Holländische und flämische Maler des XVII. Jahrhunderts*, Leipzig, 1960, p. 144; B. Nicolson, "The 'Candlelight Master,' a Follower of Honthorst in Rome," *Nederlands Kunsthistorisch Jaarboek*, XI, 1960, pp. 121 ff. (153); B. N[icolson] in *Burlington Magazine*, CIV,

1962, p. 310; C. Carr, *Saint Sebastian Attended by Irene, An Iconographic Study* (Oberlin Master's Thesis, typewritten), 1964, pp. 70 ff.; H. Gerson in *Kindlers Malerei-Lexikon*, I, Zürich, 1964, pp. 563 f.; W. Stechow, "Terbrugghen in America," *Art News*, LXIV, October 1965, pp. 47 ff. (50 f.); J. Rosenberg, S. Slive, E. H. ter Kuile, *Dutch Art and Architecture, 1600–1800* (The Pelican History of Art), Baltimore, 1966, p. 25 (and plate 9A).

TITO, SANTI DI. Born in 1536 in Borgo San Sepolcro. In Florence pupil of Sebastiano da Montecarlo, perhaps also of Angelo Bronzino. Member of the Company of St. Luke in 1554. Active in Rome from 1558 to 1564, afterwards again in Florence until his death in 1603.

Armorial Shield Salviati-Strozzi   *47.32*

Canvas (central part) and panel (lateral, upper and lower section), 66 × 63 in. (167.6 × 160 cm). Coll. Niccolini-Strozzi family, Florence; French & Co., New York; Charles E. F. McCann, Oyster Bay, L.I. and New York, sale in New York, November 19, 1942, no. 685 (as by Bronzino); R. Zinser, New York. Gift of R. Zinser, 1947.   *Fig. 25*

A modern painted and gilded coronet surmounting the shield (see the illustration in the 1942 sale) has been removed.

The suggestion that this escutcheon, traditionally given to Bronzino, is much more closely related to the work of Santi di Tito was first made by Philip Pouncey (*in litteris*, 1958). This is borne out by the very close resemblance to the signed *Holy Family* in a private collection in Vienna, illustrated in G. Arnolds, *Santi di Tito, pittore di Sansepolcro*, Arezzo, 1934, pl. XXXII, and dated by him (p. 44) ca. 1576–78; in this picture, the heads of the Christ Child, St. John, and the Madonna are practically identical with those of the two putti and the right caryatid in the present work. Workshop participation is probable. The Salviati-Strozzi wedding for which the shield was made, may have been that of Maddalena, daughter of Lorenzo Strozzi and Dianora di Pierantonio Bandini, and Marchese Lorenzo Salviati, 1598 (Litta pl. XXI).

TREIMAN, JOYCE. Born Joyce Wahl in Evanston, Ill., in 1922.
Studied at Stephens College and the University of Iowa. Active in Chicago.

Sculpture I   *60.3*

Canvas, 50¼ × 38 in. (127.6 × 96.5 cm). Signed, lower right: Treiman. Gift of the artist, 1960.

The canvas received a purchase prize from the Ford Foundation
Program for Visual Artists, 1960.

TURNER, JOSEPH MALLORD WILLIAM. Born in Lon-
don in 1775. First copied and colored prints for J. R. Smith. In 1789 a pupil
of the Royal Academy, where he first exhibited water colors in 1790;
associate member 1799, full member 1802, professor 1807. Oil paintings
rare before 1800. Extensive travels in Great Britain, France, Switzerland,
the Netherlands and Italy (first in 1819). Active chiefly in London; died
in Chelsea in 1851.

View of Venice: Ducal Palace, Dogana, with Part of San Giorgio
44.54

Canvas, 25 × 36⅝ in. (63.5 × 93 cm). Coll. Sir Francis Chantrey,
1841 (bought at the Royal Academy Exhibition); after his death
(1841) acquired by W. J. Broderip; sale W. J. Broderip, London,
June 4, 1853, no. 89, bought by a Mr. Egg; Coll. T. Horrocks Miller,
Singleton Park, Poulton-le-Fielde, Lancashire (1889–94); Duveen
Brothers, New York; from them acquired in 1925 by Mrs. F. F.
Prentiss, Cleveland. Prentiss Bequest, 1944.   *Fig.* 92

Painted in (or shortly before) 1841, when it was first exhibited;
according to Thornbury (1862) it was actually painted for Chantrey
and at his death "much damaged by an ignorant dealer," a story
taken over by Armstrong but not borne out by the present state of
the picture. Labels on the back prove its identity with the painting
exhibited in 1889 and 1894 by T. Horrocks Miller; the reference to
the Chantrey picture of 1841 is corroborated—beyond the un-
ambiguous description of the view—by the fact that with the
picture there was passed on to Mrs. Prentiss a label which rightfully

belongs to no. 542, *The depositing of the three Pictures by John Bellinus*, of the same exhibition.

Exh.: London, Royal Academy, 1841, no. 53; *ibid.*, 1889, no. 141; London, Guildhall, 1894, no. 78; "Masterpieces of Painting, Treasures of Five Centuries," Columbus, Ohio, Gallery of Fine Arts, 1950, no. 36; "Paintings by J. M. W. Turner," Toronto Art Gallery, 1951, no. 13; "Paintings and Drawings from Five Centuries" (AMAM), New York, Knoedler Galleries, 1954, no. 58; "Turner in America," Indianapolis, John Herron Art Museum, 1955, no. 44; "Notable Paintings from Midwestern Colleges," Omaha, Nebraska, Joslyn Art Museum, 1956–57; "Comparisons," Toronto Art Gallery, 1957, no. 30; "The World of Art in 1910," New Orleans, Isaac Delgado Museum of Art, 1960; "Significant Forms—The Changing Character of Western Art," Andover, Mass., Addison Gallery, Philips Academy, 1961; "Birth of Impressionism," New York, Wildenstein & Co., 1963, no. 63; "Impressionism and its Roots," Iowa City, University of Iowa Gallery of Art, 1964, no. 9.

Lit.: G. W. Thornbury, *The Life of J. M. W. Turner*, London, 1862, II, pp. 382 and 403 (ed. of 1877, pp. 179 and 604); Sir Walter Armstrong, *Turner*, London, 1902, p. 234; A. J. Finberg, *The Life of J. M. W. Turner*, Oxford, 1939, p. 506, no. 539.

TWACHTMAN, JOHN HENRY. Born in Cincinnati in 1853. Pupil of F. Duveneck, studied later in Munich, Paris and Venice; again in Europe in 1880. Active in New York, where he was a co-founder of the group of the "Ten American Painters" in 1898. Died in Gloucester, Mass., in 1902.

Seascape   *16.2*

Canvas, 19¾ × 23⅝ in. (50.2 × 60 cm). Signed, lower right: J. H. Twachtman. Gift of Homer H. Johnson, New London, Ohio, 1916.

Fig. 193

Probably painted about 1890.

Exh.: "John Henry Twachtman," Cincinnati (Ohio) Art Museum, 1966, no. 32.

Lit.: J. D. Hale, *The Life and Creative Development of John H. Twachtman*, Columbus (Ohio State University Ph.D. thesis, unpublished), 1957, no. 396.

VALLOTTON, FÉLIX. Born in Lausanne in 1865. Studied at the Académie Julian in Paris, 1882–85. Predominantly a print maker until 1900 when he resumed painting more actively. Worked chiefly in Paris, where he died in 1925.

The Crowd 1894   *58.57*

Panel (hardwood like poplar), 10⁹⁄₁₆ × 13¾ in. (26.8 × 34.9 cm). Stamped on the back: "Blanchet.....Paris." Coll. Elisabeth Lotte Franzos, Vienna and Washington. Franzos Bequest, 1958.

Fig. 110

Listed as "Une pochade: Foule" among the works of 1894 in the artist's "Livre de Raison" (H. Hahnloser-Bühler, *Félix Vallotton et ses amis*, Paris, 1936, p. 280, no. 223); for a stylistically close parallel cf. *Le Promenoir des Folies-Bergère* of 1895 (Exhibition Félix Vallotton, Kunsthalle, Basel, 1957, no. 18).

VAUTIER, BENJAMIN, THE YOUNGER. Born in Geneva in 1895, son and pupil of Otto Vautier the Elder. Traveled in Italy and France. Active in Geneva.

View of Billancourt 1930   *37.39*

Canvas, 20 × 25½ in. (50.8 × 64.8 cm). Signed, lower right: Benj. Vautier 1930. Coll. Mrs. Malcolm L. McBride, Cleveland. Gift of Mrs. McBride, 1937.

Billancourt is situated on the Seine, southwest of Paris.

VELDE, ESAJAS VAN DE. Born in Amsterdam ca. 1591. Son of a Flemish immigrant painter, Anthony van de Velde. From 1610 on living at Haarlem, member of the painters' guild in 1612. Moved to The

Hague in 1618, active there until his death in 1630. Landscape and genre painter and etcher.

Summer Landscape (Road to Emmaus) *58.42*

Panel (oak), 8⅛ × 12⁹⁄₁₆ in. (20.6 × 31.9 cm). Signed, lower right: E.VAN.DEN.VELDE. Coll. Anna Maria van Diemen, Amsterdam, who in 1675 married Gerolamo Paressi, ancestor of Marchese Raffaello Mansi Orsetti, Lucca, who owned it in 1928; Frederick Mont, New York. Purchased from R. T. Miller, Jr. Fund, 1958.

Fig. 56

The panel had a companion piece representing a *Winter Landscape with the Flight into Egypt* which has been lost sight of since 1928 (illustrated by Stechow, 1947 and 1966). As the form of the signature proves (Stechow 1947), this pair was painted before 1618; it can probably be dated as early as ca. 1613. It retains a double traditional bond ("season" and "religious scene") and some stylistic connection with Gillis van Coninxloo, but foreshadows the achievements of the following generation of landscape painters with remarkable stylistic freedom.

Exh.: "Capolavori della pittura olandese," Rome, 1928, no. 124; "The Young Rembrandt and his Times," J. Herron Art Museum, Indianapolis, 1958, no. 34; "An American University Collection" (AMAM), Kenwood (London County Council), 1962, no. 34; "Seventeenth Century Paintings of Haarlem," Allentown (Pa.) Art Museum, 1965, no. 82.

Lit.: W. Stechow, "Esajas van de Velde and the Beginnings of Dutch Landscape Painting," *Nederlandsch Kunsthistorisch Jaarboek*, I, 1947, pp. 83 ff.; A. Bengtsson, *Studies on the Rise of Realistic Landscape Painting in Holland, 1610–1625 (Figura*, III), Stockholm, 1952, p. 58 n. 44; H. Gerson, "Enkele vroege werken van Esajas van de Velde," *Oud Holland*, LXX, 1955, pp. 131 ff.; E. Haverkamp Begemann, *Willem Buytewech*, Amsterdam, 1958, p. 41 and p. 218; E. Plietzsch, *Hollandische und flämische Maler des XVII. Jahrhunderts*, Leipzig, 1960, p. 95 n. 1; W. Stechow, *Dutch Landscape Painting of the Seventeenth Century (National Gallery of Art, Kress Foundation Studies in the History of European Art*, I), London, 1966, pp. 20 f.

VENNE, ADRIAEN VAN DE. Born in Delft in 1589. Trained
as goldsmith. Active as painter, illustrator and poet in Middelburg 1614–25
and The Hague from 1625, where he died in 1662.

Allegory of Poverty   *60.94*

Panel (oak), 21½ × 16⅝ in. (54.6 × 42.2 cm). Inscribed on scroll
near feet of main figure: "'t Sijn ellendige beenen die Armoe
moetē draegē" ("it is miserable legs that have to bear poverty").
Inscribed on the back: "Van der Vinne, Rth [Reichsthaler] 175.—"
(18th or early 19th cen.). Coll. Dukes of Saxe-Coburg-Gotha
(probably acquired by Duke Ernst II, 1745–1804), exhibited in the
Museum Friedenstein in Gotha, Cat. 1890, no. 228; G. Cramer,
The Hague. Purchased from Mrs. F. F. Prentiss Fund, 1960.

Fig. 59

The location of the companion piece (Allegory of Wealth: "it is
strong legs that can bear wealth"), no. 227 of the Gotha Catalogue
of 1890, is unknown. A slightly larger copy of the present picture
(panel 24¾ × 18½ in.) was in the Autumn Exhibition of the Alfred
Brod Gallery, London, 1962, no. 57 (with wrong attribution to
"Pseudo-van de Venne"), and is now in the H. H. Weldon Coll.,
New York, wrongly identified with the Gotha picture (Exh.
"Northern Baroque Paintings and Drawings from the Collection of
Mr. and Mrs. Henry H. Weldon," Providence, R.I., 1964, no. 27).
A smaller version is in Coll. Edgar Feder, New York (with com-
panion piece). The same pair but *en grisaille* is in the Museum
Boymans-van Beuningen in Rotterdam, Cat. 1962, no. 2194, panel
62 × 50 cm, there tentatively identified with the pictures of the
sale in Amsterdam (F. Muller) on May 14, 1912, no. 179.

Lit.: D. Franken, *Adriaen van de Venne*, Amsterdam, 1878,
p. 56, no. 28 or 29 (erroneously as grisaille); L. J. Bol, "Een Mid-
delburgse Brueghel-groep, VIII: Adriaen Pietersz. van de Venne,
schilder en teyckenaar. B. Haagse periode, 1625–1662," *Oud Holland*, LXXIII, 1958, pp. 128 ff. (131 n. 10); M. Bernhard, *Ver-
schollene Werke der Malerei*, Munich, 1965, p. 130.

VLAMINCK, MAURICE DE. Born in Paris in 1876. Self-
taught, started painting at twenty-five; exhibited first in 1904. Active

mostly in the country (Beauce, La Tourillière, Nesles-la-Vallée), in later years in Rueil la Gadelière, where he died in 1958.

Landscape with a Village   *44.23*

Canvas, 19¼ × 21¾ in. (48.9 × 55.2 cm). Signed, lower right: Vlaminck. Private Collection in New York; Karl Lilienfeld, New York. Purchased from R. T. Miller, Jr. Fund, 1944.   *Fig.* 121

Painted ca. 1911–12; a similar view, called *Village, Rueil*, is in the Chicago Art Institute (no. 31.517) and likewise assumed to have been painted about 1912. Cf. also the *Petite Ville avec L'Église* of ca. 1911 in the Hermitage in Leningrad (Exh. "Chefs-d'œuvre de la peinture française dans les musées de Leningrad et de Moscou," Paris, 1965/66, no. 101).

River Landscape   *57.1*

Canvas, 21¼ × 25½ in. (54 × 64.8 cm). Signed, lower right: Vlaminck. Gift of Mrs. Joseph L. Lilienthal, Menlo Park, Calif., Mrs. Ann L. Tryon, Beverly Hills, Calif., and Mr. Philip Lilienthal, Berkeley, Calif., 1957.   *Fig.* 122

Painted ca. 1913; in this year, Vlaminck worked together with Derain, whose influence is noticeable here along with that of Cézanne.

WALDO, SAMUEL LOVETT and JEWETT, WILLIAM. Waldo was born in Windham, Conn., in 1783. Pupil of J. Stewart in Hartford ca. 1799, then active on his own in Hartford, Litchfield (Conn.), and Charleston, S.C. 1803–06. 1806–08 in London with West and Copley. Settled in New York in 1809; collaborated with William Jewett from 1818 to 1855. Associate member of the National Academy, 1847. Died in New York in 1861.
Jewett was born in East Haddam, Conn., in 1789 or 1790. From 1812 apprentice and assistant, from 1818 associate of Waldo in New York until 1855. Died in Bayonne, N.J., in 1874.

Portrait of Charles Grandison Finney *16.6*

Panel (hardwood like poplar), 32½ × 25½ in. (82.6 × 64.8 cm). Gift of Lewis Tappan, New York, to Oberlin College, 1858. *Fig.* 156

The sitter (1792–1875), the famous revivalist, came to Oberlin as a teacher of theology in 1835 and was President of the College from 1851 to 1866. In his letter of deed, April 1858, Lewis Tappan (1788–1873), a close friend and sponsor of Finney, wrote: "The picture was painted about twenty years since by an excellent artist and was considered a good likeness. Mr. Finney will recollect sitting for it." Finney, however, had severed the connection with his church in New York by 1837, and it is probable that the picture was painted at (or before) that time. While no documentary evidence has become available the traditional attribution of the picture to "Waldo and Jewett" is borne out by its style. Very close to it in style is another portrait of a preacher, *Rev. Gardiner Spring* in the Metropolitan Museum in New York (Cat. 1965, p. 177, no. 97.17.1), which is signed by both Waldo and Jewett, and dated 1831.

WATSON, ANGÈLE. Born Angèle Hamendt in St. Nicolas, Belgium. Pupil of Alice Ronner in Brussels, of the Slade School in London, and of Sir William Orpen. Active in New York.

Negro Family Before 1937 *38.24*

Canvas, 50 × 36 in. (127 × 91.4 cm). Signed, lower right: Angèle Watson. Anonymous Gift, 1938.

Exh.: "Portraits, Flower Paintings and Drawings by Angèle Watson," New York, Arden Gallery, 1937, no. 10.

WAUGH, FREDERICK JUDD. Born in Bordentown, N.J., in 1861. Pupil of T. Eakins at the Pennsylvania Academy in Philadelphia 1880–81 and of the Académie Julian in Paris. Active in Philadelphia 1885–92, on the Channel Island of Shark and in St. Ives (Cornwall). Died in Provincetown, Mass., in 1940.

Bailey Island, Maine   Before 1925   *25.10*

Canvas, 24½ × 29½ in. (62.2 × 74.9 cm). Signed, lower right:
Waugh. George E. Gage Gallery, Cleveland. Purchased by the
Oberlin Art Association and the Department of Fine Arts, 1925.

Fig. 201

WEENIX, JAN (THE YOUNGER).   Born in Amsterdam in
1640. Son and pupil of Jan (Giovanni Battista) Weenix the Elder. Active
in Amsterdam, Utrecht 1664–68 and Düsseldorf (works for Bensberg
Castle, 1702–12). Died in Amsterdam in 1719.

Decorative Panel with a Musical Party   *53.3*

Canvas, 129¾ × 68 in. (329.6 × 172.7 cm). Coll. F. Reekers, Amsterdam, sale in Amsterdam (F. Muller), Feb. 5, 1923; William
Randolph Hearst, sale cat. New York (Hammer Galleries), 1941,
p. 324, no. 526; French & Co., New York. Gift of Edwin C. Vogel,
New York, and the R. T. Miller, Jr. Fund, 1953.   *Fig.* 80

Part of a series of five panels which was still together in the
Hearst sale, 1941. These decorated an upstairs room in no. 99,
Nieuwe Heerengracht, Amsterdam, where in 1953 the walls still
showed the spaces left empty by their removal. Since that house is
apparently of a somewhat later date than the paintings (second
quarter of the 18th century, see J. G. Wattjes and F. A. Warners,
Amsterdams Bouwkunst en Stadsschoon, 1306–1942, Amsterdam,
1943, p. 126) the latter must have been transferred from their
original location, and the room adjusted to them. Four of the
panels are of the same size; two of them, *Children Playing with a
Dog* and a *Harbor Scene with an Equestrian Monument*, are now in
the main lobby of the Hotel Carlyle, New York; the whereabouts
of the fourth of this size, which shows a large peacock in the foreground, is unknown as is that of the large (339 × 318 cm) piece with
a hunting scene (seen through a "window"), which occupied the
center of one main wall of the room. Painted ca. 1700, somewhat
earlier than the generally similar panel of 1713 in sale, Paris
(Galliéra), March 30, 1963, no. 30. At least one of the five panels
carries the signature of the artist.

WEISSENBRUCH, JAN HENDRIK. Born in The Hague in
1824. Pupil of B. J. van Hove, A. Schelfhout and the Academy at The
Hague. Active in The Hague until his death in 1903.

Landscape
19.9

Panel (oak), 9½ × 11½ in. (24.1 × 29.2 cm). Signed, lower right:
J. H. Weissenbruch. Coll. A. Augustus Healy, Brooklyn, N.Y.
(1909). Gift of A. A. Healy, 1919. *Fig.* 103

Exh.: Brooklyn Museum of Art, 1909.

WERFF, ADRIAEN VAN DER. Born in Rotterdam in 1659;
pupil of Eglon van der Neer. Active in Rotterdam from 1676 until his
death in 1722. Court painter to the Elector Palatine in Düsseldorf in 1697,
knighted by him in 1703.

Jacob Blessing the Sons of Joseph
63.30

Panel (oak), 24⅟₁₆ × 18⅟₁₆ in. (62.5 × 47.5 cm). Sale in Amsterdam,
June 5, 1765, no. 1; Coll. King Frederick II of Prussia, Castle
Sanssouci near Potsdam, by 1770 (probably bought from the Paris
art dealer Mettra in 1767); Kings of Prussia and German Emperors,
House Hohenzollern, until 1925; private collection in London; sale
at Christie's in London, May 24, 1963, no. 152 (bought in). Purchased from Mrs. F. F. Prentiss Fund, 1963. *Fig.* 81

Berlin Museum seal and inventory number (I, 547) on the back.
A companion piece, representing the *Blessing of Jacob by Isaac*
according to *Genesis*, XVIII, 1–4, early misinterpreted as a *Dis-
missal of Hagar*, shares the same history with the present panel
until 1925, when it was returned by the Hohenzollern to Sans-
souci (cat. 1930, no. 141), where it remained until its disappearance
during the last world war.

A late work (ca. 1710–20) of Adriaen van der Werff, as already
recognized by M. Oesterreich in 1770, and one of the earliest
known examples of the use of Prussian blue (Buck 1964–65).

Exh.: Sanssouci Gallery, 1770–ca. 1833; Berlin Museum, before
1837–1906 (no. 481 in Cat. of 1837, no. 510 in Cat. of 1886).

Lit.: G. Hoet and P. Terwesten, *Catalogus of naamlyst van
schilderijen*, III, The Hague, 1770, p. 451; M. Oesterreich, *Be-*

schreibung der Königlichen Bildergallerie und des Kabinetts im Sans-souci, Potsdam, 1770, p. 112; C. Decker, *Arrangement du Cabinet à coté de la Grande Galérie Royale des Tableaux de Sans-Souci,* Berlin, 1773; Friedrich Nicolai, *Beschreibung der königlichen Residenzstädte Berlin und Potsdam,* second edition, 1779, II, p. 924, and third edition, Berlin, 1786, III, p. 1211; Friedrich Rumpf, *Beschreibung der äussern und innern Merkwürdigkeiten der Königlichen Schlösser in Berlin, Charlottenburg, Schönhausen, in und bey Potsdam,* Berlin, 1794, p. 178; John Smith, *A Catalogue Raisonné . . .,* IV, 1833, p. 212, no. 114, and *Supplement,* 1842, p. 558, no. 30; C. Hofstede de Groot, *Beschreibendes und kritisches Verzeichnis . . .,* X, 1928, p. 241, no. 17; W. Stechow, "Jacob Blessing the Sons of Joseph, by Adriaen van der Werff," *AMAM Bulletin,* XXII, 1964–65, pp. 69 ff.; Richard D. Buck, "Adriaen van der Werff and Prussian Blue," *ibid.,* pp. 74 ff.

WEST, BENJAMIN. Born in Springfield, Pennsylvania, in 1738. Pupil of William Williams in Philadelphia (1747); subsequently active in Lancaster, Pa., and New York. Traveled in Italy, 1760–63; settled in London in 1763. Co-founder of the Royal Academy (1768) and its President, 1792–1805 and 1806–20; Painter to the King, 1772. Member, Institut de France 1803, Berlin Academy 1812, Accademia di San Luca, Rome 1816. Died in London in 1820.

Jacob Blessing the Sons of Joseph   1766   *61.70*

Canvas, 40⁄¹⁶ × 51 in. (101.8 × 129.5 cm). Remains of a signature, lower left: B...... 66. Coll. Earl Grosvenor, London, before 1802; although the picture is not listed in John Young's catalogue (1820/21) it must have remained in the Grosvenor (later Marquises, then Dukes of Westminster) family until sold by Hugh Richard Arthur, Duke of Westminster, London (Sotheby's), July 15, 1959, no. 128; John Nicholson Gallery, New York. Purchased from R. T. Miller, Jr. Fund, 1961.   *Fig.* 151

Engraved by Valentine Green (Exhibition Society of Artists, 1768, no. 246, but published by Boydell only in 1778; see Alfred Whitman, *Valentine Green,* London, 1902, no. 165, mezzotint) and by J. Rogers (with slight alterations).

The remains of the date on the picture prove that it was painted in 1766. A presumed companion piece (40×50 in.) representing *Elisha Raising the Son of the Shumanite* and now in the J. B. Speed Memorial Museum in Louisville, Kentucky (A. F. Page, "A Biblical Story: Benjamin West," Speed Museum *Bulletin*, XXIV, 1964, no. 4, pp. 5 ff.) is dated 1765 or 1766 (mezzotint by V. Green, 1768, Whitman 166), had been exhibited alone in 1767 (no. 175) and was shown in a *special* West Exhibition in 1768 (no. 121), thus not as a companion piece of the present picture. Their treatment as pendants was probably suggested by Green's prints, both made and exhibited together in 1768 (Society of Artists, nos. 245 and 246). The suggestion of their being companion pieces would be more plausible if the Speed Museum picture was intended to represent the story of *Elijah Raising the Widow's Son* (1 Kings XVII, 21–24), rather than the Elisha scene (2 Kings IV, 34–37)—on the frequent fusions of the two scenes cf. *Reallexikon zur deutschen Kunstgeschichte*, IV, 1958, col. 1400—because *Jacob's Blessing* was sometimes considered prophetic of Baptism, and Elijah seen as the predecessor of St. John the Baptist; and while Green's print of the Oberlin picture is inscribed with its subject, his print of the Louisville painting bears no title at all. The 1959 sale catalogue identified the Speed Museum picture as the *Elijah Raising the Widow's Son* exhibited at the Royal Academy in 1775, no. 334, but this was evidently a different picture, painted in 1774 (Galt 1820, p. 226) and now in the Philadelphia Museum of Art (retouched in 1819). A signed preparatory drawing for the Oberlin picture (date 1768 added later) at the Kennedy Galleries, Cat. 1967, no. 1.

Exh.: London, Society of Artists, 1768, no. 177; "Benjamin West," New York, Graham Gallery, 1962, no. 16.

Lit.: Joel Barlow, *The Columbiad*, Philadelphia, 1809, II, p. 184 (based on a list put at Barlow's disposal by West in 1802); John Galt, *The Life and Works of Benjamin West*, London, 1820, II, p. 220; A. Graves, *The Society of Artists of Great Britain, 1760–1791 . . .*, London, 1907, p. 275 (for the year 1768) no. 177.

General Kosciusko 1797   46.46

Panel (mahogany), 12⁵⁄₁₆ × 17⅜ in. (31.3 × 44.1 cm). Signed, lower left: B. West / 1797. On a sheet of paper, left, can be read: "Gen'

Co....osko, Lo.do." Coll. of the artist (1802, see Barlow, 1809), sold in London (Robins), May 22–25, 1829, no. 138, bought by "Bone," most probably H. P. Bone, the miniature painter, who was in close contact with the Neeld Family, owners of a large collection of pictures by West; L. W. Neeld, Grittleton House near Chippenham, Wilts., sold in London, July 13, 1945, no. 175; M. Knoedler & Co., New York. Purchased from R. T. Miller, Jr. Fund, 1946.

Fig. 152

Thaddeus Kosciusko (Tadeus Kósciuszko, 1746–1817), Polish military leader and statesman, and hero of the American War of Independence, is shown lying on a couch in his London domicile, the Sablonière Hotel, at 30 Leicester Square (formerly Hogarth's residence), with a view of St. Paul's through the window. His head wound had been inflicted in the Polish defeat of 1794 at Maciejowice where Kosciusko had been taken captive; it had not healed during his imprisonment in Russia, from which he was released in 1796; he also had a bad leg injury. Kosciusko arrived in London on May 30th, 1797, was feted liberally, and portrayed by West— the present picture, begun on June 7th, as stated in the Farington Diary—, by Richard Cosway, and (in wax) by Catherine Andras (Hamilton 1952). He left London for Bristol and Philadelphia after a stay of about two weeks. An engraving after the picture, indicated as existing in Barlow's list (1809), has not been identified.

Exh.: Royal Academy, London, 1798, no. 618; "Pictures and Drawings by the Late Benjamin West, Esq., President of the Royal Academy," London, 1823, no. 63; "The Art in America in the Eighteenth Century," AMAM, 1946, no. 18; "From Colony to Nation," Chicago Art Institute, 1949, no. 130; "They gave Us Freedom," Williamsburg (Colonial Williamsburg and the College of William and Mary), 1951, no. 48; "The French in America, 1520–1880," Detroit Institute of Arts, 1951, no. 244; "Paintings and Drawings from Five Centuries" (AMAM), Knoedler Galleries, New York, 1954, no. 54; "The Century of Mozart," W. R. Nelson Gallery of Art, Kansas City, 1956, no. 106; "Masterworks from American University Museums," European Tour, sponsored by the College Art Association, 1956–57, Cat. Malmö no. 48, Cat. Utrecht no. 48, Cat. Lyons no. 40; "Art Across America," Munson-Williams-Proctor Institute, Utica, N.Y., 1960, no. 109; "Benjamin

West," Graham Gallery, New York, 1962, no. 4; "Style, Truth and the Portrait," Cleveland Museum of Art, 1963, no. 47 (color repr.); "Treasures from the Allen Memorial Art Museum," Minneapolis Institute of Arts, 1966.

Lit.: Joel Barlow, *The Columbiad*, Philadelphia, 1809, II, p. 186; *The Port Folio*, VI, no. 6, Dec. 1811, p. 552; J. Galt, *The Life and Works of Benjamin West*, London, 1820, II, p. 231; A. Graves, *The Royal Academy of Arts*, London, 1906, VIII, p. 216; A. Graves, *Art Sales*, London, 1921, III, p. 331; J. Greig (ed.), *The Farington Diary by Joseph Farington, R.A.*, London, 1923, I, p. 210; R. Wittkower, "An Exhibition of American Art in Chicago," *Burlington Magazine*, XCI, 1949, p. 254; Virgil Barker, *American Painting: History and Interpretation*, New York, 1950, pp. 204 f.; Chloe Hamilton, "A Portrait of General Kosciusko by Benjamin West," *AMAM Bulletin*, IX, 1952, pp. 81 ff. (reprinted in Polish: "Portret Kósciuszki pędzla Benjamina Westa," *Biuletyn Historii Sztuki*, XXV, 1963, pp. 77 ff.).

WHITESIDE, FORBES. Born in Vancouver, B.C., in 1918. Studied and taught at the Minneapolis School of Art and the University of Minnesota. Since 1951 teaching at Oberlin College.

Warm Journey 1951   *53.223*

Board, 28 × 40 in. (71.1 × 101.6 cm). Signed, lower left: Whiteside '51. Purchased from Mrs. F. F. Prentiss Fund, 1953.

WILLARD, ARCHIBALD M. Born in Bedford, Ohio, in 1836; moved to Wellington, Ohio, in 1853. Was primarily a carriage painter until 1873 when he went to study in New York. Mostly active in Cleveland, where he died in 1918.

Deacon Jones' Experience   *04.1210*

Canvas, 16 × 23 in. (40.6 × 58.4 cm). Signed, lower right: AWillard (A and W in ligature). Coll. J. F. Ryder, Cleveland (1874); Charles F. Olney, Cleveland, who bought it in Cleveland in 1893. Olney Gift, 1904.
                                              Fig. 171

Painted ca. 1873 as a genre scene and acquired by J. F. Ryder, who had chromo lithographs made of it and commissioned Bret Harte to write a poem on the picture in order to make it respectable (1874); the title is that of Harte's poem.

Exh.: "Wellington Centennial Exhibition," Wellington, Ohio, 1955.

Lit.: James F. Ryder, *Voigtländer and I in Pursuit of Shadow Catching*, Cleveland, 1902, pp. 220 ff.

WITTE, EMANUEL DE. Born in Alkmaar in 1617. Member of the guild in 1636. Active in Rotterdam 1639–40, Delft 1641–51, and Amsterdam from 1652. Died (by his own hand) in Amsterdam in 1692.

Interior of the Old Church at Delft   1653 or 1655   *43.279*

Panel (oak), 19½ × 16 in. (49.5 × 40.6 cm). Signed, lower left: E De Witte 1655 (last digit not quite certain and probably retouched, perhaps originally a 3). Probably Coll. D. Katz, Dieren, 1934 (as dated 1653); D. Katz, Dieren, 1938; Schaeffer Galleries, New York. Purchased from the R. T. Miller, Jr. Fund, 1943.   *Fig. 64*

View from the main choir towards north-west into St. Mary's Choir and St. George's chapel; in the center the epitaph of Gerard Welhouc (see the photograph reproduced in Manke, fig. 25).

Exh.: Probably Exh. Arnhem, D. Katz, 1934, and The Hague, D. Katz, 1934, no. 32; Exh. Amsterdam, D. Katz, 1938, no. 90; "Dutch and Flemish Paintings," Dieren, D. Katz, 1938, no. 112; "Dutch Painting," Providence, R.I., Museum of the School of Design, 1938, no. 62; "Seventeen Masterpieces of the Seventeenth Century," New York, Schaeffer Galleries, 1939, no. 17; "Paintings and Drawings from Five Centuries" (AMAM), New York, Knoedler Galleries, 1954, no. 45; "Dutch Seventeenth Century Paintings and Drawings," Akron, Ohio, Art Institute, 1956, no. 24; "Ten Baroque Paintings," Ohio State University School of Art Gallery, 1964, no. 5.

Lit.: E. Trautscholdt in Thieme-Becker, XXXVI, 1947, pp. 124 (lower right) and 125 (upper left); Ilse Manke, *Emanuel de Witte, 1617–1692*, Amsterdam, 1963, pp. 31, 40, 82 f. (cat. no. 20), and 118 f. (cat. no. 179).

WRIGHT, JOSEPH, *called Wright of Derby*. Born in Derby in 1734. Pupil of Thomas Hudson in London 1751–53 and 1756–57. After having painted portraits and genre scenes in Derby and other small English towns he visited Italy 1773–75 and was afterwards active in Bath 1775–77, and Derby, where he died in 1797. Member, Royal Academy, 1784.

Dovedale by Moonlight
51.30

Canvas, 24⅝ × 30⅝ in. (62.5 × 77.8 cm). Signed, lower center: I. W. Coll. Edward Mundy, Markeaton near Derby (bought from the artist); William Martin, Broadstairs, Kent; R. Langton Douglas. Purchased from R. T. Miller, Jr. Fund, 1951.
Fig. 86

The valley of Dovedale is ca. 14 miles north-east of Derby.

The companion piece, likewise signed with initials and of the same size, represents Dovedale at day-light and is now in the Collection of Sir John Crompton-Inglefield, Parwich Hall near Ashbourne, Devonshire (Nicolson, 1958, no. 24, known to have come from the Mundy Coll.). Wright's account book lists among pictures of the mid-1780's: "A View in Dove Dale Morn. Companion in Do. Moonlight 3 qrs. Sold to Ed. Mundy Esqr." at £31 sh10 each (Ms. in the National Portrait Gallery, London, as transcribed by Mr. Benedict Nicolson; Bemrose, 1885, p. 123); "3 quarters" corresponds to the size of the Oberlin and the Crompton-Inglefield pictures. The latter collection preserves an unsigned copy (25 × 30 in.) of the present painting, on loan to the Derbyshire County Council, exhibited in the Wright exhibition at Derby in 1934 as a scene at Tissington Spires [Dovedale] (cf. color plate in *Connoisseur*, LXXXVII, Jan. 1931, opp. p. 3). A third version (30 × 36 in.), also unsigned, is in the Derby Museum and Art Gallery.

Exh.: "Pictures, Painted by J. Wright, of Derby," London, Robin's Rooms, Covent Garden, 1785, no. XIX (most probably); "Joseph Wright of Derby, 1734–1797," New York, Durlacher Bros., 1960, no. 22; "Nature and Natural Phenomena in Art of the Eighteenth Century," Vassar College Art Gallery, Poughkeepsie, N.Y., 1964, no. 24.

Lit.: W. Bemrose, *The Life and Works of Joseph Wright*, *A.R.A.* . . ., London, 1885, pp. 22 and 123; Chloe Hamilton, "A Landscape by Wright of Derby," *AMAM Bulletin*, XII, 1954–55, pp. 17 ff.; [B. Nicholson], Cat. Exh. Joseph Wright of Derby, The Arts Council, London (Tate Gallery) and Liverpool (Walker Art Gallery), 1958, p. 28.

WUCHERER, FRITZ. Born in Basel in 1873. Pupil of Anton Burger in Cronberg near Frankfurt, 1892–94; in Paris, 1895–97. Active in Frankfurt and (from 1901) in Cronberg, where he died in 1948.

Taunus Mountains in Winter   Before 1900   *23.3*

Canvas, 31½ × 45 in. (80 × 114.3 cm). Signed, lower right: FWucherer (F and W in ligature). Coll. Dr. and Mrs. D. P. Allen, Cleveland, acquired in Munich in 1900. Gift of Mrs. F. F. Prentiss, 1923.

Exh.: "Art Loan Exposition," Cleveland, 1913, no. 183 D.

YOUNG-HUNTER, JOHN. Born in Glasgow in 1874; attended the Royal Academy in London, where he exhibited from 1895. Traveled in Italy 1899–1900. Moved to the U.S.A. in 1913 and was active in New York and in Taos, New Mexico (by 1942), where he died in 1955.

Portrait of Henry Churchill King   1922   *23.4*

Canvas, 50 × 40 in. (127 × 101.6 cm). Signed, upper left: J. Young-Hunter 1922. Gift of Mr. and Mrs. J. Young-Hunter, 1923.

The sitter (1858–1934) was President of Oberlin College, 1902–1927.

Lit.: D. M. Love, *Henry Churchill King*, New Haven, 1956, frontispiece.

YUNKERS, ADJA. Born in Riga (Latvia) in 1900. Studied in Leningrad, Berlin, Paris and London. Active in New York since 1946; has taught there at the New School for Social Research and the Cooper Union.

August 18, 1959   1959   *64.46*

Gouache on paper, 14½ × 18½ in. (36.8 × 47 cm). Gift of Mr. and Mrs. André Emmerich, 1964.

ZAHRADNICZEK, JOSEPH. Born in Vienna in 1822. Pupil of
the Vienna Academy, 1838 ff. Died in Vienna in 1844.

View in the Prater, Vienna   *44.55*

Canvas, 12⅛ × 9⅞ in. (30.8 × 25.1 cm). An otherwise illegible long
signature, lower right, begins with a "Z." Coll. Mrs. F. F. Prentiss,
Cleveland. Prentiss Bequest, 1944.   *Fig.* 94

Formerly called "School of Fontainebleau," but the motif and
the style of the picture are clearly derived from similar views by
F. G. Waldmüller, such as the *Parthie aus dem Prater* of 1831 in
Hamburg (B. Grimschitz, *F. G. Waldmüller*, Salzburg, 1957, pl.
18). The signature is almost certainly that of Zahradniczek, as was
first pointed out by Heinrich Schwarz (orally, 1949).

ZAO-WOU-KI. Born in Peking in 1920. Studied at the Hong Chow
School of Art 1935–41; taught there, 1941–47. Since 1948 active in Paris
and Geneva.

Landscape 1951   *57.65*

Canvas, 25⅝ × 31⅞ in. (65.2 × 81 cm). A stylized signature in illegible Chinese characters, lower right. Signed on the back of
canvas: ZAO-WOU-KI 1.51. Coll. Cadby-Birch Gallery, New York;
Norbert Schimmel, New York. Gift of Norbert Schimmel, 1957.

ZIEM, FELIX. Born in Beaune in 1821. Attended the Art School at
Dijon; 1840 in Marseilles, 1841 in Italy, 1841–43 in Russia, then active in
Paris, where he exhibited at the Salon from 1849. Visited Venice annually,
1845–92. Died in Paris in 1911.

Grand Canal, Venice Before 1890   *04.405*

Canvas, 10½ × 10¾ in. (26.7 × 27.3 cm). Signed, lower left: Ziem.
Coll. Charles F. Olney, Cleveland, acquired in 1890. Olney Gift,
1904.

Sculpture

AMERICAN, second half 19th Century

Eve *00.127*

White marble, H. 37½ in. (95.3 cm). Signed with monogram on base: WS. Provenance unknown.

The monogram does not correspond to that of William Wetmore Story (1819–95) and the style of the figure is more graceful, the proportions more slender than Story's; an attribution to him is therefore hazardous although an "Eve in Paradise, Statuette" is listed (without date) as his in Mary E. Phillips, *Reminiscences of William Wetmore Story*, Chicago—New York, 1897, p. 298. The possibility of an attribution to the latter's son, Waldo Story, remains open; his figures are in any case more elegant than his father's (see E. March Philips, "Waldo Story," *Magazine of Art*, 1903, pp. 137 ff. and 273 ff.).

ARP, HANS (JEAN). Born in Strasbourg in 1888. Studied in Weimar 1907 and in Paris 1907–08. Active in Munich 1912, Zürich 1916 (cofounder of *Dada*), Cologne 1918–19, and Paris from 1922; died in Basel, 1966. Painter and author.

Bird Tower (Château d'Oiseaux) 1963 *64.37*

White marble, 9¾ × 9 × 5¼ in. (24.8 × 22.9 × 13.3 cm). Coll. Sidney Janis Gallery, New York. Purchased from General Fund, 1964.

Fig. 278

This is the smaller version of two, both in marble; the larger one (50 × 46 × 29.5 cm) is now in Coll. Robert W. Sarnoff, New York. Both versions were made in 1963. Five bronze versions of the Oberlin marble are scheduled to be cast.

Lit.: A. Tacha Spear, "Arp's 'Château d'oiseaux' (Oberlin College)," *Burlington Magazine*, CVIII, 1966, p. 262.

AUSTRIAN (?), second half 14th century.

The Virgin Mary   *58.89*

Wood (linden), traces of old polychromy, H. 27¾ in. (70.5 cm). Coll. Elisabeth Lotte Franzos, Vienna and Washington. Franzos Bequest, 1958.

The back uncarved.

Companion piece of the following entry; from a Crucifixion group.

St. John the Evangelist   *58.90*

Wood (linden), traces of old polychromy, H. 28¾ in. (73 cm). Coll. Elisabeth Lotte Franzos, Vienna and Washington. Franzos Bequest, 1958.

The back uncarved.

Companion piece of the preceding entry; from a Crucifixion group.

AUSTRIAN (?), late 15th century.

Christ Entering Jerusalem   *58.93*

Unfired clay (?) relief, 6 × 6⅞ × 1 in. (15.2 × 17.5 × 2.6 cm). Coll. Elisabeth Lotte Franzos, Vienna and Washington. Franzos Bequest, 1958.

AUSTRIAN (?), ca. 1530.

Christ Tied to the Flagellation Post   *58.91*

Wood (hardwood) relief, traces of gold and dark paint, 18⅝ × 7½ × 1⅞ in. (47.3 × 19.1 × 4.8 cm). Coll. Elisabeth Lotte Franzos, Vienna and Washington. Franzos Bequest, 1958.

Fragment of a *Flagellation of Christ* from an altarpiece. Perhaps South German (Bavarian or Swabian).

BARTHÉ, RICHMOND. Born in Bay St. Louis, Missouri, in 1901. Studied at the Art Institute of Chicago, the Art Students League in New York, and with C. Schroeder. Active in New York and St. Ann, Jamaica.

Head of a Negro   *39.6*

Terracotta, bronze colored, H. 10⅝ in. (27 cm). Signed on back of neck: BARTHÉ. Anonymous Gift, 1939.

From the artist's student days (so stated by the artist, *in litteris*, 1965).

Lit.: C. Dover, *American Negro Art*, New York Graphic Society, 1960, pl. 70, as "Shoeshine Boy."

African Head   *46.50*

Terracotta, H. 8 in. (20.3 cm). Signed on back of neck: BARTHÉ. Coll. Mrs. Malcolm L. McBride, Cleveland. Gift of Mrs. McBride, 1946.

Made in 1935 or shortly before (see reproduction in *Art Digest*, IX, August, 1935, p. 18).

BARTHOLOMÉ, PAUL-ALBERT. Born in Thivernal (Seine-et-Oise) in 1848. Active in Paris as a painter until 1886; afterwards as a self-taught sculptor. Died in Paris in 1928.

Girl Crouching (Grief)   *04.471*

Brass, natural color, 2½ × 6½ × 3½ in. (6.4 × 16.5 × 8.9 cm). Signed on base: APBartholomé (APB in ligature); stamped "H 491" and (in circle) SIOT-DECAUVILLE.PARIS FONDEUR. Coll. Charles F. Olney, Cleveland. Olney Gift, 1904.

Cast of a detail from the *Monument aux Morts* in Père-Lachaise Cemetery, Paris (1895–99). Bartholomé exhibited single bronze studies for the Monument from 1887 on, and the *Crouching Girl* was shown in 1889 (M. Demaison, "M. Bartholomé et le Monument aux Morts," *Revue de l'art ancien et moderne*, VI, 1899, pp. 265 ff.[268]). It seems that the present cast antecedes the completion of the monument; Olney cannot have acquired it after ca. 1898.

BENSON, STUART. Born in Detroit in 1877. Attended the Joseph Gies School of Art in Detroit. Active in Colle-sur-Loup (France) and in New York. Died at sea in 1949.

Woman of Avignon 1933   *00.128*
Bronze, hollow cast, black-green patina, H. 16¾ in. (42.5 cm). Signed on back of left shoulder: S. BENSON / '33. Foundry mark to right of signature: CIRE/C. VALSUANI/PERDUE. Gift of Mrs. Duggett Benson.

BOLOGNA, GIOVANNI (DA), ALSO CALLED GIAMBOLOGNA, FOLLOWER OF. Born in Douai in 1529. Pupil of Jacques Dubroeucq in Mons. Went to Italy in 1550; after two years spent in Rome, he settled in Florence where he was active until his death in 1608.

Mercury   *45.26*
Bronze, helmet and staff gilded, H. 22 in. (55.9 cm). Said to come from the Guicciardini family in Florence; Coll. F. A. Stern, New York. Purchased from the R. T. Miller, Jr. Fund, 1945. *Fig. 244*

Right hand (with part of lower right arm) and left foot replaced. Wings on helmet and feet, and upper part of caduceus missing. Several casting flaws.

Basically identical with the original versions on a small scale preserved in Vienna and Naples. These slightly precede the large statue in Florence (1580; see E. Dhanens, *Jean Boulogne*, Brussels, 1956, pp. 125 ff.) but are substantially later than the bozzetto in Bologna (1564); in them, the helmet has three openings (over forehead and ears) and the left hand holds the caduceus between thumb and index finger. The present piece shows practically no chasing; the treatment of the hair is very summary and somewhat crude. Its quality is nevertheless quite superior to the ordinary later versions and it is possibly still of the artist's lifetime. However, the small finger of the left hand is less detached from the other fingers than in the Vienna and Naples versions, and this deviation from the Mannerist custom may speak for a 17th century origin, particularly if the restoration of the right hand—with a comparable non-Mannerist change in the index finger—was made to conform with the lost part (a similar "correction" is found in the version in Berlin, no. 144, in that recently acquired by the Minneapolis Institute of Arts, and others).

BONHEUR, ISIDORE-JULES.
Born in Bordeaux in 1827. Brother of Rosa Bonheur. As painter, pupil of his father, Raymond Bonheur. Exhibited at the Salon from 1848. Active in Paris from 1849 until his death in 1901.

Lioness   04.1285
Bronze, green patina, 8⅛ × 8⅜ × 4⅝ in. (20.6 × 21.3 × 11.7 cm). Signed on ground: I. BONHEUR. Coll. Charles F. Olney, Cleveland. Olney Gift, 1904.   *Fig.* 262

CARPEAUX, JEAN BAPTISTE.
Born in Valenciennes in 1827. Moved to Paris in 1842; studied at the Academy, 1846–50, and in Rome, 1854–59. Active in Rome, Paris, and London (1871). Died at Castle Bécon near Asnières in 1875. Painter and etcher.

Neapolitan Fisherboy   1857   04.1141
Bronze on octagonal base, H. 13⅝ in. (34.6 cm). Light brown patina. Signed above base, back left: B. Carpeaux Rome 1857. Stamped (behind right foot): M (with eagle) PROPRIÉTÉ/CARPEAUX. Coll. Charles F. Olney, Cleveland. Olney Gift, 1904.
Fig. 260

The original plaster of which this statuette (with the same octagonal base) is a reduced version is in the Louvre; the plaster was exhibited at the Salon in 1858. A marble version (36 in. high) is in the National Gallery in Washington (Kress Coll. 1945, p. 204, with a companion piece of a *Girl with a Shell*). See further: *European Art in the Virginia Museum of Fine Arts*, 1966, p.115, no. 210.

COPTIC, 5th–6th century A.D.

Capital   52.1

Limestone, traces of yellow and red color throughout, 19 × 22 × 8½ in. (48.3 × 55.9 × 21.5 cm). Coll. P. Mallon, New York. Purchased from R. T. Miller, Jr. Fund, 1952.   *Fig.* 230

Acanthus foliage with a lotus blossom at the top.

Portion of a Frieze   51.4

Limestone, traces of color on the animals, 14 × 7⅝ × 1¾ in. (35.6 × 19.4 × 4.4 cm). Gift of P. Mallon, New York, 1951.   *Fig.* 231

Said to have come from Ahnas (Heracleopolis Magna), and in general similar to other animal friezes connected with the Ahnas style (J. Beckwith, *Coptic Sculpture*, London, 1963, no. 76), but flatter. The treatment of the heavily stylized acanthus foliage is more closely related to the upper part of the 6th century frieze from the monastery of Apa Spollo, Bawit, Upper Egypt, in the Louvre (Beckwith, no. 93); see also the *Eros with a Fish* from Oxyrhynchus (Bahnasa), in the Seattle Museum, dated "late 5th or 6th century" by Beckwith (no. 58).

Lit.: E. Capps, Jr., "Note on a Coptic Relief," *AMAM Bulletin*, IX, 1951–52, pp. 5 ff.

DAVIDSON, JO. Born in New York in 1883. Pupil of G. de F. Brush and H. A. MacNeil in New York. Studied at the École des Beaux-Arts in Paris. Active in Paris, Spain 1938, Lahaska (Pa.), and New York from 1910. Died at Bercheron near Tours, France, in 1952.

La Pasionaria (Dolores Ibarruri) 1938 *39.35*

Alloy of tin and lead with copper coating, H. 8⅝ in. (22 cm). Signed on back: JO DAVIDSON / BARCELONA / 1938. Stamped under signature: C (in circle) 1938. Anonymous gift (through Kendall K. Mussey), 1939. *Fig. 274*

The sitter was a heroine of the Spanish loyalists during the civil war of 1938.

Exh.: New York, Arden Galleries, 1938; Washington, Whyte Gallery, 1939.

Lit.: *Art Digest*, Jan. 15, 1939.

DEGAS, EDGAR HILAIRE GERMAIN. Born in Paris in 1834. As painter, pupil of L. Lamothe (1855); 1856–57 in Italy. Afterwards active in Paris; 1873 in New Orleans. Died in Paris in 1917. His activity as a modeler in wax was completely unknown during his lifetime.

Dancer at Rest, Hand on Hips, Left Leg Forward *55.33*

Bronze, brown patina, H. 14¾ in. (37.5 cm). Signed at back between feet: Degas; near right foot foundry mark: CIRE/PERDUE A. A. HÉBRARD/O/8 (set O, no. 8). Thin bronze base cast with figure. Coll. Curt Valentin, New York. Purchased from R. T. Miller, Jr. Fund, 1955. *Fig. 266*

As the caster's stamp indicates, this is subject no. 8 (out of 72) of set O (out of 22) cast by Hébrard between 1919 and 1921; it is no. 21 of the exhibition of these casts held in Paris in 1921, and no. XXI of von Matt-Rewald's catalogue (1956). The date of the original wax statuette cannot be established more exactly than "1882–95."

Exh.: "Closing Exhibition—Sculpture, Paintings and Drawings," New York, Curt Valentin Gallery, 1955, no. 19, with wrong illustration (Rewald XXII); "Edgar Hilaire Germain Degas," Los Angeles County Museum, 1958, no. 102.

Lit.: J. Rewald, *Degas, Works in Sculpture, a Complete Catalogue*, New York, 1944, p. 22, no. XXI; L. von Matt and J. Rewald, *Degas Sculpture*, New York, 1956, p. 145, no. XXI.

DESPIAU, CHARLES. Born in Mont-de-Marsan (Landes) in 1874. Went to Paris in 1891, pupil of H. Lemaire and E. Barrias. Active in Paris, where he died in 1946.

Mrs. Stone ("oreilles cachées") 55.34

Bronze, black patina, 14¼ × 8 × 9¼ in. (36.2 × 20.3 × 23.5 cm). Signed on the neck, back right: C. Despiau; foundry mark and cast number, back left: CIRE/C. VALSUANI/PERDUE. 4/5. Coll. Curt Valentin, New York. Purchased from R. T. Miller, Jr. Fund, 1955. *Fig.* 273

One of the five casts made in 1926/27; in the latter year, a version was exhibited at the "Première exposition annuelle d'un groupe de sculpteurs" (see *Cahiers d'art*, II, 1927, "feuilles volantes," no. 10, ill. on p. 5). A plaster version was exhibited in the Berlin *Sezession* in 1930 (repr. *Kunst und Künstler*, XXVIII, 1930, p. 237; Deshairs 1930, pl. 38). The same sitter was represented in a similar bust ("oreilles découvertes") made at the same time (Deshairs 1930, pl. 39; terracotta version 1958 with Roland, Browse and Delbanco in London, *Burlington Magazine*, C, 1958, Dec., pl. XXXI; one of the five bronze versions of this type is in the Museum of the Rhode Island School of Design in Providence).

Exh.: "Closing Exhibition—Sculpture, Paintings and Drawings," New York, Curt Valentin Gallery, June 1955, no. 22.

Lit.: Karl Scheffler, "Moderne Plastik, Ausstellung der Berliner Sezession," *Kunst und Künstler*, XXVIII, 1930, pp. 234 ff. (236, plaster version); Léon Deshairs, *Despiau*, Paris, 1930, p. 82.

EGYPTIAN, ca. 2300 B.C. (early VI dynasty).

Relief from the Tomb of Ny-ankh-Nesut 43.302

Limestone, painted, 15 × 48½ × ca. 1 in. (38.1 × 121.9 × ca. 2.5 cm). Coll. Jacob Hirsch, New York, acquired in Geneva in 1922. Purchased from R. T. Miller, Jr. Fund, 1943. *Fig.* 215

The relief, showing six servants bringing sacrificial gifts to the deceased, comes from the early sixth dynasty tomb of Ny-ankh-

nesut at Saqqara, said to have been excavated in 1918. Other reliefs
from the same tomb are in the Fogg Art Museum of Harvard
University, Cambridge, Mass. (2 pieces; *Bulletin*, V, 1936, pp. 30
ff.), the Cleveland Museum of Art (6 pieces; *Bulletin*, XVII, 1930,
pp. 136 ff.), the Worcester Art Museum (*Bulletin*, XXIII, 1932,
p. 11), the Kansas City Gallery (H. Ranke, *The Art of Ancient
Egypt*, Vienna, 1936, pl. 204), the Honolulu Academy of Arts
(*Bulletin*, V, 1937, p. 59), the Los Angeles County Museum
(Breasted 1947) and the Geneva Museum (*Guide illustré*, no. 9,
1963, p. 10); four other pieces from the estate of J. Hirsch were
sold in Lucerne (Ars Antiqua) on May 2, 1959, nos. 1–4. The
name of Ny-ankh-nesut appears on an unpublished upright relief
from this series in the Geneva Museum (acquired 1955), where he
has the title of Leader of Boats and High Priest of Heliopolis. The
name of King Tety which occurs on one of the reliefs provides a
terminus post quem for the tomb.

Lit.: J. H. Breasted, Jr., "Six Pieces of Egyptian Sculpture,"
Bulletin of the Art Division of the Los Angeles County Museum, I,
1947, no. 2, pp. 3 ff. (p. 11 n. 7); see also W. S. Smith, *A History of
Egyptian Sculpture and Painting in the Old Kingdom*, London,
1946, p. 208.

EGYPTIAN, ca. 2050 B.C. (XIth dynasty).

Papyrus   *58.71*

Limestone relief, traces of red, green and blue paint, 18¼ × 10½ ×
4¾ in. (46.4 × 26.7 × 12.1 cm). Coll. Metropolitan Museum of Art,
New York. Purchased, 1958.   *Fig. 216*

Cleaned in 1958.

Fragment of a relief from the Temple of Mentuhotep II at Deir
el Bahri, Thebes, excavated by E. Naville for the Egypt Exploration
Fund 1903–07; this fragment was given to the Metropolitan Museum of Art (see *Bulletin of the Metropolitan Museum*, II, 1907,
p. 22, and E. Naville, *The XIth Dynasty Temple at Deir-el-Bahari*,
I, London, 1907, pp. 1 ff.).

EGYPTIAN, ca. 1950 B.C. (XIIth dynasty).

Frieze with "Kheker" Ornament   *58.113*

Limestone, painted red and blue, 33¼ × 12⅞ × 4⅝ in. (84.5 × 32.7 × 11.7 cm). Coll. Metropolitan Museum of Art, New York (acc. no. 12.180.241). Purchased, 1958.

Cleaned and mended in 1958.
Block of a relief from the Tomb of Daga at Sheikh 'Abd el Qurneh, Thebes, on which see N. de Garis Davies, *Five Theban Tombs*, London, 1913, pp. 28 ff.

Fragment of a Male Figure   *58.111*

Limestone relief, painted in red and green, 9⅛ × 7¼ × 1¹⁵⁄₁₆ in. (23.2 × 18.4 × 3.3 cm). Coll. Metropolitan Museum of Art, New York (acc. no. 09.180.82). Purchased, 1958.

From the South Pyramid of Sesostris I at Lisht, excavated by the Metropolitan Museum in 1908–09.

EGYPTIAN, ca. 300 B.C. (early Ptolemaic period).

Head of a Priest   *52.2*

Black granite, H. 5 in. (12.7 cm). Coll. Mrs. Paul Mallon, New York. Purchased from R. T. Miller, Jr. Fund, 1952.   *Fig. 217*

Nose broken.
Probably fragment of a statuette of a priest supporting a shrine (*naophoros*).

ENGLISH (?), second half 12th century.

Chessman: Knight   *48.310*

Ivory, with traces of gold and red color, 2⅛ × 1¾ × 1¹¹⁄₁₆ in. (5.5 × 4.5 × 4.3 cm). Coll. Count Karl Saint-Hilaire, 1672; Baroness Rosina Josefa von Drahotusch; Maria Charlotte Saint-Hilaire, who married a Count Wilczek; Counts Wilczek, Castle Kreuzenstein near Vienna; E. and A. Silberman, New York. Purchased from R. T. Miller, Jr. Fund, 1948.   *Fig. 234*

Well preserved except for the lost eye insets (pearls?).

A companion piece is in the Museo Nazionale, Florence (Goldschmidt 1926, no. 177); a very similar piece (a rook) is in the Louvre (*ibid.*, no. 180). The hypothesis of an English origin of these pieces is gaining ground among scholars; Goldschmidt attributed them to France.

Exh.: "Arts of the Middle Ages, 1000–1400," Boston Museum of Fine Arts, 1940, no. 128; "An American University Collection" (AMAM), Kenwood (London County Council), 1962, no. 2; "Treasures from the Allen Memorial Art Museum," Minneapolis Institute of Arts, 1966.

Lit.: A. Goldschmidt, *Die Elfenbeinskulpturen der romanischen Zeit, XI.–XIII. Jahrhundert*, Berlin, 1926, IV, p. 6, no. 178; Beatrice F. Griffith, *Treasure under Glass from the British Isles in the United States of America*, Harrisburg, Pa., 1963, p. 32; J. Beckwith, "A Game of Draughts," *Studien zur Geschichte der europäischen Plastik, Festschrift Theodor Müller*, Munich, 1965, pp. 31 ff. (p. 36 n. 15).

EPSTEIN, JACOB (SIR).   Born in New York in 1880. Studied at the École des Beaux-Arts and the Académie Julian in Paris, 1902–05. From 1905 active in London, where he died in 1959.

Marchesa Casati 1918   *50.10*

Bronze mask, brown patina, 12 × 11⅞ × 7½ in. (30.5 × 30.2 × 19.1 cm). Coll. Ferargil Gallery, New York (1927); D. W. Prall, Berkeley, California (1927–1950). Purchased from Friends of Art Fund, 1950.   *Fig. 272*

On the sitter and the circumstances of the making of the bust see the artist's *Let There Be Sculpture*, New York, 1940, p. 77.

Other versions are in the Philadelphia Museum of Art (Elkins Coll.; Bronze, with gold patina) and in Coll. Lady Moorea Wyatt

(Epstein Memorial Exhibition, Edinburgh Festival Society, 1961, no. 61). One was in the sale of the Ruskin Art Galleries of Birmingham in London, Nov. 24, 1932 (reproduced in *Apollo*, XVI, 1932, p. 304).

Exh.: "Sculpture by Jacob Epstein," New York, Ferargil Galleries, 1927.

Lit.: D. W. Prall, *Aesthetic Judgment*, New York, 1929, p. XV and pls. 14–16; L. Richards, "Epstein's Bronze Mask, 'Marchesa Casati,' " *AMAM Bulletin*, VII, 1949–50, pp. 47 ff.

ETRUSCAN, early 5th century B.C.

Warrior   *43.116*

Bronze, solid cast, H. 7½ in. (19.1 cm). Coll. Alphonse Kann, Paris, sale in New York, I, Jan. 6–8, 1927, no. 81; D. G. Kelekian, New York. Purchased from R. T. Miller, Jr. Fund, 1943.   *Fig. 218*

The missing right arm can be assumed to have brandished a spear as in similar votive figures of the "striding warrior" type, on which see E. H. Richardson in the *Journal of the Walters Art Gallery*, VII–VIII, 1944–45, pp. 105 ff. The figure wears the Etruscan version of an Attic helmet, with cheek pieces turned up.

Exh.: "The Etruscans: Artists of Early Italy," Walters Art Gallery, Baltimore, 1958.

Lit.: Emeline Hill Richardson, "The Etruscan Origins of Early Roman Sculpture," *Memoirs of the American Academy in Rome*, XXI, 1953, pp. 77 ff. (100).

FLANNAGAN, JOHN BERNARD. Born in Fargo, North Dakota, in 1895. Studied painting at the Minneapolis Institute of Arts, 1914. Began working in stone in 1926. From 1924, active in New York, where he died in 1942.

Mother and Child   *42.24*

Cast stone, 14½ × 12 × 8⅜ in. (36.8 × 30.5 × 21.2 cm). Coll. Mrs. Malcolm L. McBride, Cleveland. Gift of Mrs. McBride, 1942.

Fig. 276

Smaller version, made in 1933 (according to Miller, 1942), of the red sandstone group (42¾ in. high, finished in 1934/35) in the Fogg Art Museum of Harvard University, Cambridge, Mass. (design for a skyscraper court).

Lit.: Dorothy C. Miller, "The Sculpture of John B. Flannagan," Exhibition Catalogue, New York, Museum of Modern Art, 1942, p. 40.

FLEMISH, ca. 1640.

Madonna and Child   *61.113*

Boxwood, 3 in. high (7.6 cm). Coll. Edward Lubin, New York. Purchased from Friends of Art Fund, 1961.   *Fig. 255*

Back fully worked out.

The present state of our knowledge of Netherlandish sculpture of the 17th century does not permit a more exact attribution of this piece. It was formerly listed as French ca. 1600; the new suggestion is due to Theodor Müller (*in litteris*, 1966), who is specifically reminded of some works by Artus Quellinus the Elder. There exists indeed some kinship between the boxwood Madonna and the *Ara Coeli Madonna* by Quellinus at St. Gudule in Brussels (fig. 160 in K. Fremantle, *The Baroque Town Hall of Amsterdam*, Utrecht, 1959) even though the former follows a more conservative pattern.

FLEMISH (?), mid 17th century.

The Virgin Mary   *58.45*

Bronze, gilt and chased, H. 9¹⁄₁₆ in. (23 cm). Private Coll., Amsterdam; M. Komor, New York. Purchased from R. T. Miller, Jr. Fund, 1958.   *Fig. 253*

Companion piece of the *St. John the Evangelist* (following entry). From a group of the *Crucifixion*. A former attribution to Guillielmus Kerricx is unacceptable; for a characteristic contrast see his *St. Magdalene* of 1700, reproduced in *Gentse Bijdragen tot de*

Kunstgeschiedenis, XIII, 1951, p. 81. The Oberlin bronzes are considerably earlier and reflect a much more direct connection with the work of François Duquesnoy. For the heads and the drapery compare also some figures from the confessionals on the north wall of St. Paul's in Antwerp, which are usually attributed to the workshop of Artus Quellinus the Elder (see S. Leurs, *Barokkerken te Antwerpen*, Antwerp, 1935, pls. XLIV ff.). Ludwig Burchard is reported to have favored an attribution to Augsburg, ca. 1650.

Exh.: "An American University Collection" (AMAM), Kenwood (London County Council), 1962, no. 4a.

St. John the Evangelist   *58.46*

Bronze, gilt and chased, H. 9⅜ in. (23.8 cm). Private Coll., Amsterdam; M. Komor, New York. Purchased from R. T. Miller, Jr. Fund, 1958.   *Fig. 254*

Companion piece of *The Virgin Mary* (preceding entry), which see for other information.

Exh.: "An American University Collection" (AMAM), Kenwood (London County Council), 1962, no. 4b.

FRENCH (Poitou), ca. 1155.

Bishop Grimoard Standing on a Bull   *48.1*

Limestone in three blocks, 80 × 22 × 21⅝ in. (203.2 × 55.9 × 54.9 cm). Inscription on a slab (two blocks, 12 × 34½ × ⅞ in., 30.5 × 87.6 × 2.3 cm): D̄S: MISEREATUR: GRIMOARDI: PICTAVENSIS EP̄Ī: ET: ARNAVDI ARCHIDIACONI: P̄AT: N̄R̂: (God have mercy on Grimoard, Bishop of Poitiers, and on Archdeacon Arnaud. Pater Noster).

Together with 48.2, originally placed on the façade of the Benedictine Abbey Church of Les Moreaux (Vienne; south of Poitiers), to the left and right of the archivolt of the main portal, with the inscription slab in between (see the reproduction in Kingsley Porter, 1923, fig. 1065); sold by the appropriate French authorities and acquired in 1932 by Joseph Brummer, New York. Purchased from R. T. Miller, Jr. Fund, 1948. *Fig. 232*

Bishop Grimoard succeeded Bishop Adelelme (1128–40) in 1141 and died in the same year or in 1142. Archdeacon Arnaud is mentioned in documents between 1142 and 1155. The bull on which Grimoard is standing, together with Adelelme's lion, must be related to the inscription still legible on the gateway: "Ut fuit introitus templi sci Salomonis / sic est istius in medio bovis atque leonis." Although the temple of Solomon was actually not flanked by such animals, the inscription proves that a symbolical context was intended here; Gaillard's explanation (1954) that the bull and lion were conceived as purely decorative elements and interpreted symbolically *ex post* by a clergyman is hardly acceptable.

The head of this figure, still visible in 1844 (Rédet; see the reproduction in Stechow, 1949), had already been removed in 1865 (Brouillet); at that time a mitred head (probably this one) was mentioned as being placed in a niche of the transept but no trace of it can be found today (Gaillard 1954). The right hand was probably raised in blessing.

It is possible (though denied by Gaillard, 1954) that the statues of the two deceased bishops reflect the well-authenticated feud between Archdeacon Arnaud (who had the nickname "qui non ridet") and Gilbert de la Porée, Bishop of Poitiers from 1142 (Stechow 1949); in any case, the inscription suggests their erection as commemoratives to both Arnaud and the two deceased bishops, *i.e.* after 1155, rather than before 1142, as Kingsley Porter (1923) implied. The style of the statues and of comparable ones in Poitou and Saintonge was connected with Spain by Gaillard (1954). On the related statues from St. Martin at Angers now at the Yale University Museum see Ludwig Schreiner, *Die frühgotische Plastik Südwest-Frankreichs*, Graz, 1963.

Lit.: L. Rédet, "Notice sur l'ancienne abbaye des Moreaux," *Mémoires de la société des antiquaires de l'ouest*, XI, 1844, pp. 277 ff.; De Longuemar, "Épigraphie du Haut Poitou," *ibid.*, XXVIII, 1863, pp. 207 f.; A. Brouillet, *Indicateur archéologique de l'arrondissement de Civrai*, Civrai, 1865, pp. 356 ff.; A. Kingsley Porter, *Romanesque Sculpture of the Pilgrimage Roads*, Boston, 1923, I, pp. 318 f., figs. 1065–1068; W. Stechow, "Two Romanesque Statues from Poitou," *AMAM Bulletin*, VII, 1949–50, pp. 28 ff.; G. Gaillard, "Deux sculptures de l'abbaye des Moreaux à Oberlin, Ohio," *Gazette des Beaux-Arts*, 6. ser., XLIV, 1954, pp. 81 ff.; R. Crozet, "Recherches sur la Cathédrale et les Evêques de Poitiers des origines au commencement du XIII. siècle," *Bulletin de la société des antiquaires de l'ouest*, 4. ser., VI, 1962, pp. 361 ff. (373 f.).

FRENCH (Poitou), ca. 1155.

Bishop Adelelme Standing on a Lion 48.2

Limestone in three blocks, 75½ × 23 × 13⅛ in. (91.7 × 58.4 × 33.2 cm). Inscription on a slab (two blocks, 12 × 35¾ × ⅞ in., 30.5 × 90.8 × 2.3 cm): D̄S̄ MISEREATUR GVILELMI: ADALELMI PICTA-VENSIS EP̄Ī: ET: ARNAVDI: ARCHIDIACONI: PAT: NR: (God have mercy on Guillaume Adelelme, Bishop of Poitiers, and on Archdeacon Arnaud. Pater Noster). *Fig. 233*

Companion piece of 48.1; see there.

FRENCH, middle 14th century.

Madonna with Child 40.38

Limestone, H. 45½ in. (115.6 cm). Coll. Joseph Brummer, New York. Purchased from R. T. Miller, Jr. Fund, 1940. *Fig. 238*

Back partly worked out, most completely in the headdress. Head of the Child missing; upper part of Mary's crown damaged.

The statue seems to belong in the northern part of France but hardly one of the main centers. As William H. Forsyth has pointed out (*in litteris*, 1966), a Madonna "from St. Denis" (cast in the Trocadéro; photo Giraudon 5859) may represent the archetype; it is indeed very close to the Oberlin figure in practically all important details (drapery, the motifs of the Madonna's right arm and of the Child's left arm with the fruit), except for the right arm of the Child which in the Oberlin statue is shown playing with Mary's head veil. The latter motif is not by itself rare but the form in which it appears here, with four fingers apparently covered by the veil, is unusual. The Trocadéro figure is distinctly earlier in style; the date and general style of the Oberlin statue is more closely approximated by a Madonna in the Besançon Museum (found in Château-Farine near Besançon; comm. W. H. Forsyth) and an ivory Madonna in sale Hans Wendland, Berlin, April 24, 1931, no. 273, pl. 60.

FRENCH, late 14th century.

Wing of a Diptych Upper register: **Entombment**; lower register: **Adoration of the Magi** *47.47*

Ivory relief, 4⁵⁄₁₆ × 2¾ in. (10.9 × 7 cm). Coll. Adolph Loewi, Los Angeles. Purchased from R. T. Miller, Jr. Fund, 1947. *Fig. 235*

For the iconography of the *Magi* and the decorative elements of this piece see R. Koechlin, *Les ivoires gothiques français*, Paris, 1924, II, no. 343, and for the *Entombment*, no. 354, where Joseph of Arimathea has an identical attitude. However, the style of the figures is more comparable to Koechlin no. 823 ("décadence," dated in the early 15th century by Koechlin) and to a diptych in sale Otto Bernheimer, Munich, Dec. 9, 1960, no. 189 (dated, much too early, in the second quarter of the 14th century).

Exh.: Berea College, Berea, Kentucky, 1947.

FRENCH (?), ca. 1500.

St. Hubert (?) *43.119*

Wood (probably walnut), painted and gilt, high relief, 38 × 27 × 6½ in. (96.5 × 68.6 × 16.5 cm). Coll. French & Co., New York. Purchased from R. T. Miller, Jr. Fund, 1943.

Polychromy partly damaged; the trumpet is new. Behind the dominating figure of the mounted Saint riding toward left, there are, in a landscape, the stag with the Crucifix between his antlers, dogs, the Saint kneeling, the Saint leaving his castle for the hunt, and a chapel. It is not impossible that the story refers to St. Eustace rather than to St. Hubert.

Probably from Northern France, or possibly the Southern Netherlands.

GERMAN (South), early 17th century.

Crucified Christ 58.92

Boxwood, stained dark, H. 8¼ in. (21 cm). Coll. Elisabeth Lotte Franzos, Vienna and Washington. Franzos Bequest, 1958.

Back fully carved. Right arm, toes and hanging lappet of loin cloth (on dexter side) missing. Left arm separate.

A variation on the type of Crucifix made popular by several versions of Giovanni da Bologna; the head is particularly close to that of the large bronze of 1594 in the St. Michael's Church in Munich (see the detail, fig. 172 in E. Dhanens, *Jean Boulogne*, Brussels, 1956).

GERMAN (South), second half 17th century.

Two Standing Lions with the Bavarian Coat-of-Arms 62.16

Ivory, H. 10¼ in. (26 cm). Coll. Otto Bernheimer, Munich, sale in Munich, Dec. 9, 1960, no. 222; Edward Lubin, New York. Purchased from Mrs. F. F. Prentiss Fund, 1962. *Fig. 257*

Part of the tail of the right lion and second coat-of-arms missing.

Nine screw holes on the under side of the rim of the hollow base indicate that the group was originally attached to a piece of furniture or such. The shield with the arms of the Bavarian Electors (quartered, first and fourth fusils paly bendy, second and third a crowned rampant lion with double tail) is affixed to a perpendicular support; the support for a second shield is visible on the back.

The workmanship of the lathe-turned center piece suggests the hand of a member, or an assistant, of the Zick family of Nuremberg, possibly from the circle of Lorenz Zick (1594–1666). The attribution to the circle of Christop Angermair (Bernheimer sale cat.) is not convincing.

GERMAN (South?), ca. 1700.

St. John under the Cross   *51.15*

Ivory, H. 7¹³⁄₁₆ in. (18.3 cm). Coll. Victor Spark, New York. Purchased from R. T. Miller, Jr. Fund, 1951.   *Fig. 258*

Right lower arm and left hand missing. Back flat and unworked. No close parallels have been discovered so far; but the figure was most probably carved in South Germany or Austria toward 1700.

Exh.: "An American University Collection" (AMAM), Kenwood (London County Council), 1962, no. 3; "Treasures from the Allen Memorial Art Museum," Minneapolis Institute of Arts, 1966.
Lit.: B. N[icolson], *Burlington Magazine*, CIV, 1962, p. 310.

GERMAN (Swabian), ca. 1500.

Standing Christ Child   *49.86*

Wood (hardwood), H. 17¼ in. (43.8 cm). Coll. Eugene Garbáty, New York. Gift of Eugene Garbáty, 1949.   *Fig. 243*

Polychromy renewed. Cross on globe modern.
The nude standing Christ Child, often clad sumptuously, was a favorite devotional image from about 1300, particularly in convents (see H. Wentzel, s. v. Christkind, in *Reallexikon der deutschen Kunstgeschichte*, III, 1954, col. 590 ff.). The present type, with right hand raised in blessing and holding the globe in his left, became very frequent in the late fifteenth and early sixteenth centuries and was exported in large quantities from the Netherlands but also often carved in North and South Germany. The specific type of the modest Oberlin figure may very well have been the very slightly larger one (49 cm) in the Museum in Ulm, re-

produced in *Die Kunst und das schöne Heim*, LX, 1961/62, p. 95. The renewal of the polychromy makes the assignment of a more exact date hazardous.

GERMAN (Upper Rhine), ca. 1515.

St. Anne, Mary and the Child (Anna Selbdritt)   *42.52*

Wood (linden), painted and gilt, 19⅝ × 16½ × 3½ in. (49.8 × 41.9 × 8.9 cm). Coll. Chauncey J. Blair, Chicago (1916); French & Co., New York. Purchased from R. T. Miller, Jr. Fund, 1942.

Fig. 241

The original polychromy and gold are reasonably well preserved. Most probably, the two half-circular openings on the upper right and left of the tabernacle were originally occupied by half figures of Joseph and Joachim, as in Martin Schaffner's contemporary tabernacle in the Victoria and Albert Museum in London, reproduced in A. Feulner, *Die deutsche Plastik des 16. Jahrhunderts*, Florence-Munich, 1926, pl. 31 (observation of Miss Sherrill Rood).

The relief is almost certainly from the Upper Rhine; stylistic parallels can be found in the (somewhat later?) Dangolsheim Altarpiece of 1522 (St. Lawrence Chapel of Strasbourg Cathedral), which also contains similar motifs in the tracery of the predella (Otto Schmitt, *Gotische Skulpturen des Strassburger Münsters*, Frankfurt, 1924, II, fig. 275). Echoes of the art of Nicolaus Gerhart are still noticeable in the Christ Child and the organization of the background (Epitaph of 1464).

GERMAN, mid 15th century.

Man of Sorrows   *44.161*

Wood (porous hardwood), back fully carved, polychromy renewed, H. 25¾ in. (65.4 cm). Coll. Raymond S. Stites, Washington, D.C. Gift of Mr. Stites, 1944.

Lower left arm and hand are missing; the toes of the right foot are new.

The left hand was doubtless raised in a gesture revealing its wound from the inside; see the examples following the basic pattern established by Hans Multscher, illustrated in G. von der Osten, *Der Schmerzensmann*, Berlin, 1935, figs. 114 ff.

Probably by a Swabian artist; an origin in central Germany (Thuringia?) must also be considered possible.

Exh.: Berea, Kentucky, Berea College, 1947.

GERMAN (?), early 17th century.

Hercules   *53.237*

Bronze, hollow cast, brown patina, H. 11¼ in. (28.6 cm). Coll. Baroness René de Kerchove, New York. Gift of Baroness de Kerchove, 1953.

The exaggerated leaning pose points to a German (Bavarian?) rather than Flemish origin of this bronze but no exact parallels have been discovered so far.

GREEK, 5th century B.C. (Roman copy, 2nd century A.D.)

Head of Athena   *39.139*

White (Pentelic?) marble, 11⅜ × 7¼ × 8⅝ in. (28.9 × 18.4 × 21.9 cm). Coll. Edward Capps, Sr., Princeton. Gift of the owner, 1939.

Fig. 221

Break at the neck at a sharp angle. Damaged: nose, upper lip, lower right lip, both ear lobes; surface scratched and rubbed. Eyeballs (originally separately inset) mostly missing; traces of metal suggest the loss of bronze eyelashes on upper lids.

The treatment of the top of the head indicates clearly the original presence of a bronze helmet fastened with bronze dowels and shaped very similarly to that of the Athena Parthenos of Pheidias (Capps 1953).

The head, said to have been found in Salonika, is evidently a Roman copy, probably of the Hadrianic or Antonine period, after a Greek work of the Pheidian school (third quarter of the fifth century B.C.), possibly the Athena Parthenos itself.

Lit.: E. Capps, Jr., "A Marble Head of Athena from Salonika," *AMAM Bulletin*, X, 1952–53, pp. 77 ff.

GREEK, 4th century B.C. (Roman [?] copy after).

Male Torso   *41.43*

White marble, H. 17½ in. (44.5 cm). Coll. Joseph Brummer, New York. Purchased from R. T. Miller, Jr. Fund, 1941.   *Fig.* 222

Missing: Head, left arm, most of right arm, left leg under the knee, right leg below middle of upper thigh. Holes on the shoulder blades (for wings?) may be post-antique.

Probably a Roman copy, of considerable merit, of Praxiteles' *Apollo Sauroktonos*, or a very closely related Praxitelian work. It is possible that the right chest and the right arm (which is closer to the body and extends further across the chest than that of the *Sauroktonos*) are an old substitution taken from another ancient torso; this entire part is joined to the bulk of the statue by means of a broad plaster insert, and the shape of the right side of the chest does not convincingly correspond to that of the left. Remains of a (tree-trunk?) support on the left leg are found at approximately the same spot as on the Vatican *Sauroktonos*. The similarity of the present marble to the Praxitelian *Eros* (New York, Cat. G. M. A. Richter, 1954, no. 107, pl. LXXXVI, and elsewhere) is not quite so close, but the possibility of bronze wings having been inserted in the shoulder blade holes indicates that the piece may at one time have been made up as an *Eros*.

GREEK, ca. 200 B.C.

Lion Attacking a Bull   *48.28*

White marble, 17½ × 28 × 7 in. (44.5 × 71.1 × 17.8 cm). Coll. S. Pozzi, Paris, sale in Paris (Petit), June 25, 1919, no. 364; G. A. van

Haeften, The Hague (1923); D. A. Hoogendijk, Amsterdam. Purchased from R. T. Miller, Jr. Fund, 1948.   *Fig.* 223

Head and legs of the bull, and hind part of the lion missing.

The marble seems to be of an Asia Minor type (G. E. Mylonas, orally, 1948), and the origin of the group in Pergamon is probable; see the lion of the northern frieze of the Pergamon Altar in Berlin (*Die Altertümer von Pergamon*, VII, 2, p. 270). An almost identical small bronze in Vienna (Reinach, *Répertoire*, II, 721, 4) is valuable for the reconstruction of the missing parts of the present marble but embodies less energy and tenseness. Judging from the description, an identical or very similar marble was in the Theseion in Athens (Reinhard Kekulé, *Die antiken Bildwerke im Theseion zu Athen*, Leipzig, 1869, p. 1, with mention of replicas).

The subject, occasionally adopted as a city emblem (Akanthos) was also sometimes interpreted as a symbol of death; the present group may therefore have served as the crowning piece of a sepulchral monument (Scheurleer 1923). A comparable lion with similarly stylized hair appeared in the Myron C. Taylor sale in New York, Nov. 11, 1960, no. 876 (as Greek, 4th cent. B.C.).

Lit.: C. W. Lunsingh Scheurleer, "Grieksche Oudheden in Nederland," *Oudheidkundig Jaarboek*, III, 1923, pp. 201 ff.; W. Stechow, "Selected Acquisitions of European Art, 1947–1948," *AMAM Bulletin*, V, 1948, p. 25.

GREEK, first century A.D.?

Head of a Bearded Man   *41.42*

White (Pentelic?) marble, 8½ × 5¼ × 6½ in. (21.6 × 13.3 × 16.5 cm). Coll. J. Brummer Gallery, New York. Purchased from R. T. Miller, Jr. Fund, 1941.   *Fig.* 224

Nothing is known of the provenance of this head. It may come from an Attic funeral stele (G. Karo, orally, 1941) or from some other kind of relief.

GREEK, late second century A.D.

Fragment of a Sarcophagus *40.39*

White marble (Proconnesian? de Grüneisen 1930), 20 × 33¾ × 9⁷⁄₁₆ in. (50.8 × 85.7 × 24 cm). Private Coll., Smyrna, 1901 (probably); Art Trade, Smyrna (1924); Coll. Vladimir de Grüneisen, Rome? (1930); J. Brummer Gallery, New York (1937). Purchased from R. T. Miller, Jr. Fund, 1940. *Fig.* 225

Fragment of central gable and adjacent intercolumniation; probably from the end of a sarcophagus.

The man with the Phrygian cap may well be Odysseus, from a representation of the *Theft of the Palladium* by him and Diomedes (Capps 1945), rather than a Parthian prisoner.

Probably executed in Ephesus and closely related to other sarcophagi of a similar type and provenance (Morey 1924; Capps 1945; Lawrence 1951).

Exh.: "The Dark Ages," Worcester, Mass., Art Museum, 1937, no. 36.

Lit.: J. Strzygowski in *Byzantinische Zeitschrift*, X, 1901, p. 726; G. Mendel, "Catalogue des monuments grecs . . . Brousse," *Bulletin de correspondance hellénique*, XXXIII, 1909, pp. 245 ff. (333, no. 12); E. Weigand, "Baalbek und Rom," *Jahrbuch des archaeologischen Instituts*, XXIX, 1914, pp. 37 ff. (73); C. R. Morey, "The Sarcophagus of Claudia Antonia Sabina and the Asiatic Sarcophagi," *Sardis*, V, part 1, Princeton, 1924, p. 43; W. de Grüneisen, *Collection de Grüneisen, Catalogue Raisonné* (*Art Chrétien Primitif du Haut et du Bas Moyen Age*), Paris, 1930, p. 44, no. 157 A; C. R. Morey, "Art of the Dark Ages: A Unique Show," *Art News*, XXXV, Feb. 20, 1937, pp. 9 ff. (16); E. Capps, Jr., "A Lydian Sarcophagus from Smyrna," *AMAM Bulletin*, II, 1945, pp. 53 ff.; M. Lawrence, "Additional Asiatic Sarcophagi," *Memoirs of the American Academy in Rome*, XX, 1951, pp. 119 ff. (147 f.); C. Vermeule, "Roman Sarcophagi in America: A Short Inventory," *Festschrift für Friedrich Matz*, Mainz, 1962, pp. 98 ff. (104).

GREENBAUM, DOROTHEA. Born Dorothy Schwarcz in New York in 1893. First studied painting; as a sculptress self-taught. Active in New York and Princeton, N.J.

Young Woman 1939   *40.36*

Cast stone, H. 14¾ in. (37.5 cm). Coll. Robinson Gallery, New York. Purchased from Friends of Art Fund, 1940.   *Fig.* 275

HUNTINGTON, ANNA VAUGHN HYATT. Born Anna Hyatt in Cambridge, Mass., in 1876. Pupil of H. H. Kitson in Boston, and of H. A. MacNeil and G. Borglum in New York. Active in New York and Bethel, Conn.

Young Red Stag ca. 1935   *37.40*

Bronze, brown-green patina, H. 12⅞ in. (32.7 cm) with base. Signed on ground, right back: Anna Hyatt Huntington. Foundry mark on base, rear: ROMAN BRONZE WORKS / N.Y. Gift of the artist, 1937.

ITALIAN (Friuli?), middle 14th century.

Madonna with Child   *44.45*

Wood (hardwood like poplar), old polychromy partly preserved, H. 32 in. (81.3 cm). Coll. Robert Lehman, New York. Gift of Robert Lehman, 1944.   *Fig.* 236

  The closest stylistic parallel is offered by works from the Friuli region, particularly by the (greatly superior) figure of S. Eufemia in Segnacco, illustrated in G. Marchetti and G. Nicoletti, *La scultura lignea nel Friuli*, Milan, 1956, pl. 15 (also in Enzo Carli, *La scultura lignea italiana*, Milan, 1960, fig. LXXIX and text p. 71), in which the organization of the drapery and the shape of the face are very similar; compare also the statue of S. Nicolò in Martignacco (Marchetti-Nicoletti pl. 18), which is a provincial version of the "umbro-sienese" Bishop in the Bargello in Florence (Carli pl. 26).

ITALIAN (Tuscan?), first half 17th century.

Mask of a Faun   *54.61*

Bronze, green patina, 12¼ × 9⅝ in. (31.1 × 24.4 cm). Coll. Bardini,

Florence; Adolph Loewi, Los Angeles. Purchased from R. T. Miller, Jr. Fund, 1954. *Fig.* 252

Purported to be from either Pietro Tacca's share in the Monument to Ferdinand I of Tuscany at Leghorn (1615–27) or one of the same artist's fountains made 1626 ff. to supplement that monument but placed in the Piazza dell'Annunziata in Florence in 1641 (see for this date *Rivista d'arte*, XIII, 1931, p. 162). The fountains —as executed—lack no such parts; the monument may at one time have been planned to incorporate fountain elements but there is no certainty about this. The faun mask as water spout does occur repeatedly at that time but the present piece is certainly not Tacca's own work.

ITALIAN (Umbrian), ca. 1500.

St. Sebastian 61.77

Poplar and spruce, polychromed. H. 61 in. (160 cm). Private coll., Munich; Kurt Rossacher, Salzburg. Purchased from R. T. Miller, Jr. and Mrs. F. F. Prentiss Funds, 1961. *Fig.* 240

The figure is constructed of several pieces, important joins occurring at shoulders, above elbows and in left leg and foot. A series of blocks have been set in the back from neck to buttocks covering the hollow center indicated by X ray. Narrow blocks in the back of the thighs suggest similar treatment there. A dowel hole in the rear of the base probably indicates that the statue was once attached to a column or tree trunk. The holes from which arrows once protruded have been filled. Condition is good, the only loss being a wedge of wood including part of the base and the fourth toe of the left foot. Scattered paint losses on back and face with unrepaired losses appearing on the loin cloth. The paint has been removed from the hair but tiny fragments remain in the deepest recesses. There is a slight scattering of termite holes over the surface.

The figure is related in pose and style but is superior in quality to a St. Sebastian in San Francesco at Stroncone, one of a number of wooden statues of this saint from villages in the vicinity of Terni.

Of these the best known, originally from San Gemini, is now in the gallery at Perugia. Gottschewski's attribution of the San Gemini figure to Antonio Rizzo ("Eine Holzstatue des Antonio Rizzo," *Zeitschrift für bildende Kunst*, XLIII, 1908, pp. 31–2) and the one at Stroncone to a pupil of Rizzo was refuted by Geza Francovich ("Gruppo di sculture in legno umbro-marchigiane," *Bollettino d'arte*, VIII, 1928–9, pp. 481 ff.) who considered both Umbrian works but carved in a Paduan-Venetian style popularized in this region through the paintings of Niccolò Alunno. E. Carli (*La scultura lignea italiana*, Milan, 1960, p. 104) refers to them as belonging to the current "veneto-alunesca." Margrit Lisner ("Deutsche Holzkruzifixe des 15. Jahrhunderts in Italien," *Mitteilungen des Kunsthistorischen Institutes in Florenz*, IX, 1960, pp. 196–97) attributes the San Gemini St. Sebastian to an Umbrian artist influenced by German (or Austrian) work represented by a series of crucifixes isolated by her. Anatomically the St. Sebastians from San Gemini, Stroncone and Oberlin belong to this Italo-German tradition, one in which the pattern made by the rib cage and clavicle is emphasized over that of the musculature. Compared with the crucifixes, however, these Sebastians are modelled in a fuller, somewhat more plastic style. Lisner (pp. 192, 194) postulates more than one German workshop in Terni during the last half of the 15th century. It is possible that the provincial Italian craftsman who carved the Oberlin St. Sebastian at the turn of the century had some training in such a shop or at least had access to its models and copybooks. Besides the basic pattern of the torso the drawstring loin cloth which appears more frequently in Umbria than elsewhere is made up of many fine folds, a characteristic of the larger and more elaborately draped loin cloths on the crucifixes in Terni. The veining confined to arms and legs is produced by the application of string to the wood which is then covered with gesso before painting, one of several methods used in the German crucifixes. The elaborate curls do not resemble those on the crucifixes but they do follow models more popular in Germany and Austria than in Italy. However, the enormous influence of Verrocchio in Umbria must not be discounted and the arrangement of the curls on the back of the head of the Oberlin figure is very close to that of St. Thomas on Or San Michele.

The material indicates an Umbrian provenance in that the main body of the statue from head through the base is poplar, a wood commonly used for Umbrian panel paintings, while a sample taken from a finger is spruce, a wood also used in Umbria (J. Marette, *Connaissance des primitifs par l'étude du bois*, Paris, 1961, p. 54).

ITALIAN (Venetian), second quarter 16th century.

A Satyr tied to a Tree (Marsyas?)   *57.58*

Bronze, brown patina, H. 11⅞ in. (30.2 cm). Coll. G. Cramer, The Hague. Purchased from R. T. Miller, Jr. Fund, 1957.   *Fig.* 245

Faulty cast; the right knee of the satyr is lacking.

No other version of this bronze seems to be known.

Formerly attributed to Andrea Riccio. The bronze resembles some works tentatively attributed to Desiderio da Firenze (cf. the seated drinking satyr in Vienna, L. Planiscig, *Venezianische Bildhauer der Renaissance*, Vienna, 1921, fig. 424) but does not seem to be by the same hand.

Exh.: "Decorative Arts of the Italian Renaissance, 1400–1600," Detroit Institute of Arts, 1958, no. 263; "The Renaissance Image of Man and the World," Columbus, Ohio, Gallery of Fine Arts, 1961, no. 53; "An American University Collection" (AMAM), Kenwood (London County Council), 1962, no. 7; "Renaissance Bronzes in American Collections," Smith College Museum of Art, Northampton, Mass., 1964, no. 15; "Treasures from the Allen Memorial Art Museum," Minneapolis Institute of Arts, 1966.

ITALIAN (Venetian?), late 16th century.

Chronos   *57.89*

Bronze, hollow cast, green patina, H. 7 in. (17.8 cm). Coll. John D. Graham, New York; J. J. Klejman, New York. Purchased from R. T. Miller, Jr. Fund, 1957.   *Fig.* 246

The lacking lower right arm and right leg below the knee were never cast; there are two holes between the shoulder blades.

This seems to be a cast, apparently unique, of an incomplete or mutilated bozzetto for the bronze of a *Chronos* preserved in at least two versions: (1) Dresden, formerly Grünes Gewölbe (W. Holzhausen in *Jahrbuch der preussischen Kunstsammlungen*, LX, 1939, p. 177 as "Art des Bernini"), and (2) Rhode Island School of Design, Providence. The right leg is here stretched out to the left beyond the globe, the left leg is spread wider to the right than in the present bozzetto and detached from the globe; the right arm reaches across and nearly joins the left hand; large wings are inserted. The two bronzes in Dresden and Providence are carefully chased giving them an appearance seemingly at great variance with the bozzetto but all structural elements are essentially the same except for the left leg.

The work seems to come from the circle of Alessandro Vittoria; the right leg and the drapery of the complete version may be compared with those of the *St. Jerome* terracotta of the former Berl Coll. in Vienna which was tentatively (but not convincingly) given to Vittoria himself by Planiscig (*Venezianische Bildhauer der Renaissance*, Vienna, 1921, p. 467, fig. 488).

Exh.: "An American University Collection" (AMAM), Kenwood (London County Council), 1962, no. 6; "Treasures from the Allen Memorial Art Museum," Minneapolis Institute of Arts, 1966.

ITALIAN (Venetian), ca. 1600.

Venus   53.235

Bronze, dark brown patina, H. 10¾ in. (27.3 cm), circular bronze base cast in one piece with the figure. Coll. Baroness René de Kerchove, New York. Gift of Baroness de Kerchove, 1953.

Fig. 250

Another cast of this bronze is with Julius Böhler in Munich (Cat. June–Sept. 1966, no. 29, as Tiziano Aspetti). Its motif is closely related to a *Venus Marina*, 1963 at Drey Gallery in New York (attributed to Tiziano Aspetti but more probably from the workshop of Alessandro Vittoria), and to the *Juno* at Vienna (Leo Planiscig, *Die estensische Kunstsamml'ung*, I, Vienna, 1919, p. 130, no. 197, and *Venezianische Bildhauer der Renaissance*, Vienna, 1921, p. 474, fig. 498, as workshop of Alessandro Vittoria). However, the style of the present figure deviates from that of these two bronzes and places it nearer Niccolò Roccatagliata.

Exh.: "The Renaissance Image of Man and the World," Columbus, Ohio, Gallery of Fine Arts, 1961, no. 58.

ITALIAN (Venetian?), early 17th century.

Boy Strangling a Goose   44.37
Bronze, hollow cast, black patina, H. 8⅝ in. (21.9 cm) without base. Coll. Alphonse Kann, Paris, sale New York, I, Jan. 6–8, 1927, no. 369; Robert Lehman, New York. Gift of Robert Lehman, 1944.

Variation on an antique bronze group by Boethos known through several marble copies (e.g., in the Munich Glyptothek). This work had been more faithfully imitated in Renaissance bronzes (e.g., in Vienna: W. Bode, *Die italienischen Bronzestatuetten der Renaissance*, Berlin, 1922, pl. 93). The present bronze is more likely to be of Venetian (circle of Roccatagliata) than of Florentine origin (as suggested in the Alphonse Kann catalogue, 1927).

ITALIAN (Venetian), late 17th century?

Minerva   48.92
Bronze, gilt, H. 10½ in. (26.7 cm). Coll. Adolph Loewi, Los Angeles. Purchased from R. T. Miller, Jr. Fund, 1948.   *Fig. 251*

This bronze figure, formerly attributed to Tiziano Aspetti, was considered a late Mannerist, possibly German or Netherlandish work of around 1600 by several connoisseurs. However, the discovery of a *Venus* forming the companion piece of another cast of the Oberlin version (Cambridge, Fitzwilliam Museum, no. 19-1950, ex Coll. Henry Harris, sale at Sotheby, Oct. 24, 1950, no. 93, the pair as *Mars* and *Venus*) makes an attribution to the period around 1600 appear most improbable because of the decidedly late baroque features of the *Venus*, particularly her hair. While the natural alternative to a late Mannerist attribution would be one to the 18th century (proposed by several other scholars) the heavy build and some other features of these figures such as the modelling of the faces may well point to a lingering on of Mannerist elements into the advanced 17th century rather than to an outright Rococo origin. The attribution to Venice and the late 17th century was first suggested by J. Pope-Hennessy (*in litteris*, 1965).

Exh.: "Masterworks from American University Museums," European Tour, sponsored by the College Art Association, 1956–57, Cat. Malmö no. 2, Cat. Utrecht no. 2, Cat. Lyons no. 44; "An American University Collection" (AMAM), Kenwood (London County Council), 1962, no. 5; "Treasures from the Allen Memorial Art Museum," Minneapolis Institute of Arts, 1966.

ITALIAN (?), first half 17th century.

Pegasus   *56.66*

Bronze, black patina, 7¹⁵⁄₁₆ × 9 in. (20.2 × 22.9 cm). Coll. R. Stora, New York. Purchased from the R. T. Miller, Jr. Fund, 1956.

Fig. 249

The bronze was attributed to Hubert Gerhard by R. Stora and later called South German, ca. 1600. However, as T. Müller, Munich, pointed out (*in litteris*, 1957), the agitated shape of ground, mane and tail point to a somewhat more advanced date, and he assumed Italian rather than German origin. Some kinship with the rustic horses in works by Stradanus and, even more, Antonio Tempesta is evident; there is still a distinctly Mannerist flavor to this work, and the authorship of a northern artist under Italian (Florentine?) influence must still be considered possible.

Exh.: "The Renaissance Image of Man and the World," Columbus, Ohio, Gallery of Fine Arts, 1961, no. 57.

Lit.: R. Wittkower, "The Vicissitudes of a Dynastic Monument: Bernini's Equestrian Statue of Louis XIV," in: *De Artibus Opuscula XL; Essays in Honor of Erwin Panofsky*, New York, 1961, pp. 497 ff. (p. 510 n. 57).

ITALIAN, 17th century.

Christ Carrying the Cross   *51.1*

Stucco relief, 4⅝ × 8⅛ in. (11.7 × 20.6 cm). Gift of Frederick B. Artz,
Oberlin, 1951.

JACQUOT, CHARLES.   Born in Bains (Vosges) in 1865. Pupil of
A. Falguière and J. P. Aubé in Paris. Exhibited at the Salon from 1885.
Active in Paris until after 1906.

The Angelus   1888   *04.492*

Bronze, hollow cast, dark brown patina, H. 32¾ in. (83.2 cm) with
base. Signed on the base: C. Jacquot, and incised: BLOT Ft. Coll.
Charles F. Olney, Cleveland, acquired before 1894. C. F. Olney
Gift, 1904.   *Fig.* 264

The plaster was exhibited at the Salon of 1887, no. 4112 (as
"Prière aux Champs"), where it was awarded the state medal. A
bronze version was exhibited in the Salon in Paris, 1888, no. 4263,
from the E. Blot Collection, quite possibly the present one which
Blot may have chased (cf. inscription); another one is in the Museum at Épinal.

   Exh.: Art Loan Exhibition, Cleveland, 1894, p. 84, no. 20 (without name of artist).

KIRCHNER, ERNST LUDWIG.

   See under Paintings.

Standing Female Nude   *55.29*

Wood (hardwood), oiled and painted (black hair), H. 38 in. (96.5
cm). Coll. Curt Valentin, New York, acquired from the artist's
estate in 1950. Purchased from R. T. Miller, Jr. Fund, 1955.

                                                                   Fig. 271

The title "Eve" appears first in 1952; a reproduction with the
title "Stehendes Mädchen" is found in the article by L. de Marsalle,
"Über Kirchners Graphik," *Genius*, 1920, II, pp. 251 ff. (252),

shown against a large unidentified painted foil. The traditional date 1919 seems acceptable although most carved pieces of the Swiss period are less expressionistic. For the face and the shoulder motif compare the painting of *The Wanderer* of 1920 (W. Grohmann, *Das Werk E. L. Kirchners*, Munich, 1926, pl. 71).

Exh.: "Ernst Ludwig Kirchner," New York, Curt Valentin Gallery, 1952, no. 30; "In the Flat and Round," Cincinnati Art Museum, 1952; "Treasures from the Allen Memorial Art Museum," Minneapolis Institute of Arts, 1966.

KONTI, ISADORE. Born in Szombathely (Steinamanger, Hungary) or in Vienna in 1862. Studied at the Vienna Academy. Active in Vienna until 1887; in Rome in 1889. Settled in Chicago in 1892, in New York in 1893. Member of the National Academy, 1905. Active in New York until his death in 1938.

Dying Melodies 1912 *19.3*

Bronze, hollow cast, dark brown patina, H. 27¾ in. (70.5 cm). Signed, in front of base to left: Cop. B. I. Konti / 1912. Foundry mark, lower back: ROMAN BRONZE WORKS N. Y. Gift of Andrew H. Noah, Akron (Ohio), 1919.

LARCHE, RAOUL FRANÇOIS. Born in Saint-André-de-Cubzac (Gironde) in 1860. Pupil of F. Jouffroy, A. Falguière and E. Delaplanche in Paris. Exhibited at the Salon from 1884. Active in Paris, where he died in 1912.

Loie Fuller, the Dancer *62.33*

Brass (lamp), H. 18¼ in. (46.4 cm). Signed on drapery, right below: RAOUL LARCHE. Foundry mark: SIOT-DECAUVILLE. PARIS (in circle)/FONDEUR. Gift of Mrs. Robert Gale, Mrs. Caroline Macnaughton and Fred R. White, Jr., 1962. *Fig. 268*

Probably made in 1900, when the famous dancer (1862–1928) attracted much attention at the Exposition Universelle. The founder, E. Siot-Decauville, died in 1909. Other casts are in the Museum of Modern Art, New York (acc. no. 266.63; see *Bulletin* XXX, 1963, nos. 2–3, p. 36), and in sale London (Sotheby's), April 19, 1966 (*Burlington Magazine*, CVIII, 1966, April, p. VI). A similar figure-lamp of the same subject is reproduced in *Apollo*, LXXXIII, 1966, p. 68.

LAURANA, FRANCESCO, ATTRIBUTED TO. Born in Vrana near Zara (Dalmatia) ca. 1420/25. 1458 active in Naples, 1461–66 at the court of René of Anjou at Angers, 1467/68–71 in Sicily, 1474 in Naples, from 1477 again in Southern France, last mentioned in 1500.

Portrait of Triboulet (?)   *54.23*

White marble relief, oval, 10½ × 8⅛ × 2½ in. (26.7 × 20.6 × 6.4 cm). Coll. M. Komor, New York. Purchased from Mrs. F. F. Prentiss Fund, 1954.   *Fig. 237*

Cleaned in 1965.

The identification of the sitter rests on the signed and dated (1461) bronze medal representing the same macro-cephalic court jester whose identity with Triboulet is traditionally assumed but not firmly authenticated. Triboulet was the most famous of the jesters in the service of René of Anjou (from at least 1447 until his death in 1466). The attribution of the relief to Laurana (Tietze-Conrat 1955) must rest primarily on its similarity to the same medal and to the marble relief with the portrait of Pietro Speziale in Militello, not an authenticated but a probable work of Laurana (Rolfs 1907, pp. 281 ff. and pl. 30); but there are also some compa-rable heads on the relief with *Christ Carrying the Cross* in St. Di-dier in Avignon (Rolfs 1907, pl. 66 ff.), a work at least designed by Laurana though probably executed with the help of French sculp-tors. There are too many uncertainties with regard to Laurana's work to accept the attribution with complete confidence, but circumstances clearly favor it. It is possible that the marble portrait was made on the occasion of the death of the jester, the more so as the fool's scepter of the medal has been eliminated; Laurana was still at the court of René of Anjou in 1466 when Triboulet died.

Exh.: "The Renaissance Image of Man and the World," Co-lumbus, Ohio, Gallery of Fine Arts, 1961, no. 47.

Lit.: E. Tietze-Conrat, "A Relief Portrait by Francesco Laurana," *AMAM Bulletin*, XII, 1954–55, pp. 87 ff. (condensed version in *Art Quarterly*, XVIII, 1955, pp. 319 ff.); E. Tietze-Conrat,
Dwarfs and Jesters in Art, London, 1957, pp. 5, 41, 43, 45 ff., 102.

LORMIER, ÉDOUARD. Born in St. Omer in 1847. Pupil of F.
Jouffroy in Paris. Exhibited at the Salon from 1866. Died in Paris in 1919.

The Fisherman   *26.3*

Bronze, hollow cast, brown patina, H. 19½ in. (49.5 cm) with base
of rocky beach. Signed on the ground: E LORMIER; foundry
mark: circle with insignia in the center (ax, pliers and pinchers?)
and inscription SUSSE FRÈRES EDITEURS. PARIS. Coll. Mrs.
F. F. Prentiss, Cleveland. Gift of Mrs. Prentiss, 1926.

LÜCKE, JOHANN CHRISTIAN LUDWIG VON (?). Born
ca. 1703, probably in Dresden. Presumably pupil of B. Permoser. Early
study travels in France, Holland and England. Active in Meissen, Dresden,
Hamburg, Copenhagen and Danzig, where he died in 1780.

Bust of Voltaire   56.42

White marble, H. 5¾ in. (14.6 cm). Coll. R. Stora, New York. Gift
of Frederick B. Artz, Oberlin, 1956.

Tip of the nose broken.
A variant of the bust said to have been presented to Voltaire by
Frederick the Great in 1775, another small version of which is
reproduced in M. von Boehn, *Modes and Manners*, tr. J. Joshua,
London 1935, IV, p. 166. The attribution to Lücke is uncertain.

MAILLOL, ARISTIDE. Born in Banyuls-sur-Mer (Pyrenées
Orientales) in 1861. Studied painting with A. Cabanel in Paris, 1882–86;
as sculptor (after ca. 1900) self-taught. Active in Banyuls, Paris from 1895
and Marly-le-Roy, where he died in 1944.

Action in Chains 1905–06 *50.4*

Bronze, hollow cast, brownish black patina, H. 12½ in. (31.8 cm). Signed with monogram (M in circle) on base near left foot. Coll. Ambroise Vollard, Paris; Swiss dealer (bought from Vollard); E. Weyhe, New York; from him acquired in 1941 by Curt Valentin, New York. Purchased from R. T. Miller, Jr. Fund, 1950.

Fig. 270

Study for the "Action in Chains" figure of the monument erected to Louis-Auguste Blanqui at Puget-Themiers near Grenoble about 1906 (commissioned in 1905). According to Lucien Maillol, Aristide's son, as quoted by Curt Valentin, only three casts of this bronze are known to exist. One is in a private collection in New Orleans (Exh. "Early Masters of Modern Art," Isaac Delgado Museum of Art, 1959, no. 20); a second version once in C. Valentin's Gallery (Exh. "The Heritage of Rodin," 1950–51, no. 44, and on loan to the Minneapolis Institute of Arts, see its *Bulletin*, XL, March 3, 1951, p. 44) is in Coll. Mrs. John Dalrymple, Minneapolis (same *Bulletin*, XLVIII, 1959, p. 9). One was with George Seligmann in New York in 1950. A related drawing is in the Metropolitan Museum in New York (Ritchie 1945, p. 79).

Exh.: "College Collections: an exhibition presented on the occasion of the dedication of the Kresge Art Center, Michigan State University," East Lansing, 1959, no. 65.

Lit.: C. Ritchie, *Aristide Maillol*, Exh. Cat. Albright Art Gallery, Buffalo, N.Y., 1945, p. 78; J. Rewald, *Maillol*, London—Paris—New York, 1939, p. 16 and pl. 80 (not with certainty the same version).

MARIOTON, CLAUDIUS. Born in Paris in 1844. Studied with E. Lavasseur, A. Dumont and J. G. Thomas. Active in Paris, where he died in 1919.

Diogenes in Search of an Honest Man 1883 *04.494*

Bronze, brown patina, H. 31½ in. (80 cm) with base. Signed on the base: CMARIOTON (C and M in ligature). Foundry mark:

B.COLIN&Cie PARIS. Coll. Charles F. Olney, Cleveland. Olney Gift, 1904.

Smaller bronze version of a plaster cast (180 cm high) exhibited in the Salon of the Société des artistes français in 1883 (Cat. Exposition Nationale, 1883, no. 1064). A large bronze version stands on the Square du Temple in Paris.

MASTER OF THE NAKED FEMALE FIGURES. Probably a northern artist active in Florence in the workshop of Giovanni da Bologna, ca. 1590.

Seated Nude Cutting Her Toe Nails
54.22

Bronze, hollow cast, 4⅜ × 2³⁄₁₆ × 2⁹⁄₁₆ in. (11.1 × 5.5 × 6.5 cm). Coll. Eugene Garbáty, New York. Purchased from Mrs. F. F. Prentiss Fund, 1954.
Fig. 247

Other versions of this bronze, with slight deviations, are in the Samuel H. Kress Collection (Cat. by J. Pope-Hennessy, London, 1965, no. 469), in Vienna (Cat. Planiscig, 1924, no. 234 as Central Italian, 2nd half 16th cen.), in Berlin (Cat. Bange 1930, no. 144 as Netherlandish-Italian, 2nd half 16th cen.), in the Ashmolean Museum in Oxford, and elsewhere.

Exh.: "The Renaissance Image of Man and the World," Columbus, Ohio, Gallery of Fine Arts, 1961, no. 54.

MINNE, GEORGE. Born in Ghent in 1866. Pupil of J. Delvin in Ghent, later of C. van der Stappen in Brussels. Settled in Laethem-St. Martin in 1899; 1914–18 in Wales. Died in Laethem in 1941.

Standing Youth
58.88

White marble, H. 17 in. (43.2 cm) with marble base. Coll. Elisabeth Lotte Franzos, Vienna and Washington. Franzos Bequest, 1958.
Fig. 267

Mended breaks at both ankles.

Apparently an early work, very close to the *Grand Blessé* of 1894 (L. van Puyvelde, *George Minne*, Brussels, 1930, pl. 12); compare also the nude youths of the *Well* (*ibid.*, pl. 16) and of the Volders Monument (W. Radenberg, *Moderne Plastik*, Düsseldorf-Leipzig, 1912, p. 60), both of ca. 1898.

MOORE, HENRY. Born in Castleford (Yorkshire) in 1898. Studied at the Art School in Leeds and the Royal College of Art in London. In Paris and Italy, 1925. Taught at the Art School in Chelsea and the Slade School in London. 1947–48 in New York, 1951 in Greece. Active in London.

Reclining Figure, No. 1 1945 *56.18*

Bronze, green patina, 6½ × 15 × 5¼ in. (16.5 × 38.1 × 13.3 cm). Coll. R. J. Sainsbury, London; J. J. Klejman Gallery, New York. Purchased from Mrs. F. F. Prentiss Fund, 1956. *Fig. 277*

One of seven casts (see W. Grohmann, *The Art of Henry Moore*, London, 1960, p. 6). Other casts: W. Grohmann, pl. 35; J. P. Hodin, *Moore*, New York, 1959, pl. 11; J. J. Sweeney, *Henry Moore*, Exhibition at the Museum of Modern Art, New York, 1946, p. 82 and p. 91, no. 53; *Interior Design*, Feb. 1958 (Coll. Lily Harmon, New York). A polished brass version is in the Nelson Rockefeller Coll., New York; see *Art in America*, 1965, no. 2, pp. 37 f., ill. p. 40). A small bronze model for this figure is in the Joseph Hirshhorn Coll., New York. Closely related is a drawing of two reclining figures (Sweeney, p. 82).

Exh.: Venice, Biennale, 1948, no. 29; London, Tate Gallery, 1951; "An American University Collection" (AMAM), Kenwood (London County Council), 1962, no. 8.

Lit.: H. Read, *Henry Moore, Sculpture and Drawings*, third ed., London, 1949, pl. 106 g.

MOREAU, MATHARIN. Born in Dijon in 1822, son of Jean-Baptiste-Louis-Joseph Moreau. Pupil of his father and of E. J. Ramey and A. Dumont in Paris (1841). Prix de Rome, 1842. Exhibited at the Salon from 1848. Active in Paris, where he died in 1912.

Greek Maiden   Before 1887   *04.1149*

Bronze, hollow cast in separate pieces, H. 10¼ in. (26 cm). Signed on back leg of chair: Moreau. Coll. Charles F. Olney, Cleveland, acquired before 1887. Olney Gift, 1904.   *Fig. 261*

According to Olney, originally connected with a black marble clock.

MÜLLER, GEORG?   Born in Munich in 1880. Parents moved to U.S.A. in 1886. Pupil of W. von Mauch in Chicago, and of W. von Rue-mann and E. Kunz in Munich. Studied with Hermann Hahn, 1909–12. Active in Munich, where he died in 1952.

Standing Woman   *57.13*

Bronze, hollow cast, dark brown patina, H. 13 in. (33 cm). Coll. Roy G. Pearce, Akron, Ohio (acquired ca. 1922 from Germany). Gift of Dr. R. G. Pearce in memory of his wife, Margery McKenney Pearce, 1957.

A foundry (?) mark (back, center) remains unidentified.

The attribution must rest on a combination of the donor's vague recollection of the artist's name and stylistic evidence which is not entirely convincing.

NETHERLANDISH, early 17th century.

Expulsion from Paradise   *59.114*

Ivory, H. 7⅛ in. (18.1 cm). Coll. Paul Ludwig Silten, Berlin (1923); Blumka Gallery, New York. Purchased from R. T. Miller, Jr. Fund, 1959.   *Fig. 256*

Right calf and right arm of Adam repaired. Old breaks in Adam's neck; instep, toes and ankle of his left foot; fingers of his right hand; and in Eve's right calf and tip of left foot.

The present state of our knowledge of Netherlandish sculpture of the 16th and 17th centuries does not permit a more exact attribution of this outstanding work. However, its Netherlandish origin is hardly doubtful; its style foreshadows that of much later works such as Pieter Xavery's group of Adam and Eve of 1671 in the Rijksmuseum in Amsterdam (*Verslag over 1960*, The Hague, 1962, opp. p. 11).

Lit.: W. F. Volbach, *Die Sammlung Silten*, Berlin, 1923, p. 15, no. 17.

PERSIAN, ca. 485–480 B.C.

Palace Guard   *43.576*

Limestone relief, 18½ × 12 × 4⁵⁄₁₆ in. (47 × 30.5 × 11 cm). Coll. D. Kelekian, New York. Purchased from R. T. Miller, Jr. Fund, 1943.

Fig. 219

Lower part of figure and staff missing.

From one of the stairways leading to either the great audience hall (apadana) of Darius, finished under Xerxes, or to the council hall of Darius at Persepolis. For reproductions of very similar figures of guards (quiver, drapery etc.) see Erich F. Schmidt, *Persepolis*, I, Chicago, 1953, pls. 59 and 83. Very similar pieces are in the Cleveland Museum of Art (no. 43.279; *Bulletin*, XIII, 1943, pp. 135 ff.) and elsewhere.

Exh.: "Art Marches On: Masterpieces of 5000 Years," Flint, Michigan, Institute of Arts, 1941.

PICASSO (RUIZ-PICASSO), PABLO.
See under Paintings.

Head of a Woman (Fernande)   1905   *55.35*

Bronze, green patina, H. 14¼ in. (36.2 cm). Signed on back, below: PICASSO. Coll. Curt Valentin, New York. Purchased from R. T. Miller, Jr. Fund, 1955.   *Fig.* 269

One of the early casts (signed only) edited by Vollard; a later edition of nine casts was made by Valsuani in 1959 (signed, numbered and stamped with Valsuani foundry mark). Casts of the early edition in the Bavarian National Museum, Munich and Coll. Justin K. Thannhauser, New York. A Valsuani cast (5/9) in Coll. Joseph H. Hirshhorn, New York.

The sitter was Fernande Olivier, who lived with Picasso from 1904 to 1912.

A closely related drawing is in the Art Institute of Chicago (Exh. "Master Drawings from the Art Institute of Chicago," New York, Wildenstein's, 1963, pl. XLIX).

Exh.: "Sculpture and Sculptors' Drawings," New York, Curt Valentin Gallery, 1953–54, no. 50; "Closing Exhibition, Sculpture, Paintings and Drawings," New York, Curt Valentin Gallery, 1955, no. 150; "Picasso, Sculpture," New York, Fine Arts Associates, 1957, no. 5; "Picasso: 75th Anniversary Exhibition," New York, Museum of Modern Art—Art Institute of Chicago—Philadelphia Museum of Art, 1957–58, p. 26 (New York, Chicago) and no. 3 (Philadelphia).

Lit.: C. Zervos, *Pablo Picasso*, Paris-New York, 1932, I, no. 323.

PLANCKH, VIKTOR. Born in Troppau (Opava) in 1904. Studied painting with V. Schufinsky, A. Boehm and B. Loeffler in Vienna. As painter active in Vienna; also received commissions in Greece, Italy and France. Was killed in the Second World War.

Seated Woman 1936   *39.11*

Bronze, green patina with brown highlights, $7\frac{1}{2} \times 4\frac{1}{2} \times 5\frac{13}{16}$ in. (19 × 11.5 × 14.8 cm). Signed in back: V Planckh 36. Coll. Mrs. Malcolm L. McBride, Cleveland. Gift of Mrs. McBride, 1939.

No other works of sculpture by this artist are known to us.

POGGINI, DOMENICO? Born in Florence in 1520. Active there from 1556 in the service of Cosimo I de'Medici. Moved to Rome in 1585 and worked for Pope Sixtus V. Died in Rome in 1590. Poet.

Gladiator Drawing his Sword   *53.236*

Bronze, solid cast, H. 8⅛ in. (20.6 cm). Coll. Baroness René de
Kerchove, New York. Gift of Baroness de Kerchove, 1953.

Fig. 248

Blade of sword and body of sheath missing.

Other versions of this bronze are in the Henry E. Huntington
Art Gallery, San Marino, Calif. (formerly Morgan Collection; Cat.
W. Bode, Paris, 1910, II, no. 128; sheath and half of sword
preserved); in the Victoria and Albert Museum, London (sword
clasped with both hands); in the former Coll. Mrs. Philip Lydig
(*Art in America*, I, 1913, p. 73, and Lydig Cat. 1913, no. 51); and
elsewhere. The attribution to Poggini cannot be considered certain;
the bronze was listed as "Italian, end of 16th century" by Bode
(*The Italian Bronze Statuettes of the Renaissance*, III, London,
1912, pl. CCXXIV, the Morgan version) and "in the style of
Poggini" in Bode's Morgan Cat. and by Grotemeyer (Thieme-
Becker XXVII, 1933, p. 188). In any case, it is later than Poggini's
bronze *Pluto* of 1571 in the Pal. Vecchio in Florence (repr. *Burlington Magazine*, LIII, 1928, p. 8).

Exh.: "The Renaissance Image of Man and the World," Columbus, Ohio, Gallery of Fine Arts, 1961, no. 55.

POWERS, HIRAM. Born near Woodstock, Vermont, in 1805.
Moved to Cincinnati in 1822 and worked for the wax cabinet of the
Western Museum, 1829–34. Later active in Washington (1834–37) and
in Florence (from 1837), where he died in 1873.

Standing Female Nude   *58.174*

White marble, H. 33¾ in. (85.7 cm). Coll. Leonard K. Graves,
Waterbury, Vermont (whose wife was the daughter of a cousin of
the artist); Edward S. Peck (grandnephew of L. K. Graves) (1941).
Gift of E. S. Peck, Los Angeles, 1958.   *Fig. 263*

The statue, said to have been in the artist's studio in Florence at
the time of his death, seems to be a fairly late work.

RIEMENSCHNEIDER, TILMANN. Born in Heiligenstadt (Thuringia) ca. 1460. Probably trained in Erfurt and Ulm. Settled in Würzburg in 1483, became citizen and master there in 1485. Active in Würzburg as sculptor in stone and wood and as a member of the city council, 1504–25. Died there in 1531.

Bust of Saint Urban

48.294

Linden, 21¾ × 13 × 7 in. (55.2 × 33 × 17.8 cm). Back finished in less detail. Base modern. Coll. Eugen Schweitzer, Berlin, sale June 6, 1918, no. 80; Henry Goldman (died in 1937), New York; A. S. Drey, New York. Purchased from R. T. Miller, Jr. Fund, 1948.

Fig. 242

Stained dark brown (probably 19th century).

Some cleavage, mostly on the back, filled in with small strips of wood, probably at a very early date. Orb and cross of the tiara, and some of its cross-shaped leaves missing.

St. Urban (Pope Urban I, 222–230) is shown with a bunch of grapes lying on his book. He was the patron saint of vineyards, and the bust was perhaps made for processions in vineyards, of which the artist owned a large number.

Carved ca. 1500 (Bier 1946). The attribution to the Hildesheim "Benediktmeister" (von der Osten 1965) is not convincing.

Exh.: Zanesville, Ohio, Art Institute, 1948; "Sculptures of Tilmann Riemenschneider," North Carolina Museum of Art, Raleigh, 1962, p. 50, no. XII.

Lit.: J. Bier, "A Bust of St. Urban by Tilmann Riemenschneider," *Art Quarterly*, IX, 1946, pp. 128 ff.; J. Bier, "A Virgin with the Christ Child by Tilmann Riemenschneider," *Register of the Museum of Art, University of Kansas*, II, no. 2, 1959, pp. 2 ff.; G. von der Osten, "Niederdeutsche Bildwerke in amerikanischem Besitz," *Niederdeutsche Beiträge zur Kunstgeschichte*, IV, 1965, pp. 101 ff. (104 f.).

RODIN, (FRANÇOIS) AUGUSTE (RENÉ). Born in Paris in 1840. Pupil of Barye and Carrier-Belleuse. Worked in the porcelain manufactory at Sèvres, 1864–71; assistant to Carrier-Belleuse and Rasbourg in

Belgium, 1871–77. Visited Florence and Rome, 1875. After 1878, active in Paris and, after 1894, also in Meudon, where he died in 1917.

The Prodigal Son (also known under the titles: **L'Enfant du siècle, The Prayer, The Supreme Appeal, Expiring Warrior, Vae Victis,** etc.) *55.32*

Bronze, dark green patina, H. 54¼ in. (137.8 cm). Signed on top of base, behind right foot: A. Rodin; foundry mark on back of base, lower right: "Alexis Rudier / Fondeur. Paris." Coll. Alexis Rudier, Paris; Curt Valentin, New York. Purchased from R. T. Miller, Jr. Fund, 1955. *Fig. 265*

Presumably cast before Rodin's death, since Alexis Rudier also died in 1917. Two earlier casts, both with the front dexter and the back sinister corner of the base open (a casting fault), are in the Tate Gallery, London (given by Rodin to the Victoria and Albert Museum in 1914), and the California Palace of the Legion of Honor, San Francisco (sold by Rodin to Mrs. Alma de Bretteville Spreckels in 1914). Another cast is in the Musée Rodin, Paris. Seven, probably all posthumous casts, sold by the Musée Rodin since Rodin's death (one to the Washington County Museum of Fine Arts, Hagerstown, Md., and one to the Slatkin Galleries, New York). The model after which all the above bronze casts were made is a limestone version, 55 in. high, in the Ny Carlsberg Glyptothek, Copenhagen (bought by its founder from Rodin in 1907). This figure is an enlargement of a smaller version of the *Prodigal Son*, 23 in. high, which exists in several bronze casts and which comes from a version of the group called *Fugit Amor* or *La Sphinge*. This group, of which several bronze casts and marble replicas are known, is in turn an enlargement of the couple found twice on the right panel of the *Gates of Hell*, above the lower right corner and in the middle of the panel (reversed). The figures of this couple were probably executed in the early '80's.

Exh.: "Auguste Rodin," New York, Curt Valentin Gallery— Minneapolis Institute of Arts—Des Moines Art Center—Portland Art Museum—Santa Barbara Museum of Art—City Art Museum of St. Louis—Cincinnati Art Museum, 1954–1955, no. 20; "Closing Exhibition—Sculpture, Paintings and Drawings," New York,

Curt Valentin Gallery, 1955, no. 166; "Rodin," New York, Museum of Modern Art, 1963, no. 36.

Lit.: A. E. Elsen, *Rodin*, New York, Museum of Modern Art, 1963, pp. 57 ff. (repr. p. 56); A. C. Tacha, "The Prodigal Son: Some New Aspects of Rodin's Sculpture," *AMAM Bulletin*, XXII, 1964–65, pp. 23 ff.

ROGERS, JOHN. Born in Salem, Mass., in 1829. Studied briefly with B. E. Spence in Rome (ca. 1857); otherwise self-taught. Member, National Academy, in 1863. Active in New York 1860 ff. and New Canaan, Conn. 1877–93, where he died in 1904.

Rip van Winkle at Home *51.75*

Plaster, H. 18½ in. (49 cm). Coll. Mrs. S. W. McCabe. Gift of Mrs. McCabe, 1951.

Made in December 1871, together with two other Rip van Winkle subjects. The actor, dramatist and painter Joseph Jefferson, famous for his portrayals of Rip van Winkle (see his painting, p. 89), posed for the main figure; the specific subject of this group goes back to Washington Irving's story, rather than Jefferson's play (see Chetwood Smith, *Rogers Groups*, Boston, 1934, p. 77).

ROMAN, first century A.D.

Corinthian Capital with Dolphins *41.45*

White marble, 10 × 14 × 13½ in. (25.4 × 35.6 × 34.3 cm). Coll. Lord Francis Pelham Clinton Hope, Deepdene, Dorking (probably there from ca. 1800), sale London, July 23, 1917, no. 190 a; J. Brummer, New York. Purchased from R. T. Miller, Jr. Fund, 1941.

Fig. 227

For the motif of dolphins with crossing tails see Eugen von Mercklin, *Antike Figurenkapitelle*, Berlin, 1962, no. 518, fig. 983, and nos. 522 a and b, figs. 993–994 (from Pompeii). Compare also his no. 583, fig. 1125 (first half of first century), for the similarly lively structure and ornament which have led some observers to believe that the present capital is a work of the Renaissance.

ROMAN (?), first century A.D. (?).

Head of a Youth
60.34

Porphyry, H. 9½ in. (24.1 cm). Coll. Morosini (not in the sales Venice, May 15, 1894 and New York, Oct. 10, 1932); unidentified sale in London, late 1950's; Melvin Gutman, New York. Gift of Mr. Gutman, 1960.
Fig. 229

This fragment was called Constantinian in the London sale, and Alexandrian ca. 300 A.D., by its last owner. The later attribution remains a distinct possibility but an earlier date and an origin in an archaizing Graeco-Roman workshop (C. Vermeule, orally, 1965) must be seriously considered.

ROMAN, early second century A.D.

Portrait of an Isis Priest
1902.1

White (Pentelic?) marble, 12 × 7⅝ × 9½ in. (30.5 × 19.4 × 24.1 cm). Coll. Dr. Joseph Cook, Boston (purchased from an antiquarian in Rome in 1881). Gift of Mrs. Joseph Cook, Boston, 1902.
Fig. 226

Nose and part of the left ear are restored. The alien bust, shown in older reproductions (Dennison 1905), has been removed.

The mark of a small cross or X above the right forehead of the man, whose head is smoothly shaven, was formerly thought to refer symbolically to the wounds received by Scipio the Elder in the Battle of Ticinus (218 B.C.) and led to the identification of a whole group of similar portraits with Scipio. It is now convincingly referred to a priest serving the cult of Isis (Dennison 1905); all such busts come from the first three centuries A.D., when the cult of Isis was very popular throughout Italy. These priests shaved their heads, and there exists written evidence of foreign priests being branded. For style and date compare the Trajanic and Hadrianic examples adduced by Vermeule (1959).

Lit.: W. Dennison, "A New Head of the so-called Scipio Type: an Attempt at its Identification," *American Journal of Archaeology*, IX, 1905, pp. 11 ff.; C. C. Vermeule III, "Oberlin's Head of an Isis Priest of the Second Century A.D.," *AMAM Bulletin*, XVII, 1959–60, pp. 6 ff.

ROMAN (Early Christian), second half 4th century A.D.

Sarcophagus Lid with Story of Jonah   *48.3*

White marble, 10¼ × 81⅞ × 9 in. (26 × 209.9 × 22.3 cm). Coll. Count Gregor Stroganoff, Rome (1909); J. Brummer, New York. Purchased from R. T. Miller, Jr. Fund, 1948.   *Fig. 228*

The center section held by the two putti, originally containing an inscription, was replaced with a "cosmati" porphyry slab surrounded by a mosaic design in black, white, red and gold, presumably in the early 13th century.

In the left section, Jonah thrown to the whale; the box-like structure above the whale is an allusion to Noah's Ark. In the right section, Jonah under the gourd after having emerged from the whale. Masks on the corners. An almost identical ship occurs on a similar sarcophagus in the Vatican Museum (Wilpert 1932, II, pl. CLXXI, 1).

Lit.: A. de Waal, "Noé-Jonas," *Römische Quartalschrift*, XXIII, 1909, pp. 250 ff.; L. Pollak and A. Muñoz, *Pièces de Choix de la Collection du Comte Grégoire Stroganoff à Rome*, 1912, p. VII (illustrated only); H. Leclercq in F. Cabrol and H. Leclercq, *Dictionnaire d'archéologie chrétienne et de liturgie*, VII, 2, Paris, 1927, col. 2607 f. (no. 136); J. Wilpert, *I Sarcofagi Cristiani Antichi*, Rome, 1932, II, pp. 202 and 215, pl. CLXXII, 6; W. Stechow, "Selected Acquisitions of European Art," *AMAM Bulletin*, V, 1948, p. 27; C. Vermeule, "Roman Sarcophagi in America: A Short Inventory," *Festschrift für Friedrich Matz*, Mainz, 1962, p. 104.

SAMMARTINO (SAN MARTINO), GIUSEPPE. Born in Naples in 1720. Pupil of Felice Bottiglieri as modeller of crêche figures; also worked in wood and marble. Active in Naples, where he died in 1793.

St. Joseph Holding the Christ Child   62.39

Polychromed wood (hardwood), H. 27¼ in. (69.2 cm). Coll. K. Rossacher, Salzburg. Purchased from Mrs. F. F. Prentiss Fund, 1962.   *Fig.* 259

Restorations in ground and paint; the left side of the robe rebuilt (with plaster?).

Comparison with Sammartino's *Nativity* scenes in the Gatti-Farina Coll., Naples (*Dedalo*, II, 1921/22, p. 391), and in the Bayerische Nationalmuseum, Munich (*Kunst und Kunsthandwerk, Meisterwerke im Bayerischen Nationalmuseum München*, Munich, 1955, pl. 170) supports the attribution to Sammartino.

SUMERIAN, ca. 2500–2400 B.C.

Bust of a Royal (?) Personage   50.13

Limestone, 6 × 5¾ in. (15.2 × 14.6 cm). Coll. Charles L. Morley, New York. Purchased from R. T. Miller, Jr. and Charles F. Olney Funds, 1950.   *Fig.* 214

Right arm broken. Lower part missing; probably to be reconstructed as a votive figure; standing, hands clasped and perhaps holding a cup.

The exact provenance of the bust is uncertain but it is reliably reported that it was known to the Abbé de Genouillac and to Père Vincent Scheil, who excavated in Mesopotamia from ca. 1895 to ca. 1910, and that the bust was found and perhaps owned by either one of them. The separate locks of hair at the back seem to be a unique feature.

Lit.: E. Capps, Jr., "A Unique Sumerian Royal (?) Personage," *AMAM Bulletin*, VII, 1949–50, pp. 39 ff.; L. Schnitzler, *Frühe Plastik im Zweistromland*, Stuttgart, 1959, pl. 13; an article by Mark A. Brandes is in preparation.

SYRIAN (?), ca. 6th century B.C.

Antelope *43.275*

Bronze, solid cast, green patina, 3³⁄₁₆ × 4 in. (8.1 × 10.2 cm). Coll. D. Kelekian, New York. Purchased from R. T. Miller, Jr. Fund, 1943. *Fig. 220*

No closely related works are known to us. The attribution to Syria, presumably based on provenance, is more acceptable than the suggestion of Persian origin.

VERROCCHIO, ANDREA, CIRCLE OF. Andrea di Michele de'Cione called Verrocchio was born in Florence in 1435. Trained as a goldsmith he later became head of an important Florentine workshop in which he practiced as a painter as well as a sculptor in bronze, marble, terracotta and silver. Active primarily in Florence he also executed works in Pistoia and Venice where he died in 1488.

Madonna and Child *44.167*

Stucco relief, 33¼ × 23¾ × 1⅞ to 3⅞ in. (84.5 × 60.3 × 5 to 10 cm). Coll. Piero Tozzi, Florence; Drey Galleries, New York, 1935; Parish-Watson Galleries, New York, 1935. Purchased from the R. T. Miller, Jr. Fund, 1944. *Fig. 239*

Well-preserved, the chief loss being part of the right hand of the child.

When purchased the relief had been cleaned of the paint with which it was once covered. Microscopic examination of fragments yield no certain evidence as to the time the paint was applied, but the fact that a few mold marks and small blemishes were allowed to remain suggest that polychromy was the original intention. These same mold marks appear in a less well-preserved replica formerly in the Dibblee Collection where it was once attributed to Leonardo da Vinci (T. A. Cook, *Leonardo da Vinci, Sculptor*, London, 1923) and which was recently sold (Christie's, London, June 2, 1964) as "workshop of Luca della Robbia under the influence of Verrocchio." Several inferior versions with variations exist in glazed terracotta, terracotta and marble. That the original was terracotta rather than marble is based on convincing visual evidence. Bongiorno (1962) dates it in the mid-80's and believes it was modelled by someone closely connected with Verrocchio who was familiar with certain workshop practices as well as with particular sculptures, paintings and drawings that come from the shop in the late 70's and early 80's either from Verrocchio's own hand, Leonardo's or other assistants. Charles Seymour, Jr., (1966) dates it in the mid-60's and thinks that the original may have been an early work by Verrocchio himself.

Exh.: New York, Drey Galleries, 1935, no. 17; New York, Parish-Watson Galleries, November, 1935; "Italian Sculpture 1250–1500," Detroit Institute of Arts, 1938, no. 55; "Masterpieces of Art," New York World's Fair, 1939, no. 432.

Lit.: W. R. Valentiner, "Leonardo as Verrocchio's Coworker," *Art Bulletin*, XII, 1930, pp. 43 ff. (85 n. 67, fig. 37); C. Ragghianti, "La mostra di scultura italiana antica a Detroit," *Critica d'arte*. XVI–XVII, 1938, p. 144 and p. 181, fig. 54; L. M. Bongiorno, "A Fifteenth Century Stucco and the Style of Verrocchio," *AMAM Bulletin*, XIX, 1961–62, pp. 115 ff.; R. D. Buck, "Report on Technical Examination," *AMAM Bulletin*, XIX, 1961–62, pp. 138 ff.; C. Seymour, Jr., *Sculpture in Italy: 1400–1500*, Baltimore, 1966, pp. 178, 247 n. 8.

Illustrations: European Paintings

1. Italian (Florentine), ca. 1330–40, *Crucifix* (p. 79)

2. Jacopo del Casentino, *Crucifixion* (p. 87)

3. Italian (Sienese), ca. 1300, *Madonna and Child* (p. 83)

4. Italian (Sienese), ca. 1350, *Madonna and Child* (p. 83)

5. Shop of Taddeo di Bartolo, *St. Margaret* (p. 147)

6. Shop of Taddeo di Bartolo, *St. John the Baptist* (p. 146)

7. Mariotto di Nardo, *Adoration of the Magi* (p. 103)

8. Neri di Bicci, *Altar Wing with Five Saints* (p. 117)

9. Giovanni Boccati, *St. John the Baptist and St. Sebastian* (p. 19)

10. Apollonio di Giovanni, *Xerxes Invading Greece*, 1463 (p. 8)

11. Guidoccio Cozzarelli, *Madonna with Child and Two Angels* (p. 40)

12. Italian (Florentine), late 15th century, *The Archangel Raphael Guiding Tobias* (p. 79)

13. Italian (Lombard), ca. 1500, *Adoration of the Child* (p. 80)

14. Vrancke van der Stockt (?), *Kneeling Donor with St. John the Baptist* (p. 143)

15. Master of the Sterzing Altarpiece, *St. Mary Magdalen* (p. 105)

16. Austrian (Salzburg), ca. 1470–80, *St. Michael Weighing Souls* (p. 9)

17. Circle of the Master of Grossgmain, *St. Augustine* (p. 104)

18. Miguel Jiménez,
Man of Sorrows (p. 89)

19. Byzantine, 17th cen-
tury (?), *Head of a Saint*
(p. 27)

20. Russian, 16th cen-
tury (?), *The Nativity*
(p. 134)

21. Circle of Pintoricchio, *The Mystic Marriage of St. Catherine* (p. 121)

22. Italian (Neapolitan), first quarter 16th century, *Madonna del Suffragio* (p. 81)

23. Giampietrino (?), *Cleopatra* (p. 63)

24. Niccolò Giolfino, *Lucretia* (p. 64)

25. Santi di Tito, *Armorial Shield
Salviati-Strozzi* (p. 150)

26. Sofonisba Anguissola,
Double Portrait (p. 7)

27. Follower of Jacopo Bassano, *Nativity* (p. 11)

28. Italian (Veronese), *A Vision of the Holy Family near Verona*, 1581 (p. 85)

29. Flemish, ca. 1500–15,
Holy Face (p. 56)

30. Flemish, early 16th
century, *Lamentation over
Christ* (p. 56)

31. Flemish, *Holy Family
with St. Anne and
St. Joachim*, 1525 (p. 57)

32. Michiel Coxie, *Portrait of Christina of Denmark*, 1545 (p. 39)

33. Maerten van
Heemskerck, *Samson
Slaying the Philistines,
Jupiter*
(p. 72)

34. Karel van Mander (?), *Rustic
Landscape* (p. 102)

35. Daniel Froeschl, *Allegorical
Figure*, 1609 (p. 58)

36. German (South) or Swiss, ca. 1520, *St. Mary Magdalen Raising the Wife of the Prince of Marseilles* (p. 62)

37. German (South) or Swiss, ca. 1520, *St. Mary Magdalen Raising a Dead Knight for Confession* (p. 62)

38. German (South), ca. 1515–20, *Portrait of a Young Man* (p. 61)

39. Barthel Bruyn the Elder, *Portrait of a Lady* (p. 25)

40. Spanish, first half 16th century, *Saint James Major* (p. 140)

41. Spanish, first half 16th century, *The Last Supper* (p. 139)

239

42. Spanish, 16th century, *The Fountain of Life* (p. 140)

43. Jacopo Ligozzi, *Portable Altar with Carrying Case*, 1608 (p. 99)

44. Pier Francesco Mola, *Mercury Putting Argus to Sleep* (p. 110)

45. Italian, mid 17th century, *The Crowning with Thorns* (p. 85)

46. G. B. Gaulli (Il Baciccio), *Death of Adonis* (p. 59)

47. Luca Giordano, *Christ Expelling the Money-Changers*, 1684 (p. 65)

48. Italian, late 17th century, *Mercury Lulling Argus into Sleep* (p. 86)

49. Anthony van Dyck, *Portrait of a Bearded Man* (p. 53)

50. Joos de Momper, *Mountainous Landscape* (p. 111)

51. Paulus Bril, *Landscape with Nymphs and Satyrs*, 1623 (p. 24)

246

52. P. P. Rubens, *The Finding of Erichthonius* (p. 132)

53. Jacob Jordaens, *An Oracle* (p. 90)

54. Hendrick Terbrugghen, *Saint Sebastian Attended by Saint Irene*, 1625 (p. 148)

55. Jan van Goyen, *Landscape with Dunes*, 1647 (p. 67)

56. Esajas van de Velde, *Summer Landscape* (p. 154)

57. Adriaen Bloemaert, *Hilly Landscape*, 1657 (p. 19)

58. Jan Davidsz de Heem, *Still Life* (p. 71)

59. Adriaen van de Venne, *Allegory of Poverty* (p. 155)

60. Nicolaes Berchem, *Resting Shepherds* (p. 14)

61. Abraham Begeyn, *Ruins of a Castle*, 1665 (p. 14)

62. Nicolaes Berchem, *The Country Farrier* (p. 15)

63. Dirck van Bergen, *The Bull* (p. 17)

64. Emanuel de Witte,
*Interior of the Old Church
at Delft*, 1653 or 1655
(p. 164)

65. Job Berckheyde,
The Bakery Shop (p. 16)

66. Michael Sweerts, *Self Portrait* (p. 145)

67. Jacob Esselens, *Portrait of a Lady* (p. 54)

254

68. Jan Steen, *A Merry Company* (p. 143)

69. Meindert Hobbema, *A Pond in a Forest*, 1668 (p. 74)

70. Follower of Claude Lorrain, *A Harbor Scene* (p. 100)

71. Gaspard Dughet, or Close Follower, *Classical Landscape* (p. 51)

72. Sébastien Bourdon, *Encampment* (p. 21)

73. Jusepe de Ribera, *Blind Old Beggar* (p. 128)

74. Alessandro Magnasco, *Landscape with Washerwomen* (p. 101)

75. Carlo Carlone, *Lamentation over Christ* (p. 28)

76. Italian (Venetian), ca. 1780, *Landscape (Capriccio)* (p. 86)

77. Rosalba Carriera, *Portrait of a Lady* (p. 29)

78. Giuseppe Bazzani, *The Death of Sapphira* (p. 11)

79. Giuseppe Bazzani, *Allegory of Peace* (?) (p. 12)

80. Jan Weenix, *Decorative Panel* (p. 158)

81. Adriaen van der Werff, *Jacob Blessing the Sons of Joseph* (p. 159)

82. Jean-Baptiste Siméon Chardin, *Still Life with Rib of Beef*, 1739 (p. 32)

83. J. M. Nattier, *Portrait of a Lady* (p. 116)

84. Frédéric Dubois, *Miniature Portrait of a Lady* (p. 48)

85. William Hogarth, *Portrait of Theodore Jacobsen*, 1742 (p. 75)

86. Wright of Derby, *Dovedale by Moonlight* (p. 165)

87. Joshua Reynolds, *The Strawberry Girl* (p. 127)

88. John Hoppner, *Mrs. Frances Henrietta Jerningham*, 1800 (p. 77)

89. Barker of Bath, *Interior of a Mill*, 1807 (p. 10)

90. Théodore Rousseau, *The Source* (p. 131)

91. Georges Michel, *Landscape* (p. 107)

92. J. M. W. Turner, *View of Venice* (p. 151)

93. Eugène Delacroix, *The Beheading of St. John the Baptist* (p. 44)

94. Joseph Zahradniczek, *View in the Prater, Vienna* (p. 167)

95. Claude Monet, *Garden of the Princess, Louvre* (p. 112)

96. Adolphe Monticelli, *Autumn Landscape* (p. 114)

97. Adolphe Monticelli, *Study in Color* (p. 115)

98. Gustave Courbet, *Castle of Chillon, Evening* (p. 38)

99. C.-F. Daubigny, *River Banks*, 1874 (p. 43)

100. C.-F. Daubigny, *A Showery Day in Spring*, 1876 (p. 43)

101. Jacobus Maris, *The Bridge* (p. 103)

102. Anton Mauve, "*The Pensioner*" (p. 106)

103. J. H. Weissenbruch, *Landscape* (p. 159)

104. Jozef Israels, *Mother and Son—Twilight* (p. 78)

105. Charles Jacque, *Sheep at the Entrance to a Forest* (p. 88)

106. Armand Charnay, *The Park of Sansac, Autumn* (p. 34)

107. Paul Cézanne, *The Viaduct at L'Estaque* (p. 30)

108. Alfred Sisley, *The Loing Canal at Moret* (p. 138)

109. Alfred Sisley, *Bristol Channel, Evening*, 1897 (p. 138)

110. Félix Vallotton, *The Crowd*, 1894 (p. 153)

111. Max Buri, *Head of a Woman* (p. 27)

112. H. E. Cross, *The Return of the Fisherman*, 1896 (p. 42)

113. Camille Pissarro, *Pont Neuf, Paris*, 1901 (p. 123)

114. H. J. Harpignies, *Landscape*, 1907 (p. 68)

115. Carl Moll, *Spring in Kahlenbergerdorf* (p. 111)

116. Emma Ciardi, *Garden of a Villa*, 1912 (p. 36)

117. P. A. Renoir, *Landscape at Cagnes* (p. 126)

118. Alexej Jawlensky, *Head of a Woman* (p. 88)

119. Karl Schmidt-Rottluff, *Parkway*, 1911 (p. 135)

120. Pablo Picasso, *Glass of Absinthe*, 1911 (p. 120)

121. Maurice de Vlaminck, *Landscape with a Village* (p. 156)

122. Maurice de Vlaminck, *River Landscape* (p. 156)

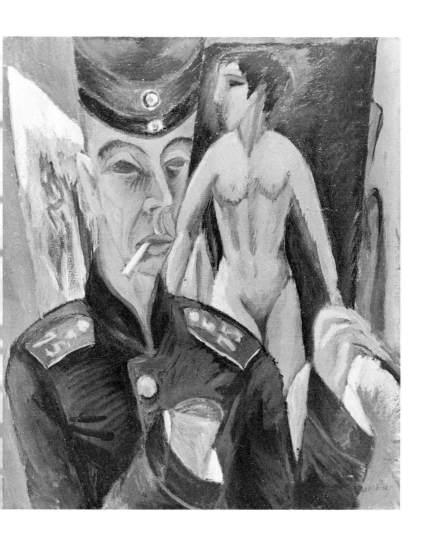

Opposite: 123. Oskar Kokoschka, *Sposalizio*, 1911 or 1912 (p. 95)

124. Ernst Ludwig Kirchner, *Self Portrait as Soldier*, 1915 (p. 93)

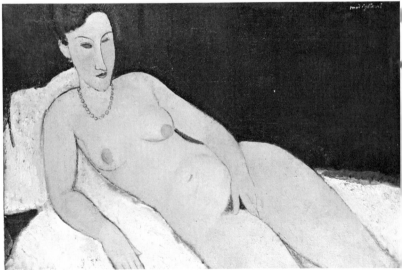

125. Amedeo Modigliani, *Head of a Man* (p. 109)

126. Amedeo Modigliani, *Nude with Coral Necklace*, 1917 (p. 109)

127. Claude Monet, *Wisteria* (p. 113)

128. Raoul Dufy, *Vence* (p. 51)

129. Raoul Dufy, *Boats at Le Havre*, 1938 (p. 51)

288

130. Paul Klee, *Flower Gardens in Taora*, 1918 (p. 94)

131. Paul Klee, *Die Paukenorgel*, 1930 (p. 94)

132. Pablo Picasso,
Woman in a Peplos, 1923
(p. 120)

133. André Derain,
Bust of a Woman (p. 45)

134. Marc Chagall,
In the Mountain, 1930
(p. 31)

135. Marc Chagall,
Green Dream, 1945
(p. 32)

136. Georges Rouault, *Three Clowns* (p. 130)

137. Georges Rouault, *Nocturne (Gethsemane)*, 1915/1939 (p. 130)

138. Carl Hofer, *The Repast*, 1932 (p. 75)

139. Giorgio de Chirico, *Self Portrait* (p. 35)

140. Henri Matisse, *Young Girl Seated*, 1936 (p. 106)

141. Georges Braque, *Blue Guitar*, 1943 (p. 23)

142. Fernand Léger, *Composition*, 1941 (p. 99)

143. Pablo Picasso, *Chair and Owl*, 1947 (p. 121)

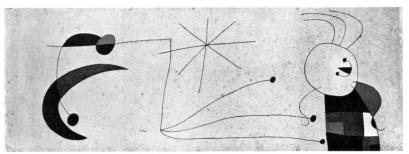

144. Joán Miró, *Woman, Bird and Serpent in Front of the Sun*, 1944 (p. 108)

145. Joán Miró, *The Spokesman of the Birds Plunges into the Night*, 1954 (p. 108)

297

146. Jean Dubuffet, *Lili*, 1947 (p. 50)

147. Jean Dubuffet, *Body of Woman*, 1950 (p. 50)

148. Jean Dubuffet, *Table with Watch and Ink Bottle*, 1951 (p. 50)

149. Kurt Schwitters, *Grey and Yellow*, 1947 (p. 136)

150. Alberto Giacometti, *Figure*, 1951 (p. 63)

American Paintings

151. Benjamin West, *Jacob Blessing the Sons of Joseph*, 1766 (p. 160)

152. Benjamin West, *General Kosciusko*, 1797 (p. 161)

153. Thomas Cole, *Lake with Dead Trees (Catskill)*, 1825 (p. 36)

154. Thomas Cole, *The Ruins* (p. 37)

155. Thomas Cole, *Sunset across the Water* (p. 38)

304

156. Waldo and Jewett, *Portrait of Charles Grandison Finney* (p. 157)

157. Thomas Doughty, *Tuckerman's Ravine* (p. 47)

158. I. J. H. Bradley, *Portrait of a Lady* (p. 22)

159. American (Ohio), ca. 1840, *Portrait of William Bushnell* (p. 7)

160. John Frederick Kensett, *The Temple of Neptune, Paestum* (p. 92)

161. John Frederick Kensett, *Mt. Mansfield* (p. 92)

165. James M. Hart, *Homeward Path*, 1882 (p. 70)

166. William Hart, *Farmington Valley*, *Connecticut*, 1866 (p. 70)

167. William Hart, *Beside the Brook* (p. 70)

168. William Hart, *Bit of Nature* (p. 71)

169. Arthur Parton, *Autumn*, 1871 (p. 119)

170. Easy Briggs, *Cows in a Pond* (p. 23)

171. Archibald Willard, *Deacon Jones' Experience* (p. 163)

172. Edward Gay, *By the Brookside*, 1875 (p. 60)

173. Jaspar Francis Cropsey, *Temple of the Sibyl, Tivoli*, 1876 (p. 41)

174. Jaspar Francis Cropsey, *Lake Wawayanda*, 1876 (p. 42)

175. W. L. Sonntag, *Autumn on the Androscoggin* (p. 139)

176. W. L. Sonntag, *Coming Storm in the Adirondacks* (p. 139)

177. Benjamin Stone, *A Peep at the Hudson* (p. 144)

178. Albert Bierstadt, *Sphinx Rock* (p. 18)

179. Edward Moran, *Ruins of Aspinwall Castle* (p. 115)

180. Julie Hart Beers, *Cattle near a Creek* (p. 13)

181. A. D. Shattuck, *The Hudson River* (p. 137)

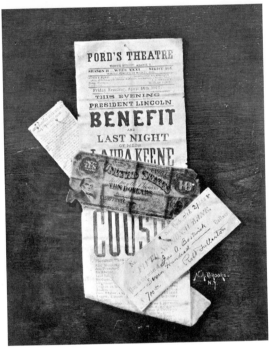

182. Victor Dubreuil, *Is It Real?* (p. 49)

183. Victor Dubreuil, *Take One* (p. 49)

184. Nicholas A. Brooks, *Handbill* (p. 24)

316

185. William M. Harnett, *Meerschaum Pipe*, 1886 (p. 68)

186. Frederick E. Church (?), "*The Letter Revenge*" (p. 35)

187. N. E. Cornwall,
*A Glimpse of Mount
Everett*, 1890 (p. 38)

188. John J. Hammer, *Mount Washington* (p. 67)

189. Ralph A. Blakelock, *California Ranch* (p. 18)

190. Joseph Jefferson, *Rip van Winkle's Nook* (p. 89)

191. Joseph Jefferson, *The Old Mill*, 1895 (p. 89)

192. William Merritt Chase, *Still Life in Copper* (p. 34)

193. J. H. Twachtman, *Seascape* (p. 152)

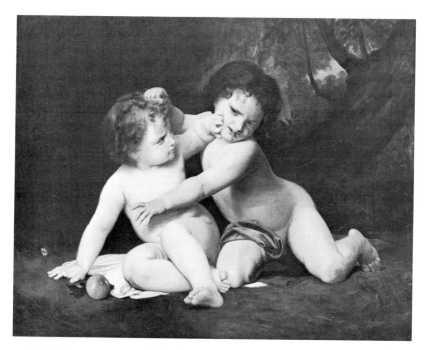

196. Robert Henri, *The Gypsy Girl* (p. 73)

194. De Scott Evans, *War (First Discord)* (p. 54)

195. Arthur B. Davies, *Child with a Toy* (p. 44)

197. Ernest Lawson, *Harlem River* (p. 98)

198. Leon Kroll, *Still Life with Lemon Tree*, 1918 (p. 96)

199. Alexander Calder, *Landscape with Country House* (p. 28)

200. Guy Pène Du Bois, *In the Wings, 1921* (p. 49)

201. Frederick Waugh, *Bailey Island, Maine* (p. 158)

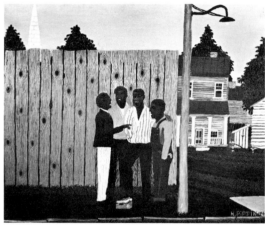

202. Paul Mays, *Harvesters* (p. 107)

203. Pop Hart, *The Hero*, 1927 (p. 69)

204. Man Ray, *Bird from Nowhere*, 1934 (p. 125)

205. Horace Pippin, *Harmonizing*, 1944 (p. 122)

206. Arshile Gorky, *The Plough and the Song*, 1947 (p. 66)

207. Richard Diebenkorn,
*Woman by a Large
Window*, 1957 (p. 46)

208. Franz Kline, *Untitled 19* (p. 95)

209. Jim Dine, *Charcoal Self-Portrait in a Cement Garden*, 1964 (p. 47)

210. Larry Poons, *Away Out on the Mountain*, 1965 (p. 123)

211. J. C. Orozco, *Mexican House*, 1929 (p. 118)

212. Jean Charlot, *Rest on the Flight*, 1943 (p. 33)

213. Guillermo Meza, *Nopalera*, 1946 (p. 107)

Sculpture

214. Sumerian, ca. 2500–2400 B.C., *Bust of a Royal (?) Personage* (p. 215)

215. Egyptian, ca. 2300 B.C., *Relief from the Tomb of Ny-ankh-Nesut* (p. 175)

216. Egyptian, ca. 2050 B.C., *Papyrus* (p. 176)

217. Egyptian, ca. 300 B.C., *Head of a Priest* (p. 177)

218. Etruscan, early 5th century B.C., *Warrior* (p. 179)

219. Persian, ca. 485–480 B.C., *Palace Guard* (p. 207)

220. Syrian (?), ca. 6th century B.C., *Antelope* (p. 216)

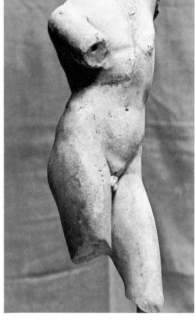

221. Greek, 5th century B.C. (Roman copy, 2nd century A.D.), *Head of Athena* (p. 188)

222. Greek, 4th century B.C. (Roman copy?), *Male Torso* (p. 189)

223. Greek, ca. 200 B.C., *Lion Attacking a Bull* (p. 189)

224. Greek, 1st century
A.D. (?), *Head of a Bearded Man* (p. 190)

225. Greek, late 2nd century A.D., *Fragment of a Sarcophagus* (p. 191)

226. Roman, early 2nd century A.D., *Portrait of an Isis Priest* (p. 213)

227. Roman, 1st century A.D., *Corinthian Capital with Dolphins* (p. 212)

228. Roman (Early Christian), second half 4th century A.D., *Sarcophagus Lid with Story of Jonah* (p. 214)

229. Roman (?), 1st century A.D. (?), *Head of a Youth* (p. 213)

230. Coptic, 5th–6th century A.D., *Capital* (p. 173)

231. Coptic, 5th–6th century A.D., *Portion of a Frieze* (p. 173)

338

232. French (Poitou), ca. 1155, *Bishop Grimoard* (p. 181)

233. French (Poitou), ca. 1155, *Bishop Adelelme* (p. 183)

234. English (?), second half 12th century, *Chessman: Knight* (p. 177)

235. French, late 14th century, *Wing of a Diptych* (p. 184)

236. Italian (Friuli?), middle 14th century, *Madonna with Child* (p. 192)

237. Attributed to Francesco Laurana, *Portrait of Triboulet* (?) (p. 201)

238. French, middle 14th century, *Madonna with Child* (p. 183)

239. Circle of Andrea Verrocchio, *Madonna and Child* (p. 216)

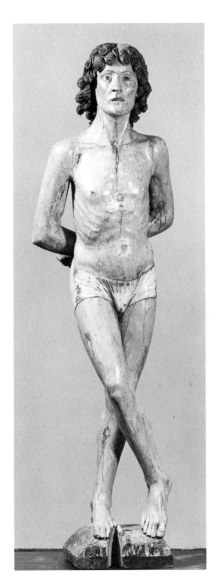
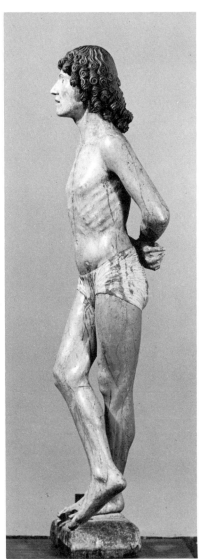

240. Italian (Umbrian), ca. 1500, *St. Sebastian* (p. 193)

241. German (Upper Rhine), ca. 1515, *St. Anne, Mary and the Child* (p. 187)

242. Tilmann Riemenschneider, *Bust of Saint Urban* (p. 210)

243. German (Swabian), ca. 1500, *Standing Christ Child* (p. 186)

244. Follower of Giovanni da Bologna, *Mercury* (p. 171)

245. Italian (Venetian), second quarter
16th century, *A Satyr (Marsyas?)*
(p. 195)

246. Italian (Venetian?), late 16th
century, *Chronos* (p. 195)

247. Master of the Naked Female
Figures, *Seated Nude* (p. 204)

248. Domenico Poggini (?), *Gladiator
Drawing his Sword* (p. 209)

249. Italian (?), first half
17th century, *Pegasus*
(p. 198)

250. Italian (Venetian), ca. 1600,
Venus (p. 196)

251. Italian (Venetian), late 17th century (?), *Minerva* (p. 197)

252. Italian (Tuscan?), first half 17th century, *Mask of a Faun* (p. 192)

253. Flemish (?), mid 17th century, *The Virgin Mary* (p. 180)

254. Flemish (?), mid 17th century, *St. John the Evangelist* (p. 181)

348

255. Flemish, ca. 1640, *Madonna and Child* (p. 180)

256. Netherlandish, early 17th century, *Expulsion from Paradise* (p. 206)

257. German (South), second half 17th century, *Two Standing Lions with the Bavarian Coat-of-Arms* (p. 185)

258. German (South?), ca. 1700, *St. John* (p. 186)

259. Giuseppe Sammartino, *St. Joseph Holding the Christ Child* (p. 215)

260. J. B. Carpeaux,
Neapolitan Fisherboy,
1857 (p. 172)

261. Matharin Moreau, *Greek Maiden*
(p. 206)

262. I.-J. Bonheur, *Lioness* (p. 172)

263. Hiram Powers, *Standing Female Nude* (p. 209)

264. Charles Jacquot, *The Angelus* (p. 199)

265. Auguste Rodin, *The Prodigal Son* (p. 211)

266. Edgar Degas, *Dancer at Rest*
(p. 174)

267. George Minne, *Standing Youth*
(p. 204)

268. Raoul Larche, *Loie Fuller, the
Dancer* (p. 200)

269. Pablo Picasso, *Head of a Woman*, 1905 (p. 207)

270. Aristide Maillol, *Action in Chains* (p. 203)

271. E. L. Kirchner, *Standing Female Nude* (p. 199)

272. Jacob Epstein, *Marchesa Casati*,
1918 (p. 178)

273. Charles Despiau, *Mrs. Stone* (p. 175)

274. Jo Davidson, *La Pasionaria*, 1938 (p. 174)

275. Dorothea Greenbaum, *Young Woman*, 1939 (p. 192)

276. John Flannagan, *Mother and Child* (p. 179)

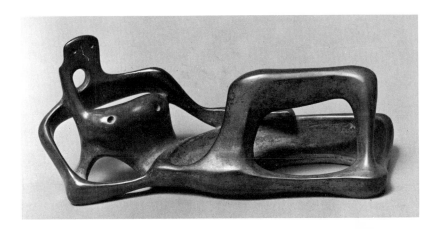

277. Henry Moore, *Reclining Figure, No. 1*, 1945 (p. 205)

278. Jean Arp, *Bird Tower*, 1963 (p. 168)